THEORY AND PRACTICE OF

FILTRATION

BY

GEORGE D. DICKEY, B.S.

Member American Chemical Society
Member American Society Chemical Engineers
Co-author of "A Textbook of Filtration"

AND

CHARLES L. BRYDEN, E.M., B.S.

Member American Chemical Society
Co-author of "A Textbook of Filtration"

MODERN LIBRARY OF
CHEMICAL ENGINEERING

REINHOLD PUBLISHING CORPORATION

330 West Forty-Second Street, New York, U. S. A.

1946

Copyright 1946 by

REINHOLD PUBLISHING CORPORATION

PRINTED IN U. S. A. BY KINGSPORT PRESS

Preface

Filtration is essentially a process of purification and, as such, occurs constantly in modern life, although frequently unnoticed and more often unappreciated. In this broadly defined sense, filtration appears as an essential part of a multitude of manufacturing processes, from sound filtration in radio and telephone operation, to vitamin extractions in medicinal preparations.

With the above in mind, it becomes evident that it would be impractical to attempt to produce an all-inclusive volume on filtration. Therefore this book has been limited to the general concept of filtration as applied to the separation of solids from liquids and gases by the use of porous media. It has been found necessary to curtail even this limitation to the extent that gas filtration is only briefly touched upon; the bulk of the text is confined to the separation of solids from liquids.

Within this scope of filtration three applications—oil, water and sewage—have seemed to warrant special chapters, viz: Oil Filters, Extractors and Expellers; Water Filtration; and Sewage Clarification and Sludge Dewatering. Aside from these three chapters, and the appendix chapter on Surface and Interfacial Separation of Immiscible Fluids, no particular application has been considered separately, but only as a part of the whole, to illustrate the functioning of different types of filtration apparatus.

The volume has been divided into two distinct parts: first, history, theory and principles, as a foundation for the proper understanding and interpretation of filtration; and secondly, the various types of filters and data pertaining thereto. History is of value, primarily, as a background to furnish a clearer understanding of the developments from early times up to and including present equipment. Theory and principles furnish established fundamental laws on which all filtration theory is based. Elaboration and modifications, in the light of present day developments, are dwelt upon, together with such mathematical interpretations as have been deemed advisable. The entire theoretical conception is of value only inasmuch as it throws light upon practical filtration problems.

The major portion of the book deals with filters and auxiliary apparatus, including typical data.

The authors wish to thank all those who so generously offered their assistance in the preparation of this volume, especially Mr. A. L. Genter,

iii

Consulting Engineer, Baltimore, Md., for his invaluable assistance on the history and the theory; Mr. M. V. Baker, Montclair, N. J., author of "Water Purification," for his suggestions dealing with the early history of water filtration; Mr. D. R. Sperry, Batavia, Ill., for his review of filtration theory and contribution of his latest ideas upon the subject; Professor B. F. Ruth of Iowa State College, Ames, Iowa, for his most helpful suggestion on filtration theory; Mr. G. G. Hawley, Reinhold Pub. Corp., New York; Professor E. L. McMillen of Lafayette College, Easton, Pa., for his assistance on filtration theory and description of laboratory testing; Dr. V. A. Kalichevsky of Woodbury, N. J., for his review of petroleum filtration; Professor W. L. Nelson of Tulsa University, Tulsa, Oklahoma, for his comments on same, and Mr. C. M. Ambler of Philadelphia for his assistance on centrifuges.

Among the many who have read some of the manuscript, offered valuable suggestions or permitted the use of some of their data, we wish to mention Mr. H. W. Munday, consulting engineer of Chicago and the following:

Mr. Anthony Anable..................................Dorr Company, New York
Dr. B. E. Anderson...................Johnson & Johnson, New Brunswick, N. J.
Mr. H. J. Angell..Goulds Pumps, New York
Mr. W. G. Bahl..............................Robinson-Branin Co., New York
Mr. E. H. Bedell...................Chemical & Metallurgical Engineering, N. Y.
Mr. K. H. Bird....................................Norton Co., Worcester, Mass.
Mr. C. C. Bryant...................General American Process Equip., New York
Mr. R. Chelminski...........General American Process Equipment, New York City
Mr. R. W. Dennam......................Tolhurst Cent. Div., East Moline, Ill.
Mr. J. R. Denton..........Worthington Pump & Machinery Corp., Harrison, N. J.
Mr. J. C. Farrant....................................Inter-Combust. Ltd, London
Dr. A. E. Flowers........................Professional Eng., Poughkeepsie, N. Y.
Mr. A. W. French, Jr............................French Oil Mach. Co., Piqua, Ohio
Mr. W. P. Gee..................................Texas Development Corp., N. Y.
Mr. F. L. Horine................................Johns-Manville Co., New York
Mr. C. E. Keefer............................Dept. Public Works, Baltimore, Md.
Mr. S. D. Kirkpatrick........Consulting Editor, McGraw-Hill Book Co., New York
Mr. Philip Kriegel.................................Spooner & Kriegel, New York
Mr. A. E. Loyd.......................Roots-Connersville Blower Co., New York
Mr. J. R. McConnell.....................American Air Filters, Louisville, Ky.
Mr. E. P. Noepel................................Wm. W. Stanley Co., New York
Mr. C. L. Peterson........Peterson Filter and Engineering Co., Salt Lake City, Utah
Mr. R. D. Prior................................Filter Media Corp., New York
Mr. P. O. Richter...................................Eimco Corp., Chicago, Ill.
Mr. W. H. Rometsch, Jr........................Fletcher Works, Philadelphia, Pa.
Mr. A. B. Sanger...............................Oliver United Filters, New York
Mr. F. E. Sebring.............The Hydraulic Press Mfg Co., Mt. Gilead, Ohio
Mr. S. A. Slack........Organic Chem. Dept., E. I. Dupont deNemours & Co., Wilmington, Del.
Mr. A. P. Smith.............................Nash Engineering Co., New York
Mr. E. G. Smith...........................Filtration Engineers, Newark, N. J.
Mr. LeRoy Van Vleeck..................Dept. Public Health, Hartford, Conn.
Mr. W. H. Withington.............................Hardinge & Co., New York

Table of Contents

Chapter 1

History of Filtration

General. The subject of filtration has long been considered as of only casual importance to the lay mind and rarely of great interest even to the scientist; yet, in its broadest sense, filtration is one of the most comprehensive of all physical operations and it has had a vital part in man's development throughout his history. Because of the lack of extensive literature upon the subject and in order to give a better background of understanding of its primary function, a brief discussion of the history of filtration may prove to be of value.

If we consider filtration as simply the separation of solids from liquids, this process, in its crudest form, was undoubtedly familiar to man as far back as the remotest antiquity when he first began to prepare food and drink for himself. From time to time this must have required some form of clarification, in other words, filtration.

Nature constantly employs filtration in an infinite variety of forms in all life activities. Although there can be no record of how man learned the simple principle, undoubtedly it was from repeated observation of some form of clarification as the purification of water by trickling through sandy soil or the accidental passage of rainwater through an outstretched skin, or similar occurrences.

Ancient Filters. In any case man has apparently known the process since the dawn of history, far beyond the earliest records, wherein it was accepted as an established practice. References are made to filtration, either directly or indirectly, in many of the earliest writings, most frequently by reference to wine making, which always means that some form of filtration was employed. As a matter of fact, wine making antedates history; but as it is only from ancient writings that a definite history can be started, we must begin with such writings. Among the first records are those of the Chinese, writing of events occurring about 2000 B.C. wherein wine is mentioned, and Biblical parchments of a somewhat later date, which abound in reference to wine and vineyards.

History credits the dissemination of wine throughout the Mediterranean to the Phoenicians; and to judge from the writings of Herodotus, Aristophanes, Democritus, Cato, Virgil, Varro, Columella and Pliny, wine making in their day had reached a high degree of perfection among the

1

Mediterranean nations. Unquestionably adequate filtration played an important part in this perfection. About 550 B.C. the very best wines known to Rome came from Carthage. They were known as "first run" and clear, and evidently were runs from crude presses.

Though the large majority of references to filtration in these early periods referred to wine making, there was occasional mention of water clarification, sufficient to establish the fact that water filtration was likewise known and practiced, but was considered of secondary importance to wine making.

Early Theory. These early writers gave some thought to the phenomenon of filtration, classifying it with evaporation. As they conceived it, distillation was the basis of all water separation; and distillation as a major subject was divided into three separate parts, *i.e.*, heat evaporation, called distillation by heat; capillary syphoning, called tube distillation; and straining, called distillation by straining.

Heat evaporation does not come under the heading of filtration and therefore no further reference need be made to it. Capillary syphoning and straining, however, are filtration and they will be taken up in some detail.

Syphoning Depicted. One of the earliest pictures of ancient syphoning was that painted on the wall of the tomb of Amenophis II (about 1450 B.C.). Somewhat later another scene, cut in the tomb of Rameses III, about 1250 B.C., depicted in a kitchen syphons drawing off liquids of various kinds. These apparently illustrated ordinary syphoning after straining and settling, and not capillary syphoning. Straining, on the other hand, while not here illustrated, was found in early pictures or carvings, as far as is known, long before syphoning; as previously stated, it was used in wine and water clarification for countless ages. In the period of Amenophis II and Rameses III straining involved the use of fabrics; and it may be of interest to point out that the word filtration itself [filter being variously specified filter, filtre, and fylter (17th century)] is presumably derived from the Latin *filtrum,* closely related to *feltrum,* felt or compressed wool, and both related to the Greek word signifying hair.

Nearer the Christian era, such well known writers as Plato in his "Symposium," written about 400 B.C., referred to capillary syphoning when he stated, "Socrates sitting down observed, 'It would be well, Agathon, if wisdom were a thing of such a kind as to flow from the party filled with it to the one who is less so, when they touch each other, like water in vessels, by means of a thread of wool from the fuller vessel to the emptier,' " thus indicating that it was a process commonly known. Again Plato's pupil Aristotle implied that straining was generally understood in his essay "De Generatione" when, in discussing the activity of the veins and pores, he compares them to "water passing through earthen vessels not sufficiently baked," which vessels were in use at that time for straining.

FIGURE 1. Siphons used about the year 1450 B.C. (2) pours a liquid into vases from the cup b; and (1) draws it off by the siphons a. (*Wilkinson*)

Filter Beds and Strainers. While fabrics were early employed as strainers for wine and water clarification and were necessary for capillary syphoning, the use of filters of charcoal or sand was not uncommon. The method employed was strikingly similar to the slow sand filters of today, using charcoal or sand as a filter medium, with downward flow through the charcoal or sand which rested on perforated false bottoms, the whole being enclosed in small vessels.

For wine filtration in ancient Rome the wealthy used colanders of silver or bronze, and the poor resorted to linen or other fabric. This class distinction held true also in China and Egypt. The primary method of separation was placing the fruit in a fabric receptacle and subjecting it to squeezing by using two poles turned in opposite directions, thus straining out the juice.

The Term "Filtration." Although filtration for a long period was considered a distillation process, the term "filtration" alone or distillation by filtration was not long in getting into written use. Galen in the second century wrote in his work "Natural Faculties" that the action of the kidneys was not unlike mechanical filters or sieves, and Palladins about the same period in his "De Rustica" stated that honey is filtered from the comb through linen cloth. Both writers were familiar with the word "filtration." It did not come into use in English until the 16th century; before that time "sifting" and "straining" were used. These terms, with, "sieve," were undoubtedly employed by early writers for what we now call filters.

For example, the unabridged Oxford Dictionary shows that "sieve" was used as "sibi," a framework with finely meshed or perforated bottom, in the year 725 in a Latin document published in England. The word "strain" has many ancient and modern meanings, but was used in English for forced filtration. Chaucer in 1386 used the term but spelled it "streignous."

When the term "filter" did come into use it was probably first applied to capillary syphoning.

Water Filtration. Water filters were described by Athanaeus of Attalia in 50 A.D., by Pliny in 77 A.D., by Rhazes in 930 A.D., by Avidenna in 1020 A.D., by Lulli in 1300 A.D., by Thomas of Aquinas in the 13th century, by Libavius in 1595, etc. Of these Lulli went to some length in describing the clarification of sea water using glass jars and jags of felt, while "The Thesaurus Alchimiae," purported to have been written by Thomas Aquinas, had much to say about distillation by filtration or wick filtration, particularly in the cascade form.

Likewise, in 1576 C. Baker, in his "Jewell of Health," wrote: "The droppings caused by a Lyste or piece of wool cloth . . . which manner of doing the Chymistes named Fyltring." (Lyste was a wick or strip of cloth.)

Athanaeus of Attalia gave distinct instructions, *i.e.*, various methods, for the filtration of drinking water. In charge of public health, he also founded a medical school at Attalia (now Antalya on the coast of Turkey), and evidently knew a great deal about sand filtration.

Pliny's "Natural History," which was actually an encyclopedia compiled by 474 secretaries or authors working for him, consists of 20,000 notices extracted from 2,000 ancient writings, some of which were very old. In one place he mentions filtering water through wool in vessels, seemingly referring to capillary syphoning. However, in a chapter on "Drunkenness"[4] he writes, "If anyone will take the trouble to consider the matter, he will find that upon no one subject is the industry of man kept more constantly on the alert than upon the making of wine; as if Nature had not given us water as a beverage the one in fact of which all other animals must use. . . . Nay, what is even more than this, that we may be enabled to swallow all the more, we have adopted the plan of diminishing its strength by *pressing* it through filter cloth."

This is thought to be the first written mention of a filter cloth and a pressure strainer or filter. Evidently Pliny thought that strength of wine was associated with turbidity. The famous Hero of Alexandria is said to have built "better" olive oil and wine presses in 100 A.D.

Stockholm Papyrus. In Stockholm there is an Egyptian papyrus known as the "Stockholm Papyrus" which, like its twin the "Leyden

Papyrus," dates from about the third century A.D. and is a compilation of Egyptian knowledge extending far beyond the periods of recorded history. Herein is described fully the process of dying fabrics and of making caustic soda. In this description, it details the first record we have of a filter used in the chemical industries; this filter must have been very ancient at the time.

The caustic soda solution was prepared by leaching wood ashes to produce a sodium and potassium carbonate solution. This was mixed with a clay suspension and thoroughly leached, then filtered through a bed of unleached lime supported on the perforated bottom of an earthenware vat. This produced a caustic soda and potash solution which was further clarified by filtering through a mat of grass. The original Greek called this device a "sebennich," to which might be traced the origin of the Latin origin of our word sieve. In any case this papyrus is claimed to be the oldest complete record of chemical recipes.

It is also of interest to note that a clay suspension was used, evidently as a filter aid, which would make it the first record of such use.

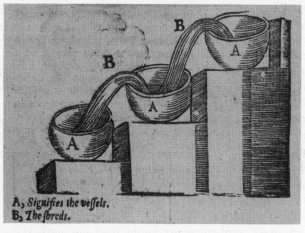

FIGURE 2. Capillary syphoning. (*John French*)

Capillary Syphoning. According to Ferdinand Hoefer in his "Historie de Chemie," filtration (meaning capillary syphoning) was first accurately described by Geber: "The liquor to be filtered is placed in a stone vessel and a jag of felt or wool cloth is placed in it, the wider part being placed to hang over the top of said vessel and reaching to a vessel below. When the liquor begins to distill the water with which the jag is moistened will distill off first and the liquor to be distilled will succeed it. If this liquor is not yet serene it must be redistilled."

In 750 A.D. the Arabian Geber or Dshabir (another alchemist) inaugurated crystallization for obtaining purer chemical products and described cleansing vitriol and alum solutions by filtering through loose layers of wool or a similar material.

Zosimas, an alchemist who probably lived in Egypt in the 4th century A.D., used oakum as a filter medium for various chemical solutions.

Despite the many references to it and the descriptions given, the action of capillary syphoning was not clearly understood at that time; in fact, there are indications that as late as the latter half of the 19th century the fact that the delivery end of the wick must be lower than the submerged end was accepted by observation of operation rather than understood as a principle.

Juncher Classification. Juncher in his "Conspectus Chemiae," published in 1730, divided filters into seven classes, but this distinction was largely one of the filter medium used, as shown by the following types he described: (1) paper filtration, wherein a folded even paper, preferably without glue, is fitted to a glass funnel, as is done today; (2) a conically woven wool which was supposed to filter suspensions not filtrable by a paper filter; (3) linen or muslin in the form of tubes, as Hippocrates sleeves, described as suitable for thick liquids; (4) filtration through chamois cloth for such materials as mercury; (5) capillary syphoning by loose threads for oil and water separation, the wick being weighted with water before filtration starts; (6) a pipe-like funnel for oil and water separation; (7) colanders or sieves for pulpy material to obtain liquor free of pulp.

Alchemist Filters. There was a small amount of filtration carried on by alchemists during the Middle Ages; but as a good deal of the earlier work, especially that of the Egyptians, had been forgotten, capillary syphoning was resorted to where sand or charcoal was not used, with occasional recourse to laboratory filtering through paper. This paper filtering was mentioned by Lenery in his "Cours de Chymie" in 1756.

While capillary syphoning gradually died out with the advance of gravity and pressure filtration, its use lingered on well into the nineteenth century for laboratory work and difficult filtration clarifications.

First Filter Patent. It is generally thought that the first filter patent ever issued was that granted to Joseph Amy by the French Government in 1789. This called for downward filtration through sand or sponge in a vessel having a false bottom. Four years previous to this Amy had applied for a patent wherein sponge was the basis for the claim; this patent was denied, which presumably is the reason for his specifying sand or sponge in his later application.

Amy established a filter manufactory and sold many household filters, including a number for large residences. In his publicity material he stated that household filters of sand in copper had been used in Paris for two centuries, but he bitterly opposed the use of copper containers on the ground that they caused verdegris poisoning. Amy claimed that sponge was a better filter medium than sand and used it in many filters, either alone or above the sand.

Cuchet and Montfort of Paris were allowed a patent on filtering water in 1806. It was at this time that street filters appeared in Paris, *fontaines marchandes,* from which filtered Seine River water was sold to the public.

In 1822 Anselme Payen, the French chemist, recommended the use of animal char for purification of water by filtration.

First British Filter Patent. The first British filter patent was granted to Peacock in **1791.** He described his invention as a new method of filtration by ascent. The unit consisted of three vessels, the first of which acted as a reservoir and receiver for the water to be filtered, which was fed to it through a pipe and a cock fitted with a bunting strainer. This vessel delivered the water to the bottom of the second vessel, in which had been placed (on a conical grating) coarse gravel followed by graded sand. A central pipe ran to the top of the vessel and down into the gravel. The filtrate was removed by an outlet in the side of the vessel, near the top of the sand. Discharge was to a third vessel, by gravity. This container acted as a storage for the filtrate and as a means of creating a head for backwashing, wherein it was filled then the supply shut off, and the water run back rapidly for cleaning, similar to modern back washes. In this filter the middle vessel was the only one which actually did any filtering, the first and third being auxiliary only.

Although Peacock anticipated the American rapid filter of the 1880's, he did not claim rapid filtration and used upward instead of downward flow and downward reverse-flow wash. Except for a trial on three British naval ships, it is not known that any filters of his type were ever used.

Modern Public Water Filters. Modern public water filtration dates from 1829, when James Simpson built some filter beds for the Chelsea Water Works Company of London. This design of slow sand filters was at first slowly and then rapidly adopted in England and on the Continent. Robert Thom of Scotland led Simpson by about a year in building a filter which was also a slow sand filter. And late in 1829 filters designed by Thom were put into use at Greenock, Scotland, employing a filter bed practically the same as Simpson's. Thom's filter rested on a false bottom of flat, perforated tile and was intended to filter either upward or downward, in either case to be cleaned by reverse-flow wash. As far as could be learned there was no evidence to show that Thom knew of Peacock's patent, and neither Thom nor Simpson took out patents of their own. Filters built by Thom were put in at Paisley, Ayr, and perhaps some other Scottish towns. With modifications, similar filters are still in use in Scotland.

FIGURE 3. Filtering by ascent. (*Peacock*)

Like Peacock's design, Thom's was an anticipation of the American rapid sand filter before coagulation was introduced, but it employed a slow rate of filtration. The essential difference between the filters of Thom and Simpson was that Thom cleaned his filter by reverse-flow wash and Simpson cleaned his by scraping off, wheeling out, washing, and returning the sand.

In 1856 Darcy took out French and British patents on a filter modeled after Thom's design, but including new features. One of these was a revolving broom for use in cleaning the surface of the filter, but it is not known whether any of the Darcy filters were ever constructed.

The Massachusetts State Board of Health opened an experimental station in 1887 at Lawrence, Massachusetts, where experiments were devoted to the study of both sewage and water treatment, the work being largely confined to intermittent sand filtration.

Allen Hazen, in dividing the history of American water filtration into three parts, attributes the first to James Kirkwood, the second to the Massachusetts Board of Health, and the third to the Louisville, Kentucky experiments. Whatever the division made, great credit should go to Kirkwood, who was sent to Europe by the City of St. Louis in 1865-66 to study water filtration methods in use abroad. Upon his return, Kirkwood made a report which American engineers regarded as classic for many years. With Kirkwood as consulting engineer, a slow sand filter was completed at Poughkeepsie, New York, in 1872, and another in Hudson, New York, in 1874. The next slow sand filters of major importance were put in at Lawrence, Massachusetts, in 1893, and at Albany in 1899.

Following the Lawrence and Albany filters intermittent sand filtration in America was more or less abandoned for water, as it was subsequently given up generally for sewage, outside of Massachusetts.

Rapid Sand Filters. The rapid sand filter in American public works had its beginning at Rahway, New Jersey, in or just before 1880, when Patrick Clark, then superintendent of the city water works, installed a small sand filter on water from the Rahway River, the surface of which was cleaned by vertically descending jets thrown by revolving perforated arms. On the same day, in June of 1882, Patrick Clark and John W. Hyatt took out separate patents, assigned to the Newark Filtering Co. Hyatt's called for stacking a number of Clark filters, one above the other, in a closed tank, each filter independent of the other except for supply and wash pipes. This was to save space. In 1882 four of these types of filter were installed by the Newark Filtering Co. on the Raritan River, for the Somerville & Raritan Water Company.

In 1884 Isaiah Smith Hyatt, brother of John Wesley Hyatt, took out a process patent on simultaneous coagulation and filtration. In 1885 filters embodying this process were installed for the Somerville & Raritan Water Co., displacing the filters of 1882. In a new plant, each filter stood on its own bottom. In place of surface-jet wash, a "sand discharge" system was used, by which the filter sand was forced up through vertical pipes from the bottom of the sand bed to an upper chamber, from which the dirty water flowed to waste. When clean, the sand was dropped back into place.

The basic principle of the Isaiah Smith Hyatt coagulation patent involved doing away with the necessity of pre-sedimentation and pre-coagulation. Fuller's Louisville rapid filtration experiments of 1895-97 showed that for highly turbid waters both were essential.

Bacterial Removal. In Europe a great impetus to water filtration was given by the discovery that sand filtration actually removed a large part of the bacteria present in the water. This proof of a long suspected fact was made by Percy Frankland at London, where he established the fact that slow sand filters of the London Water Company removed nearly all the bacteria in the applied water. This was later borne out by the cholera epidemic in Hamburg, where thousands of deaths occurred from the disease, while at Altona, which also took its water from the Elbe, there were few cases of the disease. It was noted that Altona filtered its water but that Hamburg did not. The credit, therefore, for Altona's remarkable showing was given entirely to its water filters, thus establishing in the public mind the necessity for filtered water as a disease preventive. Actually Hamburg was an exception in that for years filtration of surface waters had been the rule in England and Germany; when the Hamburg Water Works was built, filtration had been proposed by the engineer who designed it, but his recommendation was not adopted.

Intermittent Sand Filters. According to the *Journal of the American Water Works Association,* the period from 1890 to 1900 was one in which the rapid or mechanical sand filters continued in a pre-scientific stage, so far as filtering went, and although there were marked improvements in construction it was not until the next decade that their design was put on a scientific basis. This was likewise a period of intense rivalry between advocates of slow and rapid sand filters, the latter now established upon an engineering basis. With the construction of a revised rapid sand filter at Little Falls, New Jersey, under the direction of George W. Fuller, a new design in this type of filter was successfully demonstrated.

Anthracite Filters. While the customary filter medium was sand, other materials were tried at various places with more or less success, for instance, anthracite coal is sometimes used.[2] A filter plant was built at Harrisburg, Pennsylvania, in the late nineties by J. H. Fuertes, with the intention of using sand as the filter bed; but being unable to procure sand from the river and finding only anthracite, he tried the latter. It proved quite successful, although it was rather coarse and non-uniform, and necessitated a deep bed. As a result, Fuertes built anthracite filters for Dallas, Texas; Cumberland, Maryland; and Denver, Colorado. About 1928, Ripple of Denver conducted a series of comparisons between coal and sand as filtering media and published an interesting report on his findings.

House Filters. Within the past 68 years (Charles Chamberland's famous porous clay filter for removing bacteria from water dated from 1884) many varieties of household filters have been marketed which were of the faucet type for small capacities, or the basement or central-station type for large flows. One type of rapid sand filter was used on ships prior to 1914. The sand was back-washed by means of back pressure through a Venturi throat at the bottom of the case, which circulated the sand for scouring. It was a hydraulic head service and the clearing action was very rapid. These were used as gravity filters or inserted in the water line and operated under pressure. They employed sand, charcoal, diatomaceous earths, zeolites or fabrics, or metallic discs or screens as the filter medium, with intermittent cleaning at long intervals.

Disinfectants. The antecedents of disinfectants appeared between 1890 and 1900, and in the next decade the process was established. Early in 1908 hypochlorite of lime was adopted at the slow sand filtration plant of Poughkeepsie—a fact which often has been overlooked. Later in the year hypochlorite was put into use at the Chicago Stockyards, prior to filtration, and at Boonton, New Jersey, by the contractor for a new water supply for Jersey City, to avoid being forced to build filters.

Sewage Filters. An intermittent sand filter for sewage at Medford, Mass. was built before the Lawrence Experimental Station began operation in 1893; but outside of Massachusetts few intermittent sand filters were ever built to treat raw city sewage. Broadly speaking, "contact beds," in which sewage was held for bacterial action, followed intermittent sand filters for a brief period. Then came sprinkling or percolating filters of coarse material (*not* sand), freely drained, so the sewage could pass through constantly for a time and then be shut off.

The idea of sewage treatment dates chiefly from the middle of the 19th century, for although a number of ancient cities had sewers for the removal of fouled liquor, as well as for drainage, there was no thought of filtration. Carl Merckel mentions the ancient Babylonian cylinders as sewage receptacles; Layard tells of Nineveh sewers dating to the 7th century B.C.; and Schich and Warren and others have information on sewers in Jerusalem, together with the well known sewers of Rome and later of Paris—all sewage removal systems, rather than disposal involving filtration.

One of the first to propose what seems to imply sewage filtration, although not so stated definitely, was Gianibelli, who sought to interest Queen Elizabeth of England, through Lord Burghleigh (in 1591) in a scheme he had devised for cleaning "the filthy ditches of London." He pointed out that cleanliness and improved health would result, and that in addition there would be at hand a considerable water supply for firefighting—in all a most attractive proposition. Unfortunately, indifference and lack of interest in the public welfare prevented proper recognition or financial backing, and the whole idea was dropped.

While the drainage of London was the subject of legislation as early as 1225 A.D., and Paris had its few miles of sewers before 1536, the first real attempt to consider the filtration of sewage was made by the British Rivers Pollution Commission whose report was published in 1870. At that time complete removal of particles was not attempted. Where sewage-collecting systems had been provided, they were discharged into the nearest body of water regardless of the ability of the receiving waters to take care of this influent without menace.

A practical attempt to filter sewage by the use of sand was made at Merthyr Tydfil, Wales, in 1871, and at a few other places later on, but the continued use of sewage farms (dating back to the 16th century) was too much in vogue for changes to be made, and they continued so for many years. Even today sewage farms are found in Germany, France, Australia, and dry sections of the west and southwest in the United States.

It was only when a number of the sewage farms were becoming oversaturated, clogged and offensive that, in an effort to remedy the situation, sand-filter beds came to be more and more used. These were of the intermittent type, often with gravel or broken stone taking the place of sand. The sewage was fed to the filters by sprinklers for percolation, and collection was in underground drains.

Sewage Sludge Dewatering. Sprinklers or sprinkling filters are still one of the major processes of sewage disposal, while intermittent sand filters are seldom installed, although many old ones are still in use as final effluent polishers. Actually sprinkling or trickling filters are not filters at all but act to stabilize putrescible matter by contact treatment of sewage on coarse stones, as a fixed bed, in contrast to activated sludge as a moving contact medium.

Sewage sludge dewatering, however, has undergone a marked change; first, when the treatment of sludge made it possible to filter sludge on sand beds, similar to slow sand filters, and later when the art of sludge conditioning was developed to the extent that filter presses and finally continuous vacuum filters became practicable. Chemical treatment of sewage was first tried in Paris in 1740 and was used about 1857. In 1864 Bardwell obtained an English patent on treating sewage with ferric chloride. As ferric-coagulated sewage it indicated a means of coagulating sludge.

Filters have been in constant use for dewatering sludge in England since 1884. Chamber presses were first used at Aylesbury, then at Merton and Wimbledon in 1884. By 1908 these sludge presses were found in nearly every treatment plant in Wales and England.

The first chamber press installation in the United States was made at Worcester, Massachusetts, in 1898, according to the *Sewage Works Journal,* and chamber presses went into Providence, Rhode Island, in 1901, where they are still in use. The filters at Providence were originally used on chemically precipitated sludge, although they are now used on waste-activated sludge.

One of the earliest attempts in vacuum filtration of sewage sludge in the United States was by the Industrial Filtration Corporation in conjunction with the City of New York in 1914. At this time the production of briquets was the idea behind the move, and it finally was demonstrated that either the Moore open-tank filter or the rotary-drum vacuum filter could handle Imhof sludge, if the latter was sufficiently conditioned with lime and flue dust, or alum, coal dust or copperas. A rather elaborate series of Boston tanks was used to get clarity of effluent, and while the process proved practical, economically it was a failure. Some attempts at raw sludge filtration were made, but without material success, primarily from the briquetting standpoint.

The Heineken Reduction Company put in a small plant at Baltimore, Maryland, on Imhof sludge with this same idea, but the cost of conditioning chemicals and irregularities in the concentration of the sludge caused the scheme to be given up as impractical.

By the middle thirties, however, there were many installations of drum vacuum filters on sewage sludges handling primary, chemical, activated and digested sludges, and rotary-drum vacuum filters had become accepted equipment for sewage sludge dewatering.

Laughlin Filters. One of the most ingenious filters for sewage filtration was that invented by William S. Laughlin in 1932 and demonstrated at Dearborn, Michigan, and Perth Amboy, New Jersey, in large installations. This filter made use of a magnetic iron (magnetite) sand as the filter medium which was automatically cleaned by raising the sand by magnetic attraction (intermittently) for the sand washing. Laughlin later in 1938 patented an improved type of hydraulic sand filter for sewage, water, and industrial waste filtration.

Elutriation. In 1934 A. L. Genter[2] published some very interesting reports on his investigation of the filtration of sewage sludges carried on mainly in 1933. These covered a most exhaustive series of experiments upon the handling of digested and raw sludges, and concluded that by removal of the ammoniacal salts by elutriation, the use of lime could be eliminated and the requirement for ferric chloride as a conditioning agent materially reduced.

C. E. Keefer and H. Kratz, Jr.,[3] made the first large-scale tests of this process in 1933 and reported on them in 1934. The first plant installation was made at the new District of Columbia plant in Washington, which went into operation in 1937, where the elutriated sludge was handled by 500 square foot rotary-drum vacuum filters. Since then many other installations have been made.

Industrial Filters. During the time that water and sewage filters were progressing with the development of new equipment, industry itself was undergoing an awakening, and a demand soon arose for more effective filtration than that provided by sand beds, charcoal percolation, strainers or capillary syphoning, which were then the only known types. As such filters were hopelessly inadequate for industrial work, many ideas for filters were proposed and patented. Among the most economically important of these were those of Chuchet and Montfort in France and of S. McComb, J. Smith, and B. D. Calpin in America. These filters all consisted of some form of cloth media fitted on frames and suspended in containers. The chief difference between the types was that the French filters were open and the American were closed, although in these closed machines nothing was said about pressure.

Pressure Filters. As pressure filtration involved either a high-gravity head or mechanical pressure on the unfiltered mix, considerable litigation relating to the use of Montejus tanks with filter presses in beet-sugar filtration came about during the seventies in Europe, particularly in France. In 1879 H. Taridien published in Paris a history of this litigation in his "de l'Histoire de l'invention des filtres-presses," which cites an English patent to Howard in 1814, as the forerunner of the Needham filter press (patented in 1828).

In his book, Tardien describes the first crude presses that were used in the dewatering of clay slip in the ceramic industries of England and Bohemia. Filter cloths were fastened over a number of individual square wooden frames with a single hole at the top. A series of these frames were placed in a metal trough so that all the cloth but the two ends, which were solid blocks, were in firm contact. The trough was used to collect the filtrate. The slurry was first forced in by high-gravity head and then by compressed air on a reservoir of slurry. Such reservoirs were called "Montejus" (literally "juice lifters" or "juice pushers") by the French when they started using them for unclarified beet-sugar juices. Much of the litigation hinged upon the use of a Montejus for forced filtration.

Needham Press. Needham of England obtained a filter press patent in 1828 which covered the essentials of the wooden surfaces of the plate-and-frame press. A number of cells were built up by covering with filter cloth; the cells were provided with grooves for drainage and were separated by battens. The liquor was admitted to the cell chambers by multiple connections from the supply line, and longitudinal pressure was communicated by wedges and tie rods. No delivery channel or separate filtrate taps were provided.

The "Braunschweigische Machinenbau Anstalt" shows a chamber pressure filter devised to wash through the free cake surface and then to dump the cake directly into a slurry mixer in the lower filter chamber for pumping out.

Sugar Filters. Somewhat earlier than Needham, in 1824, William Cleland, an Englishman, took out patents for the clarification of sugar juices through bags and in 1830 Taylor in America patented a modification of this method, which filter up to recently was largely used in the sugar industry. In these filters the juice was fed through pipes to the various bags and allowed to drain by gravity, the whole set of bags being enclosed in a container to collect the filtrate.

The bags were closed at one end by fastening with string, while the other end was tied to a conically shaped nipple which was pressed tightly into a conical seat at the bottom of a tray. Some trays carried many bags and the liquor was run into the trays and found its way out by gravity through the walls of the bags, being collected in another tray beneath. By this means an average hydraulic head of about four feet or, approximately, two pounds' pressure was obtained—a great asset to this filtering. After each run the bags had to be removed from the containers and cleaned separately, which naturally involved a very considerable amount of time and labor.

Howard in 1834, using the first Needham patent (1828), replaced the Taylor bag filters with presses as the first attempt at pressure filtration in sugar processing.

By 1840 attempts were being made to employ pressure from air pumps, or steam, to create a partial vacuum, and also to apply water pressure mechanically through a bell device; this device, however, was not successful in application, although there was some soundness to the theory.

In order to increase the rate of flow through the bags J. Kite of Baux, England, in 1837, invented a method of forcing the juice through the bags with a force pump. Jacquier and Danek improved on this about 1864 when they perfected in Prague a filter similar to the Taylor except that they used rigid iron or wooden frames to prevent the bags from collapsing and employed pressure to force the juice through the bags from the outside inward, thus reversing the method Taylor used.

In 1874 Dehne patented a washing press, in which there was a separate connection for wash water and filtrate; and Kroog later patented an air vent to the filter frames.

This same type, with a few variations and operated by gravity, was introduced by The Société Philippe in France and by Kasalowsky in

Hungary a short time later, using Jelinek and Fry's method of purification of sugar juices with milk of lime and carbon dioxide gas, perfected in 1863.

Early Filter Media. In 1858 Dr. Julius Lowe described a filter, using asbestos as a filter medium, which could be used for filtering gelatin and corrosive liquors. In 1860 Professor Bottger employed guncotton in the filtering of liquids which acted chemically on paper; and a few years later in 1867 Dr. Gibbs made use of powdered glass as a filter medium, showing the gradually widening horizon of filter possibilities and the increasing attention paid to it by scientists. This was more true of the filter media than of the filters themselves, as their mechanical development was slow, despite the increasing interest in filter media, with the use of wool for weak acids and sand for almost every kind of slurry, in addition to the paper, felt, linen, silk, cotton, powdered glass, charcoal, etc., already mentioned.

Box Suction Filters. The first suction filter of note and acceptance was that of Bunsen, who in 1860 perfected a workable machine; for although numerous attempts to filter by vacuum had been made previously, none had been successful. Buechner devised a perforated bottom funnel for vacuum filtration about this time, which is still extensively used in laboratory work. In 1880 Gooch brought out a modification of the Bunsen filter; his filter attained wide use in chemical laboratories for solids determinations.

The growing demand for potash in the 1800's caused the rapid development of the potash beds of Germany (1860), and this brought the method of suction filtration into prominence, as leaching was the main step in the preparation of the crude potash for the market. Large false-bottomed tanks were used; the sludge was charged into them to a depth of several feet, the clear liquor being drawn through the filter medium and out of the bottom of the tanks by suction. The tanks were operated until there was a layer of solids in them three or four feet thick, when it became necessary, because of lowered filter rates and lack of room to add more sludge, to clean out the accumulated deposit and start a new cycle. The only way this cleaning could be accomplished was by getting into the tanks and digging out the filter cake with a shovel. It can be imagined what a slow, tedious and expensive procedure this was and what a destructive effect it had on the filter medium.

These open tank horizontal suction filters often went by the name of "Nutschen," from the developments in Germany, and are still sometimes referred to in the United States as Nutsch filters. In the chemical and molasses-refining industries, where free filtering precipitates were common, mechanical improvements were made whereby the filters were made portable and tipable; *i.e.*, they were mounted on trunnions and could be turned upside down, with counter-current air pressure for dumping the cake. Washing was accomplished by submerging the cake with a layer of water which was sucked through—in effect the same as the later hopper dewaterer.

Hart Drum Suction Filters. The crudeness and inefficiencies of ordinary box filters were so apparent that many inventions were claimed for making the whole process continuous and those involving a rotating drum offered the most promise. According to Genter,[2] one of the first of these drums was described in an English patent issued to William Hart and James Hart in Kent, England, in 1872, called "an improved apparatus for drying sewage precipitates, cement, paper pulp and other fluid or semi-fluid matter."

A.D. 1872, *9th December*. No 3734.

Drying Sewage Precipitates, Cement, Pulp, &c.

LETTERS PATENT to William Hart and James Hart, both of Crossness, in the County of Kent, Engineers, for the Invention of "AN IMPROVED APPARATUS FOR DRYING SEWAGE PRECIPITATES, CEMENT, PAPER PULP, AND OTHER FLUID OR SEMIFLUID MATTERS."

Sealed the 18th March 1873, and dated the 9th December 1872.

PROVISIONAL SPECIFICATION left by the said William Hart and James Hart at the Office of the Commissioners of Patents, with their Petition, on the 9th December 1872.

We, WILLIAM HART and JAMES HART, both of Crossness, in the County of Kent, Engineers, do hereby declare the nature of the said Invention for "AN IMPROVED APPARATUS FOR DRYING SEWAGE PRECIPITATES CEMENT, PAPER PULP, AND OTHER FLUID OR SEMIFLUID MATTERS," to be as follows:—

Our Invention has for its object the drying of sewage precipitates, or sewage mud, paper pulp, peat, and other fluid or semi-fluid matters, and consists essentially of a revolving drum (the cylindrical part of which is perforated or reticulated), and other apparatus in connection therewith, such drum and apparatus being arranged as herein-after described, so as to separate the water from the matter to be dried, and draw a coating of such matter on to the periphery of the drum, then to draw hot or dry air through such coating, and thereby dry it, and then to force cold air through the dried matter, and thereby detach it from the drum.

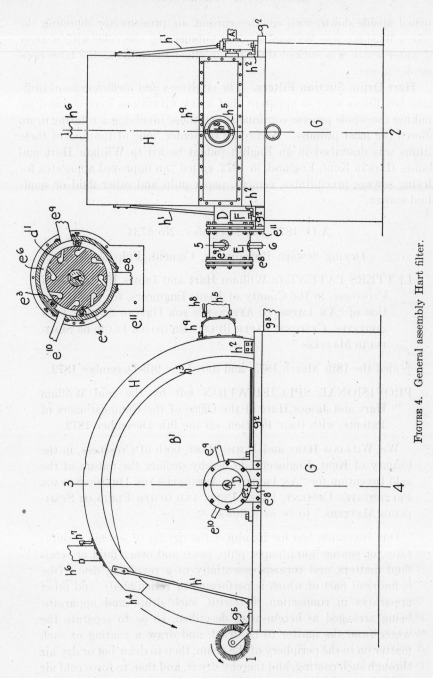

FIGURE 4. General assembly Hart filter.

Instead of drawing hot air through the coating of wet matter, cold dry air may be used when the casing H may be dispensed with.

Having now described the nature of our Invention, and the manner in which the same is to be performed, we wish it to be understood that we do not limit ourselves to the precise details herein described, as the same may be varied without departing from the nature of our Invention; but we claim as our said Invention, the improved apparatus herein-before described and illustrated in the accompanying Drawings, for drying sewage precipitates, cement, paper pulp, and other fluid or semi-fluid matters, that is to say, a revolving drum, the periphery of which is formed of wire gauze or other straining medium, the interior of the said drum being divided into chambers which are successively brought by the revolution of the drum into communication with suction and forcing pumps, so that the matter being treated is continuously drawn on to the said drum, dried, and removed therefrom at different portions of its periphery, essentially as described.

In witness whereof, I, the said William Hart, have hereunto set my hand and seal, this Ninth day of June in the year of our Lord One thousand eight hundred and seventy-three.

WILLIAM HART. (L.S.)

Witness,
> B. WILLCOX,
>> Clerk to H. H. Murdoch,
>>> 7, Staple Inn,
>>>> London.

This device covered everything essential in the modern vacuum filter (drum type) except the wire winding; in fact it even covered the use of a heating chamber over the rotating drum for further drying of the filter cake. Suction chambers, internal piping to a valve, separation of pickup from drying, providing a "blast chamber" for air removal (compressed cold air) or "blowing off" the cake, a scraper, and for paper pulp a revolving brush operating with the scraper were shown. Wire backing was provided for any filter medium, described as canvas, flannel, or other suitable straining medium (the English used "straining" for "filtering"). A roller was substituted to receive the paper pulp as detached and to deposit it on a traveling web (*i.e.*, conveyor belt).

This remarkable patent was too advanced for the times and it was

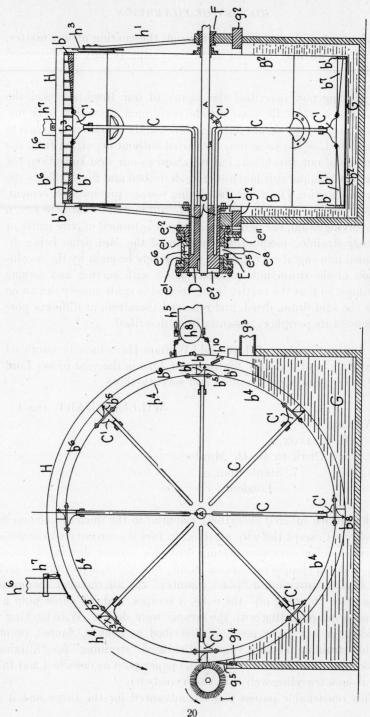

FIGURE 5. Section assembly Hart filter.

many years before continuous vacuum filters involving the features described came into commercial use.

Many later patents were taken out on various continuous filters, but with the exception of Droeshout's (Belt) and Solvay's (Drum) few of these were more than ideas, without the mechanical details being worked out sufficiently to show their practicability; and it is only within the last thirty to forty years that such filters have been perfected.

Pierre Droeshout in 1893 and 1894 patented in France and Germany a traveling belt (similar to a fourdrinier in the paper making industry) designed primarily for dewatering and washing first-carbonation lime sludge in beet-sugar practice.

Two or more suction boxes were provided under the filter belt so that the cake would be first formed and then spray-washed, the undiluted juices being drawn from the first suction compartment and the diluted juices from the spray-washed compartments. The final discharge of the washed residue was accomplished by brushing or throwing the solids from a traveling belt.

There is thus shown the provision for washing a filter cake on a continuous filter.

The Solvay filter, patented in several forms in 1896, was a filter drum of the Hart type developed for the filtration of bicarbonate of soda. The German patent covered the incidental inventions of the swinging agitator, which marks the origin of this device for drum filters.

At the time the Solvay patent was issued, continuous drum filters of this type were in wide use in Europe; the patent specifications stated: "As is well known, drum filters consist of cylinders covered by some filtering material, and, in consequence of connecting their interior with a suction valve, the liquid is drawn into their interior while the solids are deposited on the exterior surface of said cylinder from which said solids are continuously and periodically removed."

Solvay Wheel. The most widely used type of these Solvay drum filters in the United States was that designed by Edward Trump, Chief Engineer of the Solvay Company, who, between 1885 and 1896, developed a machine for the company's use. For the filtration of bicarbonate of soda, with a few modifications, this filter is still continued as a standard by many concerns.

The early continuous devices were used on a few slurries easy to filter, and it was not until counter-current decantation and continuous thickeners were perfected that drum filters came into universal use.

Moore Patents. In America two of the most important filter inventions, from the standpoint of far reaching effects, were those of George Moore, who in 1902 patented the open-tank, vacuum-leaf filter and in

1903 the multiple-compartment rotary-drum vacuum filter. Moore worked independently of European practice, and as he confined his activities to the metallurgical field, undoubtedly he was unaware of European chemical industrial developments.

In the European beet-sugar industry there were many patented ideas similar to Moore's leaf filters (which was a batch filtration device), ranging from the Danek suction filter of about 1880 to the Louis Feuillebois French patent of 1893, where reverse air pressure was used for cake discharge.

While the drum patent of Moore was antedated by Hart and others, as was his leaf filter, great credit is due to Moore for his ideas and ingenuity in both the leaf and drum filter developments.

Moore was the superintendent of a gold mill where high-grade ores were handled in large plate-and-frame filter presses, the common practice at that time for such work when cyanide extraction of gold and silver was being introduced. It so happened that the high-grade ores unexpectedly petered out and it became a question of either cheaply handling low-grade material and tailings, or closing down. The filter presses were one of the most expensive items in the extraction, and it was this step that Moore set to work to improve.

Moore conceived the idea of multiplicity of frames combined in a common unit, which would give a large area of filtering surface at a low cost as compared with the equivalent expense of the presses. At the same time the unit of leaves could be shifted, after cake formation, without the cakes touching. One of the most objectionable features of the presses, and one which prevented adequate washing, was the formation of solid cake, impossible to avoid with presses. The Moore leaves could be shifted from strong to weak liquor, to water wash and discharge, by a basket shifting crane operated by one man, an enormous saving in labor over the presses as then handled. These features made the Moore filter leaves a marked success throughout the mining world and were a prime factor in the rapid development of the cyanide process, particularly for low-grade ores and tailings.

Butters Filter. Shortly after this development an associate of Moore's by the name of Cassel patented a filter wherein the leaves remained stationary during operation, rather than being shifted, as in the case of the Moore leaves, for washing and discharge. This patent was assigned to the Butters Company, which exploited it successfully. In 1912 the U. S. Circuit Court of Appeals rendered Moore a favorable decision as to the basic nature of his patent, issued in 1904 on the process of filtering metal bearing slimes and washing out the dissolved metal values through the free cake surface. The Moore process claimed displacement wash by submergence. Several ways of doing this under suction were shown. From then on Butters, as well as others, who had developed filters along similar lines, generally conceded the validity of the Moore claims.

Kelly Filter. In 1905 David Kelly, who had worked with Moore, brought out a pressure leaf filter whereby cake formation, washing, and drying were under pressure, but leaves like Moore's were used, the cakes not being allowed to build together to form a solid cake. Discharge was accomplished by drawing out the leaves as a unit on a rail-mounted carriage. The original idea behind the Kelly filter was to eliminate the multiplicity of joints common to all chamber and plate-and-frame filters, and to provide a pressure filter with but one joint.

This was a new idea in the United States and foreign patent records and, together with his rapid method of locking the cylinder head of the traveling carriage so that it was leak-proof, it resulted in making the Kelly filter prominent both here and abroad. This device was improved by Kelly in 1914, when he introduced an air motor to telescope the horizontal carriage into the filter tank, automatically locking the head by continuous cable travel.

While the early work of Moore showed this same general design, with the exception of the locking device, Moore never followed it through to bring the filter to the market. Kelly, however, actively pushed the filter sales and demonstrated the commercial use of such a filter. Not only were numerous installations made at that time, but the machine is still standard equipment.

The Kelly filter, although much more expensive per square foot (often equalized by greater capacity), had many of the desirable features of the Moore leaf filter with the addition of pressure possibilities for the filtration of materials difficult to handle; for example it formed cakes at high pressures and at high or low temperatures, instead of the vacuum's limited range, and for this (pressure) reason it was suited to high elevations, where filters were often required for mining operations. In the chemical field the ability to jacket the shell for high-temperature work, or insulate it against heat loss in the sugar industry, were decided assets.

Sweetland Filter. About this same time another mining engineer, E. J. Sweetland, superintendent of a gold mill, was having trouble with his Butters filters because of inability to obtain high pressure, which he felt curtailed the capacity. Therefore he designed a filter which consisted of circular leaves enclosed in a clam-shelled container, which could be opened for cake discharge by swinging back the lower half. Like the Kelly press, the Sweetland was a decided success and is an important filter on the market today.

Merril, the superintendent of the famous Homestake Mining Co., of

Lead, South Dakota, devised a plate-and-frame filter press which found considerable use in pulp treatment in cyanide work. This was known as the Merril Press and provided for sluicing the filter cake with high-pressure water jets from the chambers without opening the filter. Obviously this device was of no use where dry cake discharge was desirable, but where the filtrate only was desired it saved extensive labor in filter-press operation.

Burt Filters. Another filter of the same period was the Burt revolving cylinder lined with filter mats which filtered from the inside out. The cake was discharged by being flushed out at the end of the cycle. Another Burt design was an annular shell with stationary leaves withdrawn, as were the Kelly leaves, for discharge. These filters are also still in use.

In America this entire era was one of rapid filter development and many were the types and modifications of the foregoing filters that were patented and built.

Oliver Filter. The Oliver rotary-drum vacuum filter was brought out during the same period by another mining engineer, E. L. Oliver. While Moore had patented a multiple-compartment machine, it remained for Oliver to wind the drum spirally with wire to hold the filter medium intact during cake blow-back as had been done with the Solvay type wheel. The Oliver filter appeared about 1908 and met with wide approval throughout the mining industry. A group of engineers attracted by Oliver's work attempted to effect a contract under license for such machines. Failing to do this they started to construct their own filters under the name of Portland, improving upon the surface compartment separation by cross strips over the filter medium. Later an agreement was effected with Oliver and the Portland passed out of existence as such.

Other Filters. Many modifications of the vacuum drum filters have been brought out since that time, instigated to a large extent by the growth of the chemical industry during and after the first world war. An all cast-iron drum for caustic lime mud was constructed by Mount in 1915, and in the same year an all-stoneware (Filtros) filter in disc form was offered by the General Engineering Company for acid filtration. The Mount filter was used up until recently, but the Filtros wheel did not prove as successful as was hoped.

Zenith Filter. The Zenith filter, brought out in 1914 for caustic filtration, was also an all cast-iron drum and was offered under the Moore patents. This machine, together with those with drums constructed of steel, wood, and alloys, has been widely used, as have been their successors, the Conkey filters.

Feinc Filter. A filter employing strings for cake discharge was brought out in 1919 by Wright and Young, called the Feinc filter. This filter depends on strings wound about the drum for cake discharge, rather than on air or gas pressure, somewhat similar to the early traveling belt design.

Dorrco. The Dorrco filter, using the inside of the drum for the cake building, although mentioned in the Moore patents, originated in Australia. The Dorr Company, however, took over the license rights and exploited the idea.

Conkey Dewaterer. In the hopper filter developed by Dr. H. B. Faber in 1915, there was designed a filter without a vat, the unit being composed of hoppers around a central shaft. This machine later improved under the name of the Conkey dewaterer, handles high specific gravity or coarse solids.

Sand Filters. The Oliver sand table filter brought out in 1916, consisted of a horizontally rotating vacuum bed turned against a stationary scraper. Various bucket and scoop designs, also have been tried by numerous concerns and engineers.

American Disc Filters. The American disc filter was originally constructed as a single disc composed of eight sectors. This construction was modified to include a number of discs in patents taken out by J. A. McCaskell, O. J. Salisbury, and A. L. Genter.

The filter provided for a large area in a small space; *i.e.*, a plurality of sectionalized discs spaced on a revolving shaft in a tank adapted to receive the discs collectively and having, on the cake discharge sides of the discs, numerous tank openings through which the cake fell. This was the first really successful multiple-disc vacuum filter, primarily because of the tank indentations for cake removal. It was based on the Genter patent applied for in 1918 and issued seven years later.

Vallez Filter. A somewhat similar device, but operating under pressure in a closed container and with non-sectionalized discs, was patented in 1916 by Henri Vallez, General Manager of the Bay City Sugar Company. Vallez had been experiencing trouble with the Sweetland filters due to the formation of pear-shaped cakes, which were difficult to wash. The logical procedure seemed to him to be to rotate the leaves so that all would pass through the same zone with consequent uniform cake building. This deduction proved to be correct, and the filters he so constructed gave satisfactory operation. Vallez filters are today used in sugar and other clarification work.

Filter Presses. Although the filter press was patented in the early 1800's the press as we know it today is largely the work of John Johnson of England, whether it be of the plate-and-frame type or the recessed plate design. In the early eighties Johnson devised some plate-and-frame filters for his own use, and these proved so successful that he entered the filter-press business. Johnson later came to America and started the John Johnson Filter Company. Shortly afterward T. Shriver and Company commenced building presses; their particular development was the Atkins-Shriver filter, patented in 1918, whereby a vertical press was equipped with arms for plowing off the cake as the press revolved. Their regular presses, however, were and still are standard. The Sperry, Shriver, Independent, etc., presses are all more or less alike in general design and construction, though differing in details, as a rule.

Hydraulic Press. With the success of pressure in handling extractions where vacuum was inadequate, there developed an interest in hydraulic pressure for oil extraction, primarily since here very high pressures were required. In 1877 Augustus Tucker, after ten years of experimental work, produced a hydraulic press for the extraction of juices from apples. A company was formed which has been actively pushing hydraulic presses since that time, particularly for extraction of oil from seeds, fruit, and cocoa beans.

Oil Extractors. Oil extractors and moisture expellers are products of the last thirty-five years or so, when there was applied the use of a tapering screw encased in a shell, as differentiated from the hydraulic press wherein the squeezing was performed between two or more rigid plates. In the former design the screw moves forward in revolving, the material being carried with it and the liquid being expelled at the same time. This idea was evolved from the pulp presses used in expressing water from spent cossettes in beet-sugar extraction.

While hydraulic presses and screw expellers have a rather limited field, they are of importance in this field and have contributed to many modern industries by performing a vital step in certain processes.

Oil Filters. With the discovery of mineral oil a great impetus was given to invention of separators of oil from water. The crude machines used for whale oil and vegetable oil separation were on too small a scale to be practicable. Differences in specific gravity were utilized by one type of machine, and filtering through filter cloth by another; both of these still have wide markets. Of the direct filtering designs, one of the most successful was that made for automobiles by the Puroil Filter Company in 1927, under Sweetland's patent, which consists of renewable metal cartridges. One important use of the oil filter was for cleaning exhaust steam for re-use, with consequent fuel saving. An interesting new principle applicable to separation of immiscible liquids by means of their surface and interfacial tensions has been proposed and is being developed at the present time.

Dust Collectors. Dust collectors, such as bag-house collectors, came into use to save the valuables lost in smelters and coke ovens. The great variety of gas filters, vacuum cleaners, air filters, etc., are a later develop-ment. The invention of the turbo-generator made the filtration of air a necessity, especially during the first world war; as a result, many improve-ments were made, the majority either employing a spray or wet surface to entangle the dust particles, or a direct filter medium. Today air-condi-tioning, blowers, etc. have created a great demand for filters of this type.

Edge Filters. Numerous other filters have been brought out; while different to some extent from existing types, often to a degree of marked improvement, as far as basis of design is concerned, they are still simply modifications of known types. There is one machine, however, which de-serves mention—the metallic edge filter. This filter, making use of closely laminated metallic layers as the filter media, was invented by F. H. Danchell of England in 1889. Its particular use is as a strainer for not too fine particles. After improvements made in England and the United States, many of these machines have come into use, especially for water clarification. The Cuno filter, brought out in 1931, is an Edge filter which has been widely used in railway water purification work, as well as in other fields.

Centrifuges. One of the first centrifuges was built by Penzoldt, a laborer in a piano factory in Paris in 1836. This was for separating solids from liquids, and was called a Hydroextractor. Seyring saw it and ex-ploited it, particularly in the sugar industry, obtaining an English patent in 1838.

Centrifuges, which depend on centrifugal force produced by high-speed rotation, were developed in two general types, the solid bowl and the perforated bowl. The former was largely used for separation of liquors of different specific gravities, the greatest application being found in the milk industry for cream separation.

In the perforated bowl type, crystals of salt, sugar, etc., can be whirled nearly dry. This type is widely used for such work.

In 1926-27 an attempt was made in Baltimore to use a large centrifuge (German built) on digested sludge, but it was unsuccessful because of the dirty effluent produced.

Many attempts at continuous centrifuges have been made, the ma-jority of which have been so complicated as to be impractical.

In 1933 Laughlin patented a continuous centrifuge, which worked successfully on the coarse solids.

Electrical Precipitation. Separation of dust from air by electrical precipitation is not actually filtration, but because of its importance in this class of work and its kindredship to filtration, it is worthy of some comment. The principle is not new, for as early as 1771 G. Bacarria re-corded observations on electrical discharges through smoke-filled gases.

In 1819 Rafinesque published an article in the *American Journal of Science and Arts* which was used as a basis for one of the first attempts at commercial electrical precipitation made in the 1880's by K. Moeller at Brachwede, Germany. This purported to be a large installation, but it was a failure and remained so until Cottrell began his work. In 1884 Hohfield suggested that electricity might be used for precipitating smoke particles. Guiyard in 1850 observed that if a wire charged with static electricity were plunged into a jar filled with smoke, clarification occurred.

The *Mechanics Magazine,* October 29, 1850, reported one experiment as follows: "Each portion of smoke would fly to the sides of the jar. The effect was perfectly magical. It is astounding to see how small a quantity of electricity produced a most powerful effect." These independent discoveries of the principle of electric precipitation remained in the realm of interesting experiments until 1863, when Lodge carried on more extensive investigations. The early experimenters were limited to extremely small quantities of electricity, as the largest static machine delivered only two-thirds of a milli-ampere. In 1866 Lodge and his associates applied the process to lead smelters, but the source of electricity was not sufficient to bring success.

Cottrell System. A few years later, when powerful electricity was available, Dr. Cottrell began his work. In the early years of the twentieth century a sulfuric acid plant located at Pinole in San Francisco Bay began to receive complaints about escaping acid fumes. Dr. Cottrell was asked to study the conditions and devise a remedy. He revived the Lodge experiments, and by 1905 his laboratory work had progressed to a point that justified building a commercial plant. The plant became a success, and today there are hundreds of such precipitators in operation, making recovery savings and eliminating fumes and dust nuisance.

Gas Cleaning. Gas cleaning was also attempted by means of filtration. In 1876 an Italian engineer, Belani, invented the first means of wetting blast-furnace gas to remove the flue dust. In 1884 H. Moeller was the first to filter dust from blast-furnace gases by using slag wool as the filter medium. This wool was blown from the blast-furnace slag itself.

Cataphoresis. Electricity has been applied to filtration through the phenomenon of cataphoresis (not to be confused with electrolysis) by several investigators, *e.g.,* the work of Count Schwerin on clays and peat moss, following that of Meister, Lucias, and Brunning. A hollow cylinder much like present-dry flakers was evolved to separate clays from impurities and some machines were constructed in Europe for this purpose. Making use of this electrical migration, patents were taken out in the United States by Dickey and Conrad, whereby a drum filter was aided in its vacuum filtration by cataphoresis, and Conkey filters were so constructed for special slurries difficult to handle otherwise.

Patents. As there have been over four thousand patents issued on filters and filtration in the United States alone since the opening of the patent office, not including centrifuges or special machines, any attempt at filtration history of this kind must necessarily consider only the most basic patents, and important filters in filtration development, with particular emphasis on the early history of filters as the foundation for the later work. Consequently this history of filtration has not included many later filter developments or new designs which have been recently brought out and are as yet unproved or seem to be of limited application, or otherwise not outstanding in general filtration development history.

References

1. Bolton, H. C., "Ancient Methods of Filtration," *Pop. Sci. Monthly* (1880).
2. Genter, A. L., *Sewage Works J.,* **6**, 694 (1934), and private correspondence.
3. Keefer, C. E., and Kratz, H. J., Jr., *Sewage Works J.,* **6**, 846 (1934).

Chapter 2

Theory and Principles of Filtration

General. Inasmuch as the separation or collection of suspended particles seems to have been a process always known to man, filtration is often thought of as an extremely simple operation, consisting merely of the straining out of solids from their liquids. Unquestionably, there is some justification for this in that until recently crude laboratory tests, field data, or rules of thumb were the almost universal approaches to any filtration problem.

In reality, filtration is one of the more difficult steps in chemical engineering. As such, it is desirable to have some understanding of the reaction of various materials under a definite set of conditions and the application of filtration principles in actual mechanical operation. Since any material will vary in its filterability with changing conditions, and as practically all materials differ under the same conditions, the complexity of filtration as a subject and the difficulty of applying any workable principles or formula become apparent. There are, however, some basic principles and mathematical formulas which are, sufficiently comprehensive to warrant considerable study.

In order to get as clear a picture as possible of the value of these principles and equations their development is given in considerable detail. This is particularly true of Hatschek's[6] work, as his was the first attempt to determine the underlying principles of filtration from a carefully evaluated, scientific point of view.

Hatschek started with the Poiseuille[3] formula for eddyless flow of liquids as the fundamental equation for all flow through filter cakes, a procedure which has been followed by others. He paid particular attention to particle size and filter septum, in the latter of which he differed somewhat from Lewis,[8] who followed him, with an empirical equation in a number of variations that sometimes neglected the resistance of the filter medium.

Sperry,[4] independently, without knowledge of Lewis'[7] work, developed an equation which included septum resistance with variables, in an attempt at a complete formula, while Ruth,[5b] in his recent work, gives a more tangible meaning to the constants, and seems to prefer to treat them as a separate equation, as do also McMillan and Webber.[1] The latter state that "it is generally admitted that strictly non-compressible sludges are rarely, if ever, encountered in industrial filtration. Thus we have essential agreement that a single constant pressure filtration equation is applicable to all types of sludges and basically the Sperry and Ruth[5] equations are similar."

Practically, as Genter[2] points out, "pressure produces filtrate flow simultaneously with solid packing into the cake" and "in reality the various factors of these equations in some way measure the physical properties of the solids involved. If we understand these properties, we can maintain sludge and filter conditions which influence economic optimal yields providing the filter itself is properly constructed, installed and operated." He then lists as follows the general factors to which he refers:

"1. Effective filter area.
2. Filtration pressure (pressure difference on two sides of septum).
3. Nature of solids (density, particle size, compressibility).
4. Water or solution present in sludge and filter cake and its density.
5. Rate of solids deposit in filter cake (from filtrate flow rate).
6. Resistance of filter base (cloth) to filtrate flow.
7. Resistance of filter cake to filtrate flow.
8. Time by which rate factors are measured.
9. Coefficient of viscosity of filtrate or sludge moisture.
10. Temperature."

"Through the construction and operation of mechanically operated filtration equipment the engineer aims to take advantage of these factors."

Poiseuille. In 1842 Poiseuille,[3] a French anatomist, published a formula for the eddyless flow of liquids under pressure through capillary tubes. This equation was checked by Darcy (1856)[2] and by King and Slichter (1897),[2] and proved to be correct also for flow through sand and various porous media. The formula, while not devised with filtration in mind, nevertheless is one from which all later filtration equations have been derived.

A simplified form of Poiseuille's equation for smooth flow through capillary tubes is:

$$V = \frac{\pi P r^4}{8Lu} = \frac{0.3927 P r^4}{Lu}$$

where P is pressure difference at tube ends,
r is internal capillary radius, L is length of opening,
V is flow velocity, and u is viscosity of the fluid.

Genter thinks that of prime interest here is the powerful effect of decreasing the radius of opening, *e.g.*, by reducing it to $\frac{1}{8}$ of its size the pressure must be increased over 4,000 times to get the same flow at the same tube length and viscosity. Conversely, doubling the radius produces 16 times as much flow with other factors constant.

Sperry's Filtration Equation,[4] wherein the above was used to establish the laws governing the flow of liquid through a filter cake is:

$$Q = \sqrt{\frac{2PKT}{R\%} + \left(\frac{KRm}{R\%}\right)^2} - \frac{KRm}{R\%}$$

where Q is quantity of filtrate, P is difference in pressure on two sides of the cloth, T is time of filtering, K is rate of cake deposit, $\%$ is per cent solids in sludge mixture, and Rm is resistance of filter base or cloth.

Ruth's Equation for this is:

$$(V + C)^2 = \frac{2A^2P}{\alpha Z} \left[\frac{1 - ms}{P^s}\right] (\theta + \theta_0)$$

where V is filtrate volume,
C is filtrate volume to produce a cake equal in resistance to the filter cloth,
A is filter area,
p is filtration pressure,
α is average specific resistance of dry solid,
Z is relative viscosity,
m is ratio of wet (solute-free) to dry cake weight,
s is weight fraction of solids in sludge,
θ is filtering time, and
θ_0 is theoretical time to form cake of resistance equal to cloth resistance present at start of filtration.

This is similar to Sperry's, but interprets $KRm/R\%$, relating to the filter base resistance, in terms of filtrate volume and provides for compressibility of solids, which Sperry said could be provided for by another factor in his equation.

With the above in mind and the caution that in actual plant operation equations are seldom considered, except as an indication of what effect variables may have on a filtration process, it still is most desirable to un derstand the equations which have been evolved. Therefore, the principles and formulas as set forth by the more prominent investigators will be gone into at considerable length.

Hatschek. Sixty-six years after Poiseuille, in 1908, Hatschek published his first article on filtration in the *Journal of the Society of Chemical Industry,* followed by a second article in the same journal in 1920. Hatschek was of the opinion that when materials once become ready for filtration the whole problem becomes a physical one, as the basis of operation is passage through a porous medium. On this supposition, Hatschek set up a definite relationship between particle size and filter medium voids. He stated that "the size of the pores in the septum is fixed, or has at any rate an upper limit; the largest number of pores of such size is, of course, desirable but this is a technical matter." The proper filter medium to select, therefore, was considered as the one with the largest number of these upper limit openings, within the range of permissibility and availability.

Hatschek continued with his line of reasoning in the following: "As soon as filtration commences, the pores in the surface of the filter medium are throttled, more or less by the particles which settle upon them, and, as it proceeds, the liquid has to escape through these throttled orifices and through a layer of particles of increasing thickness." This applies only to non-arching solids, and the further observation that "the structure of the layer is also fixed by the size and shape of the particles and for any given material remarkably constant," is applicable only to non-compressible solids.

Consideration of the size and shape of the particles is of importance, for uniform, solid, non-compressible spheres require smaller openings than do such solids when irregularly shaped, and they tend to form compact layers with restrictive voids. Elongated and uneven particles, on the other hand, will be held upon openings larger than themselves, and thus form "jackstraws" with maximum voids between themselves.

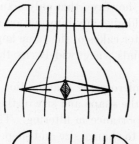

FIGURE 6a.

Particle in streamline. (*Hatschek*)

FIGURE 6b.

Particle in streamline. (*Hatschek*)

Hatschek further pointed out that particles tend to align themselves with the streamline, and that this depends upon velocity of flow and shape or particles, which naturally seek to arrange themselves so as to offer minimum resistance to the flow of the liquid. Limit values, therefore, are possible with particles of a certain shape. For example, if a particle has a rhombic pyramid shape, as shown in Fig. 6a, it may keep the position shown with respect to the streamline if the velocity is small, as the sector, that even at right angles to the latter, is such as to offer little resistance. With increasing velocities of flow, however, there will be the further effect of reducing vortices and the particles will ultimately assume the position shown in Fig. 6a.

The explanation given by Hatschek for cloudy filtrate clearing up without pressure change was that even precipitates of uniform composition contain small percentages of undersized particles. Hence these will be set in motion more quickly than the larger, and will reach the filtering surface first. There is then some throttling of the orifices of the medium by the larger particles which succeed the first flow of smaller ones. The throttled area might be small, but it would stop the small particles. He considered that this explained the statement often heard that it is not the filtering medium but the precipitate itself which acts as a filter. While this idea might hold true in leaf filters it seems contrary to observed facts in filter presses, where the larger particles are next to the filter base and the finer ones higher up. The larger particles settle more rapidly in the filter chamber, even though the velocity of particles due to filtration alone is the same.

He was correct in his observation, however, that only actual experience in the case of an unknown slurry could give any information regarding the filter-cake moisture content, since filter cakes of the same appearance and consistency but of different materials vary widely in their moisture content.

Hatschek particularly stressed microscopic examination of the solids to be filtered, in order to determine the shape and size of the particles, as he was much impressed by their importance in filtering. There was also the thought that it might be possible to change size and shape to get better filtering by altering the temperature or concentration, or both, of chemical reactions. The photomicrographs of Fig. 7 illustrate the variations in size and shape of a number of precipitates cited to emphasize this point.

Hatschek's work, as will be seen from the foregoing, consisted in pointing out the actual physical operation of filtration as he saw it, and in carrying out experiments in an attempt to prove his reasoning and deductions. In all his work he gave paramount importance to the filter medium, a point not generally agreed upon by later writers. On the other hand, his tests to prove that resistance to flow increases as the size of particles deposited in the cake decreases is conclusive, and is now an accepted principle of filtration. This follows from the Poiseuille equation, as already shown.

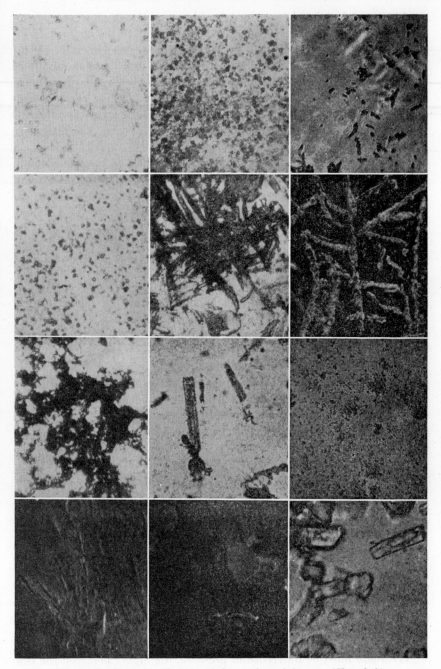

FIGURE 7. Variation in size and shape of precipitates. (*Hatschek*)

Almy and Lewis. It remained for Almy and Lewis,[7] however, to produce an equation (1912) which set down mathematically a formula intended to cover the process of filtration. Ruth and his associates (1935) in their "Studies in Filtration"[5] declared, "Existing filtration equations may be divided into two groups: those appearing in standard chemical engineering handbooks, termed the Lewis equation, and the various forms of the Sperry equation, as modified by foreign workers. The essential difference between them is the manner in which the effect of the filter base is treated."

The investigations of Lewis and Almy, which led to the formation of the Lewis equation, were carried out to determine whether the rate of flow was proportional to the pressure and the volume of filtrate could be expressed by the formula

$$R = K \frac{P^m}{V^n}$$

where R is rate of flow in cc per minute, V is the volume in cc per minute, and K is a constant. Their series of experiments, carefully detailed in their report, caused Lewis and Almy to conclude that the above formula was a true expression, the rate of flow through a filter cake not being as a rule directly proportional to the pressure and inversely proportional to the thickness of cake. It was concluded, therefore, that it was necessary only to determine the value of K, m and n to calculate the rate of flow at any pressure or thickness of cake, the rate being inversely proportional to the viscosity as expressed by K. The experiments of Almy and Lewis were upon chromium hydroxide and, according to Ruth,[5a] "their equation was generally accepted and by the logarithmic treatment of the data they secured the equation

$$\frac{DV}{D\_} = 13600 \frac{P^{27}}{V^{81}}$$

by means of which they were able to correlate their results through a pressure range to 5 to 100 pounds per square inch (0.4 to 7 kg per sq cm). Later this formula was modified to cover various conditions, although the position of the filter medium was not always clear."

Sperry. Sperry[4] in 1916 and 1917 published articles on the principles of filtration under constant-pressure conditions, wherein he lucidly described the elements of the simple operation of filtration and then passed to a formula to cover this procedure. Sperry started out with the "three indispensable conditions of filtration, *viz*:

   (1) there must be difference in pressure, the higher being on the side in contact with the mixture;

(2) there must be a filter base;

(3) there must be a filter consisting of a device to support the base and confine the mixture so the same may be placed under pressure and in contact with the filter base."

Sperry Permeability Formula. With the rate of flow known under definite conditions, Sperry stated it could be deduced from the general law under any conditions. Permeability was considered the factor that determined the rate of flow under known conditions. One of Sperry's valuable contributions at this point was the establishment of a factor for measuring permeability. The value set was defined thus: "A porous mass is said to have a permeability of 1 when a pressure of 1 lb per sq in produces a flow through a thickness of 1″ cake of 1 gallon per hour over 1 sq ft of area at 68°F."

Sperry concludes that filtration depends upon the seven following factors:

P, Pressure
T, Time
K, Rate of deposition of mixture
R, Resistance of the material
$\%$, Per cent of solids in mixture
RM, Resistance of filter base
T_1, Temperature of mixture

In addition, there are two other factors to be considered, he adds, namely, modifying pressure to allow for squeezing together of non-rigid solids as pressure increases, and the influence of gravity.

Sperry illustrated his discussion by primary drawings of a gravity filter, (Fig. 8). He showed that at the instant filtration commenced, the filter base is the entire filter medium, but, as filtration proceeds, the filter medium consists of both the base and the deposited solids; as the liquid in filtering must pass through the complete filter medium the flow decreases, assuming a constant pressure. There are thus two changing processes, he states, one the building up of the mass and the other the flow of liquid through the mass.

From this Sperry concluded that the study of instantaneous conditions there depicted reveals the fact that the rate of flow of the liquid through a porous mass is at that moment equal to the rate of flow which would obtain were there liquid only above it. "During the instant this layer of liquid is entering the cake the conditions are the same as though the liquid only were above. In actual conditions, of course, the particles of solids are not liable to be equally spaced in the liquid, but the effect of the principle is the same.

"The relation between the two processes—flow through cake and thickness of porous mass—can now be set down as follows: Rate of flow at any instant equals rate of flow of liquid only through the thickness of the porous mass at that instant. The relation between the two processes being now established, the next step is to investigate separately the laws governing each, and then by means of the common relation combine the two sets of laws to form the fundamental law of filtration." To check his deductions, Sperry formed a filter cake and measured the rate of flow through the cake under various pressures with clear water only. It was concluded that "the most interesting result of this test was the fact that it shows the rate of flow of the liquid through the cake varies as the first power of the pressure." This was due to the fact that "In non-sinuous flow the chief resistance to flow is caused by the viscosity of the liquid, while in the sinuous flow the chief resistance to flow is that due to friction between the liquid and the walls of the tube," as explained by Professor Osborne Reynolds in 1883.

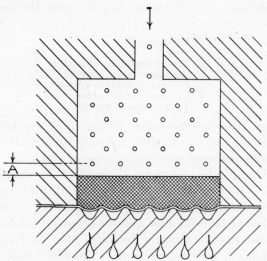

FIGURE 8. Conditions during one instant of filtration. (*Courtesy D. R. Sperry & Co.*)

There were numerous other investigators, each of whom stressed some particular point or points for consideration. A few of these will be mentioned.

Donald and Hunneman. In 1923 Donald and Hunneman[11] gave "four different methods of extracting the solid materials from the filtrate: (1) Constant-pressure: the pressure on the cake is kept constant during the run, and filtration is stopped when the volume of liquor delivered is too small; (2) constant rate: the volume of liquor delivered is maintained constant by gradually increasing the pressure during the run until the maximum pressure is reached; (3) and (4) with and without filter aid:

filter aids such as diatomaceous earth, etc., are used where the sludge is slimy and compressible." The paper described some of the work done by the Imperial College at London in investigating the application of the Lewis formula on a Sweetland press filtering "defecated sugars and syrups at a constant rate of flow, using kieselguhr as a filter aid."

Carman. It has been stated by Carman[12] in his excellent article "Fundamental Principles of Industrial Filtration," that the first essential of any filtration process is a filter septum capable of retaining solid particles suspended in a liquid and a pressure differential between the sides of the septum to drive the liquor through, leaving the solids behind as a filter cake. In particle sizes of 0.1 mm, shape and size were considered to play a part, but above this point the porosity and uniformity of particles gave assurance of a fairly constant rate. The void space was thought to be important, since it was realized that it formed a single tortuous channel of very complex shape.

Underwood. Underwood in 1926[9] concluded that "A consideration of published data shows that the rate of flow through a filter cloth appears to be proportional either to the square or the square root of the pressure according to the type of the filter cloth and the nature of the precipitate." Also that "A rational filtration formula has been proposed by Sperry, that the rate of flow through a filter cake is directly proportional to the pressure." It was also assumed that the flow through the filter cloth follows the same law. This idea has been developed by Alliot[16] and by Hinchley, Ure and Clark.[17] Underwood further stated that:

"(1)[2] Data yield is in satisfactory agreement with these formulas in cases where the resistance of the filter base is negligible compared to the filter cake.

(2) Where these conditions are not fulfilled, there is a lack of agreement, which can be expressed by the assumption that the flow through the filter cloth is not proportional to the first power of pressure but to some other power."

Bloomfield. Bloomfield,[10] discussing Hinchley's "Studies in Filtration," stated that "The total thrust (or the pressure) transmitted from the fluid prefilt to the solid support behind the filtering medium is communicated in two distinct ways: (a) through the skeleton of solid particles forming the cake, and (b) through the fluid in the interstices. It is fairly obvious that the hydrostatic pressure of the fluids must diminish progressively as it passes through the cake, from the total pressure difference P to zero at the back of the filter medium. It does not appear to be so clearly recognized that the thrust transmitted by the solid skeleton must be complementary to this, varying from zero at the surface of the cake to P at the back of the medium."

Walker and Lewis. In "Principles of Chemical Engineering" (1937) by Walker, Lewis, McAdams and Gilliland, it is stated that "Incompressible sludges are those for which an increase in the pressure on the press will not decrease the equivalent diameter of the voids between the particles. Actually it is doubtful if such sludges exist commercially." Sludges approaching incompressibility are free-filtering, and it is only the compressible sludges that are a filtering problem.

Ruth. In 1933 Ruth, Montillon and Montonna[5a] published a most interesting report of their investigation of filtration formulas and their conclusions therefrom.

They state that they used the "Lewis formula and the methods (analytical) of Baker, Waterman and Van Gilse as used by Jewett and Montonna, and the students for the first time in their scholastic experience encountered a physio-chemical phenomenon which at times displayed inexplicable, erratic behavior, and in no case exhibited a wholly satisfactory agreement with theory." They state further that Lewis and his co-workers have not attempted to picture the mechanism of the filtration process by means of which they arrived at the equation

$$R = \frac{r^{11}VP^s}{A^2 + t} \int \left(\frac{dV}{d\theta}\right) \frac{t}{V} dV.$$

Underwood,[9] Van Gilse and Van Gimmeken[22] and Pickard[24] have done so, and agree that as the suspended solids arrive at the filter surface or deposition zone of a filter cake they are impressed upon it with the entire force of the total pressure drop. Consequently they immediately contribute an additional resistance to the filtrate flow, equal to the value assigned to them by the concept of specific resistance, while the resistance of the cake previously deposited is supposed to remain unchanged. This is hard to reconcile with the appearance of a filter cake formed from a highly compressible material like ferric hydroxide. It would seem that filtration pressure itself can have no effect upon the shape of the material particles, although this is contrary to the opinion implied by some workers. They go on to say, "It is only unbalanced pressure that causes deformation and it results from the movement of the liquid relative to suspended solids. This occurs only when the latter are suddenly arrested in their free motion with the liquid by impinging upon the filter medium. The magnitude of this unbalanced pressure is equal to the kinetic energy lost by a column of water of equal area, when the column itself is deflected from its course by the arrested particle. At the surface of the cake this is small and serves only to hold the particles in place against the material previously deposited. In the layer of particles immediately below it a greater amount of kinetic energy is given up by the capillary streams, since flow becomes faster in order for the same quantity of liquid to pass through smaller openings. Thus each particle is acted upon by an unbalanced force equal to the cumulative thrust of all particles in the column above it and opposed by an equal force transmitted from the supporting septum upward through the column of particles below it. If the particles are deformable they tend to fill up the voids. This in turn requires the adjacent capillary stream of liquid to travel with still higher velocity. It is apparent that the magnitude of the viscous drag rapidly increases in the layer near the cloth. Only one citation could be found which adequately describes the pressure relation as postulated above." (Bloomfield)

Ruth further states, "When we recall that Hatschek,[4] Munning,[18] Hinchley, Ure and Clark[17] observed that when pure water is passed through a filter cake, the resistance varies with the pressure, the rate of flow, the total volume passing through and the time during which it is subjected to pressure, the problem of expressing R in terms of V from theoretical consideration of the above appears too complex to admit of solution."

"For rigid non-compressible solids it is possible to derive an equation by integration of the Poiseuillian differential expression which is quite valid. For compressible materials, however, we are unable to write R in terms of the variables affecting it. It is, therefore, impossible to integrate the equation upon a valid theoretical basis, and we are unable to predict with assurance what the exact relation between V and θ should be. It is undoubtedly parabolic, resembling the ideal non-compressible solids, but can only be approached from the experimental angle. As opposed to the Lewis equation are the treatments of Sperry,[4] Alliot,[16] Hinchley, Ure and Clark,[17] Van Gilse, Van Gimmekin and Waterman,[22] Underwood[9] and others, who agreed that the filter base must be an integral part of filtration equations. While Lewis' treatment recognizes the existence of press and filter base, its effect *per se* is not included in the integrated equation, although the method by which it might be treated has been indicated by the addition of a term or two of simpler differential expression. For this reason the Lewis equation was criticized by a number of workers. In order to avoid what has always been considered a complicated phenomenon, the Lewis equation seeks to dismiss the effect of cloth resistance by the ingenious plan of defining pressure P, to which $dv/d\theta$ through the cake is proportional, as the pressure drop through the cake alone. Webber and Hershey[25] state that although $P_t - P$ (Pressure drop through the base) is not a constant at the beginning of the filtration, it seems probable that by the time the total pressure (P_t) has been adjusted to a constant value, changes in the pressure due to pressure resistance will have become negligible, and that for most of the run a constant pressure will indicate a constant value of P."

Ruth[5b] wrote in 1937, "Although the theory underlying batch filtration, together with equations and methods for determining capacity, economic frame thickness, and optimum filtration schedules have been discussed by occasional writers over a period of years, a corresponding treatment of continuous filtration has not yet been presented." "From a theoretical point of view, no essential difference exists between the equations governing continuous filtration and those intended only for batch filtration. Since the former may be secured from a simple transformation of the latter, the 'filtration constants' determined upon a given slurry in a laboratory test press of the batch type should be directly applicable to the calculation of any desired quantity, such as the size or desired rate of rotation, which a continuous filter should have in order to filter the same type of slurry at a specified rate. Conversely, it should be possible to determine the filtration constant of a given slurry and the effective septum resistance of a continuous filter by observing the variations in its capacity at different speeds of operation. By comparing these quantities from time to time with such variations in slurry properties as are traceable to known causes, some degree of control might be exercised in the preparation or treatment of the slurry prior to filtration." "The information most frequently desired for engineering purposes is the relation between the total time of filtration and the amount of filtration accomplished."

"The equation developed should apply equally well to all types of continuous drum filters in which the filtration surface consists of a cylindrical drum," although it is somewhat different from problems which disk filters present. There should be control of particle size, agitation, etc., as well as clean discharge. Ruth's experiments showed inter-compartment leakage; they were not conclusive, but were a guide. He pointed out that in comparing batch and continuous filtration it must be remembered that in batch filtration ϕ represents the quantity of filtration performed in one cycle up to time θ. In a continuous filter, however, ϕ represents the amount of filtration accomplished per revolution. If, therefore, in continuous filtration ϕ is taken as the quantity per unit of time, $\phi = N$, where N is revolutions per unit time of the filter drum.

The Ruth constant-pressure filtration equation $(V + C)^2 = K(\theta + O_o)$ with some variations, depending upon the individual investigator, is one of the simplest and most accurate for all conditions, for both anticipation and interpretation.

According to McMillen and Webber, in 1938, in speaking of the new Ruth equations, "Predictions of larger-scale operations secured previous to this time when utilizing the Lewis equation were not satisfactory." They attributed this largely to the many formulas offered for different conditions and the various methods used in plotting test data.

Following Hatschek's idea, others have suggested that an attempt be made to obtain a table of values for specific resistance of all kinds of materials and also ascertain in what way various changes in operation and methods of preparation can affect its value. In this way design a press for a constant of the substance to be filtered.

New Sperry Formula. The most recent discussion of the theory of filtration is an article by D. R. Sperry.[4a] Of this he writes, "The following points were brought out, the method of derivation being a new simplified one.

"(1) The idea, when a given slurry is tested, of changing into constants all of the many variables with the exception of T and Q. This is done by selecting in advance constant values for what would otherwise be variable. The basic simple filtration equation thus may be used instead of the complicated general equation with its many symbols.

"(2) A graphical interpretation of the basic equation $Q = \sqrt{C}\sqrt{T+\dfrac{N^2}{C}} - N$ shows that $\dfrac{N^2}{C}$ is the time shift in axis and N is the quantity shift in axis of the ideal equation $Q = \sqrt{CT}$.

"(3) The determination of C has hitherto been a rather complicated process. The new equation presented is a simple way to find C. It is simply the difference between two consecutive quantity readings

$$C = \frac{Q_1 - Q}{\dfrac{T_1}{Q_1} - \dfrac{T}{Q}}$$

divided by the difference between their respective $\dfrac{T}{Q}$ ratios.

"(4) Since C is so easily found, it can be determined for several consecutive readings, thus making an accurate measure of the work performed, since all of the C's thus found must be alike. If they are not reasonably alike, steps must be taken to find the source of error.

"(5) The idea of 'start-run' resistance is given, showing that readings of a run may start any time after true filtration starts, even though considerable cake may be deposited. The ideal filtration curve is found regardless of the starting time after filtration commences.

"(6) The effect of sediment is discussed, showing that the thickness of cake is not necessarily proportional to the filtrate withdrawn, although the resistance is.

"(7) A method of recording, arranging and calculating filtration tests, as used by the writer, is given and an actual analysis is performed. A considerable number of analytical filtration results are given. A bibliography of filtration theory appears in the articles cited."

Conclusions. It is, of course, possible to derive equations for every conceivable filter activity and for every kind and type of filter, but while interesting, it is doubtful whether these would have any practical value. As previously pointed out, the operator or engineer can profitably use equations for anticipation of the effect of variations and for the translation of laboratory or pilot plant work into commercial operation.

Reduced to its basic terms, filtration has only three factors, all variable, for any given slurry at a constant temperature: namely, filter medium, filter cake and pressure differential; the object is to obtain the greatest capacity of the desired product in the shortest time or upon the smallest filter area (in a continuous-flow setup).

Therefore, whatever can be done to further these ends should be given first consideration, with the reservation that research is necessary for progress and that mathematical formulas play an essential part in this research with laboratory checkups as the first proving ground.

References

1. McMillan, E. L., and Webber, H. A., *Trans. Am. Inst. Chem. Eng.,* **34**, No. 3, 213 (1938).
2. Genter, A. L., *Sewage Works J.,* **13**, No. 4, 1164 (1941).
3. Poiseuille, J. L., *Compt. Rend.,* **15** (1842).
4. Sperry, D. R., *Chem. Met. Eng.,* **15**, 198 (1916); **17**, 161 (1917). *Ind. Eng. Chem.,* **13**, 986, 1163 (1911); **18**, 276 (1926); **20**, 892 (1928).
4a. Sperry, D. R., *Ind. Eng. Chem.,* **36**, 323 (1944).
5. Ruth, B. F., *Ind. Eng. Chem.,* **27**, 806 (1935).
5a. Ruth, B. F., Montillon, G. H., and Montonna, R. E., *Ind. Eng. Chem.,* **25**, 76-153 (1933).
5b. Ruth, B. F., and Kemp, L. I., *Trans. Am. Inst. Chem. Engrs.,* **33**, 34 (1937).
6. Hatschek, E., *J. Soc. Chem. Ind.,* 538T (1908); **39**, 226T (1920).
7. Almy, C., and Lewis, W. K., *Ind. Eng. Chem.,* **4**, 528 (1912).
8. Walker, W. H., Lewis, W. K., and Gilliland, E. R., "Principles of Chemical Engineering" 3rd ed., p. 397, McGraw-Hill Book Co., New York, 1937.
9. Underwood, A. J. V., *Trans. Inst. Chem. Engrs. (London),* **4**, 19 (1926); *J. Soc. Chem. Ind.,* **47**, 325 (1928); *Ind. Chemist,* **4**, 463 (1928).
10. Bloomfield, A. L., *Trans. Inst. Chem. Engrs. (London),* **3**, 38 (1928).
11. Donald, W. B., and Hunneman, R. D., *Trans. Ind. Eng. Chem. (London),* 197 (1923).

12. Carman, P. C., *Inst. Chem. Engrs. (London)*, **16** (1938).
13. Carman, J. C., *J. Soc. Chem. Ind.*, 1933, **52**, 280T.
14. Irwin, D. F., "Chem. Eng. Handbook," p. 1381, McGraw-Hill Book Co., New York (1939), *ibid.* (1941).
15. Sperry, D. R., private correspondence.
16. Alliot, E. A., *J. Ind. Eng. Chem. (London)*, **39**, 261T (1920).
17. Hinchley, J. W., Ure, S. G. M., and Clark, B. W., *Trans. Ind. Chem. Eng. (London)*, **3**, 24 (1925) *London J. Soc. Chem. Ind.*, 45IT 26.
18. Munning, Master Thesis, Mass. Inst. Tech. (1921).
19. Baker, F. P., *J. Soc. Chem. Ind.*, **13**, 610 (1921).
20. Reynoldes, Osborne, Inst. Civil Eng., Lec. to Students, 1883.
21. Waterman, H. I., and Dauvillier, A., *Rec. Trav. Chim.*, **45**, 628 (1926).
22. Waterman, H. I., Van Gimmeken, and Van Gilse, J. T., *Rec. Trav. Chim.*, **43**, 757 (1924) ; **45**, 628 (1926).
23. Jewett, E. E., and Montonna, R. E., *Chem. Met. Eng.*, **34**, 86 (1927).
24. Pickard, J. A., *Ind. Chem.*, **154**, 4186 (1928) "Filtration and Filters," London, Ernest Benn, Ltd. (1929).
25. Webber, H. C., and Hershey, R. L., *Ind. Eng. Chem.*, **18**, 341 (1926).
26. Hoxson, Work and Odell, *Trans. Am. Inst. Mining Met. Engrs*, **73**, 225 (1926).

Bibliography

Abrams, Farrow, Hartsook, S. M., Thesis, Mass. Inst. Tech. (1921).
Badger, W. L. and McCabe, W. L., "Elements of Chemical Eng.," 1st Ed. p. 456, McGraw-Hill Book Co., New York (1931). (1936).
Bain, S. W. and Wigle, A. E., *Chem. Met. Eng.*, **6**, 672 (1914).
Bellas, H. W., in "Chem. Eng. Handbook," 2nd ed. p. 1635, New York, McGraw-Hill Book Co. (1934).
Bible, N. N., Witte, M. A., and Donnel, J. W., *Ind. Eng. Chem.*, **31**, 1607 (1939).
Brumber, J. T., Thèses de la Faculté des Science de Toulouse, Douladoure Privat Toulouse (1881).
Bryden, C. L. and Dickey, G. D., "Filtration," Chemical Publishing Co., Easton, Pa., 1923.
Bull, H. B., *Kolloid—Z.*, **60**, 88 (1932).
Calvert, R., "Diatomaceous Earth," p. 130, New York, Reinhold Pub. Corp., 1930.
Comstock, S. B., Thesis, Mass. Inst. Tech. (1913).
Cogger, R. N., and Merker, H. M., *Ind. Eng. Chem.*, **33**, 1233 (1941)
Drew, Thesis, Mass. Inst. Tech., 1923.
Evans, *ibid.*, 1921.
Harris, E. W., *Ind. Eng. Chem.*, **34**, 1057 (1942).
Herman, P. A., and Bredee, H. I., *ibid.*, **55**, IT (1936).
Larian, M. G., *Trans. Am. Inst. Chem. Engrs.*, **35**, 623 (1939).
Olin, H. L., Morrison, F. W., Rogers, J. S., and Nelson, G. H., *Trans. Am. Inst. Chem. Engrs.*, **18**, 379 (1926).
Phillips, J. M., *Trans. Ind. Chem. Engrs (London)*, **3**, 35 (1926).
Porter, D. J., *Ind. Eng. Chem. (Anal. Ed.)*, **15**, 269 (1943).
Rhodes, F. H., *Ind. Eng. Chem.*, **26**, 1331 (1934).
Tatterfield, Thesis, Mass. Inst. Tech. (1922).
Walker, W. H., Lewis, W. K., and McAdams, W. H., "Principles of Chemical Engineering," 2nd ed., p. 366, McGraw-Hill Book Co., New York, 1937.
Young, G. J., *Trans. Am. Inst. Mining Engrs.*, **42**, 752 (1911).

Chapter 3
Filtration Objectives

General

Normally all filtration objectives in the separation of suspended solids from liquids or gases (the separation of dissolved solids from liquids being considered evaporation) fall into one of the following classifications:

    (1) Clarification for liquor or gas purification.

    (2) Filtration for suspended solids recovery.

    (3) Filtration for both solids and/or effluent recovery.

    (4) Leaching.

    (5) Facilitating other plant operations.

Since the points of importance differ, and since this fact affects the procedure, each is dealt with separately.

(1) Clarification

Clarification, as the name implies, refers to the removal of a relatively small quantity of suspended solids, usually for the carrying agent's purification, but at times for the recovery of valuable particles. In the latter respects this overlaps into Classifications (2) or (3).

The clarity of any liquid or gas is seldom absolute, even where brilliancy is called for; the degree of clarity is dependent upon its subsequent use, the individual project modifying the normal requirements. As an example, the extent to which fine suspensions may foul evaporator tubes determines the necessity of clarity in evaporator feed liquors; but the nature of the suspensions to be removed and the composition of the liquor to be concentrated may alter considerably the degree of the clarity requirements in any particular case. Again, in the polishing of sewage effluent, certain quantities of suspended solids are permissible, but the maximum and minimum allowance in any application depend upon local conditions.

With this in mind, the first approach to any clarification should be the degree of purification demanded, that is, the maximum allowable percentage of suspended solids in the filtrate, with the sometimes additional requirement of appearance, that is, whether filtrate brilliancy is a requisite.

Having established the effluent requirements, an examination should be made of the physical characteristics of the suspended solids to be removed—their size, shape and nature, *i.e.*, whether colloidal (not necessarily a true colloid, but as considered in filtration) semi-colloidal or crystalline.

True colloids exhibit Brownian movement, wherein the particles are in constant state of motion; these are unfiltrable directly, and with difficulty even with filter aids, concentration, cataphoresis, etc. The term *colloid*, as commonly applied in filtration, refers to those solids of such a weak structure that any appreciable pressure causes them to become distorted, either within or upon the surface of the filter medium, to the extent of filling the voids and sealing off the medium from further passage of filtrate.

Precoat and Filter Aids. Where particles of a colloidal or semi-colloidal nature are encountered in liquor clarification, a precoat and/or a filter aid are often necessary, to prevent the deposited particles from being carried by stream flow impact into the interstices of the filter medium, or filter cake after formation, thus stopping further filtration.

The precoat serves only as a protective covering upon the filter medium to prevent the particles from reaching its voids while the filter aid added to the influent serves only for particle separation in cake formation. The filter aid acts as an obstruction intervening between the particles to prevent their compacting and producing under the pressure velocity impact a more or less impervious layer in the filter medium, or if a precoat is used, upon it.

Coagulation. Another means of dealing with colloidal or semi-colloidal particles is coagulation. This applies particularly to clarification in water and sewage filtration and in industrial work to filtration of very fine solids. While floccing often can be accomplished by agitation, the use of a catalyst or, more generally, chemical treatment will cause the physical structure of the suspended solids to be changed to the extent of their losing their colloidal nature and becoming more or less crystalline, this usually being accompanied by agglomeration. Clarification by settling may follow, if the specific gravity of the particles is sufficient to give reasonably quick supernatant clarity; direct filtration may be resorted to if the filter area is not excessive or if complete supernatant clarity is demanded.

Temperature. Temperature, in its effect upon the viscosity, which in turn vitally affects the rate of flow, is a most important factor in any filtration, since the lower the viscosity the smaller the voids which can be penetrated by the liquor within a reasonable time. Occasionally temperature plays some part in altering the particle form or composition, and this will naturally affect the clarification rate.

FIGURE 9.   Clarification by coagulation.

pH.   This alteration of particles is also and to a greater extent true of the pH, proper control of which may result in a clarification otherwise impossible since an increase in alkalinity or acidity may change soft slimy solids to firm free filtering ones.

Filter Aids.   Small quantities of crystalline bodies may be present in the original mix; or they may be added for decolorizing, for absorbing or adsorbing impurities, or for other definite purposes, *i.e.*, sugar clarification, oil decolorizing, etc.   Whatever the reason for their presence, these crystalline bodies act as filter aids for improved filtration.

In some cases precoats are necessary, not because of danger of filter cloth clogging, but to allow the use of a coarser filter medium, such as metallic cloths, for longer life or for corrosion resistance.   With very fine particles which may be caught in the interstices of the filter medium where the medium will be discarded, as in blotter presses or milk clarifiers, no cake formation or holding of particles on the surface of the filter medium is attempted.

(2) Filtration for Solids Recovery

In filtration for suspended solids recovery the percentage of solids in the feed slurry must be high enough to permit a sufficiently thick deposit or cake formation for discharge as a solid mass before the rate of flow becomes materially reduced.   Cake building, cake discharge and cake washing are of vital importance in suspended solids recovery.

Cake Building. Since the filter cake is simply the solids which are left behind by the liquor in the feed slurry as it passes through the filter medium, and as the cake is formed by the collection of this layer of solids, the impact of the particles governs cake formation and structure.

Impact. The impact should be low enough at the beginning of filtration to keep the suspended particles from being driven into the filter medium voids to "blind" the medium, assuming the particles are small enough or of weak enough structure to be so driven.

Likewise, after filtration has started, the impact of succeeding particles must not scour the cake already formed or drive the particles into the voids of this cake, and finally must not compress or flatten the cake particles to the extent of checking the rate of flow. That is, the flow must not be reduced over the normal falling off with increased cake thickness, due to resistance caused by the increasing tortuous filtrate passages, except the compression encountered in plate-and-frame presses.

While the rate of flow is caused by pressure differential, the optimum is just below the point at which void particle filling or particle distortion takes place, which would more than offset the normal increase in rate of flow due to pressure increase.

The more open a cake the greater the rate of filtration, assuming that the structure is sufficiently firm to prevent scouring or washing away. This open cake, as stated previously, is the result of particle size, particle shape, particle structure and impact. Not only does the open cake increase the rate of flow through itself, but it decreases the septum resistance by enabling a more open medium to be used, since arching can be taken advantage of. This is to the extent of increasing the voids to a greater size than the particles themselves.

The velocity of flow and the compressibility of solids determine cake structure, rapidity of cake building, and consequently length of cycle. This is not altered by the fact that other considerations determine the actual thickness of deposit, such as particle size, concentration, temperature, pH, etc.

Rate of Flow. As given, the rate of flow is caused by pressure differential and is greatest at the start of filtration, falling off rapidly as cake formation commences, unless maintained by increased pressure. The constant-rate or the constant-pressure method is effected in the practical sense—which is the capacity of the filter—by solids concentration, temperature, and pH, more than by anything else. This, of course, is for a given slurry, not a comparison of slurries, and assumes that the proper filter medium has been selected and the most desirable cake formation obtained so that these resistance factors may be discounted.

Compressibility. For a given slurry, the compressibility or particle structure is probably the most important factor in rate of flow, in cake washing and in cake moisture, because it determines the cake porosity.

Temperature. As stated previously, the lower the viscosity of a liquor, the more rapidly it will penetrate a given porous body, and since the higher the temperature the lower will be the viscosity of the liquors filtered, the desirability of maintaining as high a temperature as economically possible during filtration can be appreciated. There are cases, of course, where this is more than offset by the effect of temperature elevation upon the physical structure of the solids, as in dewaxing of lubricating oils.

Naturally, the more viscous a liquor the more marked will be the visible improvement in the filtration rate by increasing the temperature; yet all lowered viscosity shows an increase. For example, a difference of 50° in some oils will show a 500 per cent increase in rate of flow.

Concentration. The concentration of suspended solids is of prime importance in cake building, in that the greater the concentration the lower will be the density of the cake. Since the impact is less, the cake will be built up the more rapidly as the percentage of solids per unit of filtrate increases, and from the rate of flow standpoint, the greater will be the agglomeration and the easier the separation of the solids from the liquids; hence the greater the filter capacity.

Many slurries will not filter at all (without filter aids) in the dilute form, but as they become concentrated they filter more and more easily, apparently starting from the point at which the particles approach one another within a distance of less than five times their diameters. The action appears similar to crystal growth in concentrations of saturated liquors, although actually in slurry concentrating the particles cohere, probably because, as they approach one another, their electromagnetic charges become strong enough to be effective.

pH. The pH as a rule does not vary greatly with an individual slurry and it is difficult to make variation or changes to increase filter rates, although at times this is possible. The structure of the particles may be changed by the increased or decreased alkalinity or acidity, which often transforms a weak colloidal structure to a rigid crystalline-like body, *i.e.*, primary sewage sludge at a pH near 7.0 is very difficult to handle, but at 9.5 it is free-filtering when conditioned with ferric chloride. This pH effect varies widely with different materials, but is surprisingly constant with any given type.

Agitation. Lack of proper agitation may cause strata of varying solids concentration, particularly with stationary leaf filters, and produce cakes of uneven thickness, with consequent poor washing and poor drying.

Other Factors. In addition to the above, which deals with an individual slurry, there is a factor which is often present, but not considered, namely, the presence of impurities in varyng percentages, depending upon the raw material source. It is too often assumed that the slurry is always the same, and changes in filtering rates have therefore been baffling to the operator; *viz.,* the increase in silica impurities will improve clay filtration as a rule, by decreasing the total solids compressibility, but the presence of magnesium in caustic calcium carbonate filtration is decidedly detrimental due to the opposite effect. Not only is the uniformity of the raw materials from varied sources important, but there must be uniformity from the individual supplier if uniformity in filtration is to be expected.

Shape and Structure. Particle shape and particle structure are of great importance to rate of flow and cake porosity, although it is not often that they can be controlled. Large, irregular crystalline particles of uniform size give the greatest rate of flow and most porous cake, the latter being best suited to cake washing and cake drying.

There is a distinct difference in cake structure depending upon the type of filter used. A plate-and-frame press confines the solids in a frame, and as filtering progresses the particles are pressed closer together, decreasing the void area until the entire frame is filled with closely packed particles.

In leaf or drum filters this does not occur, as the cake is not confined but built to a definite thickness with little compression. With continuous filters the cake is automatically removed and there is not the danger of the cake becoming too thick, as in the intermittent-leaf type. Here, as the leaves are on definite centers, overlong cake building may easily result in the cakes building up until they come together; this causes very difficult cake washing, drying and discharge problems, with the added danger of leaf distortion.

Cake Thickness. Filter capacity in clarification is measured in gallons of filtrate per square foot per hour, including the time required for cleaning, readjusting (precoating if necessary), and filter draining and filling. In the filtration for solids recovery, capacity is measured in terms of pounds of dry solids per square foot per hour, including the time for washing and drying (if part of the cycle), discharge, and filter draining and filling.

The thinner the filter cake, the more quickly can it be washed and dried; hence as thin a cake as can be discharged cleanly will give the greatest capacity, except in the case of plate-and-frame presses, where the frames must be filled.

Cake Washing. On the other hand, a thin cake may shorten the cycle too much, so that there is a disproportionate time for washing and discharge.

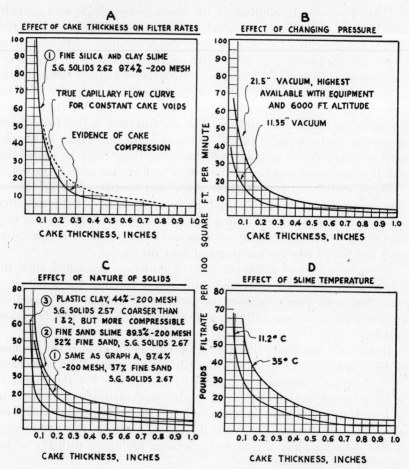

FIGURE 10. The effect of increasing cake thickness on filtration rates. (*Genter* [2])

If objectionable slurry liquors other than water are present, it becomes necessary to wash the filter cake in order to make a clean separation of the solids from the mother liquor or the mother liquor from the solids, depending upon which is valuable. In cake washing, the formation as to void and thickness uniformity is all-important, for equi-resistance is the prime requisite of wash uniformity.

Since there is no cake deposition in washing, the rate of flow is nearly constant, and where unequal resistance is present, the wash liquor follows the line of least resistance. This results in a large quantity of wash liquor being used with only partial cleaning of the cake.

In washing the mother liquor held in the voids of the filter cake as the moisture content must be removed first. Normally the displacement of this liquor is readily accomplished. The difficulty lies in removing the mother liquor which surrounds each particle as a film and is present at the point of contact of the particles. As it is held by surface tension, this mother liquor must be washed out by diffusion.

Often separation of the wash liquor into different degrees of concentration is required. The first wash, which will be high in mother liquor, must be separated from the original filtrate, as well as from the succeeding wash, in each of which the mother liquor content is progressively less.

In such a situation the make-up of the first wash liquor is commonly composed of the final wash liquor of the previous run. This does not hold true, of course, where the final wash is a neutralizer or other special liquor. With solubles difficult to wash out and for clean separation, it is often necessary to discharge the cake, repulp with wash or clean liquor and refilter, sometimes repeating this cycle several times.

Mathematically, the mother liquor left in the cake can be estimated and the number of repulpings necessary determined. For example, if the slurry has a 40 per cent soluble salt content and the filter cake a moisture content of 40 per cent before application of wash liquor, the soluble salts in the cake moisture content amount to only 16 per cent of the wet cake weight. If now the wash liquor reduces this by 90 per cent the filter cake (40 per cent moisture) is discharged into the repulper with 1.6 per cent of soluble salts. Repulped with wash liquor to a 70 per cent liquor slurry consistency, the soluble salts are reduced to 0.80 per cent in the slurry, and to 0.32 per cent in the subsequent filter cake. If 80 per cent reduction is obtained in the wash, the filter cake will be discharged with 0.064 per cent of soluble salts; and if this is too much another repulping can be made. Often in practice washing reduces the soluble salts 95 per cent or more, but the above is indicative of how definite reductions can be estimated, the one unknown being the wash reduction, although the 80 per cent used checks as a good plant average.

Cake Cracking. Occasionally cakes crack on washing due to shrinkage, usually caused by the lower viscosity of the wash liquor. In such cases a cloudy wash, one in which some washed cake has been added to the wash liquor, may be used for crack filling and restoration of uniform washing.

Submergence, where the filter cake is completely submerged in the wash liquor, as in closed-leaf presses, vacuum dewaterers or open-tank vacuum leaf filters, is the ideal method of washing. Theoretically, the mother liquor is pushed ahead of the wash liquor as a solid wall, thus quickly replacing the void mother liquor with wash liquor and giving the best final separation by diffusion.

If, in a theoretical case, a curve were plotted, using effluent mother liquor concentration as the indication of washing efficiency, a higher mother liquor concentration would continue for some time as nearly a straight line, while the filtrate was being solidly pushed ahead of the wash liquor. Then the line would drop abruptly as the wash liquor wall passed completely through the cake. The weak mother liquor concentration would continue thereafter in a slowly falling line to neutrality, somewhat as indicated in Fig. 11.

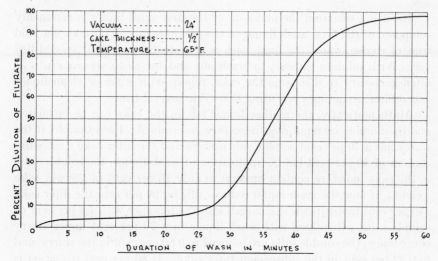

FIGURE 11.   Cake washing curve.

Sprays. The use of sprays upon drum filters, if properly selected, may flood the cake surface and approach the effect of a submergence wash. This is of particular importance where a thorough washing is necessary of a cake which tends to crack if exposed to the air. Here an excess of wash liquor is used to flood the cake, and if this excess is great enough to dilute detrimentally the feed slurry in the filter vat, a gutter may be used for diversion of this wash liquor for re-use or discard.

In the selection of sprays, wash liquor permissible, quantity of wash liquor which can be sent through the cake in a given time, and the tendency of the cake to channel, must be considered. Channeling must be considered particularly important, since washing does little good if the bulk of the liquor passes through channels. In vertical disc filters where washing is applied by sprays, it is extremely difficult to obtain or to approach flooding, even with mist sprays, since the wash is applied at right angles to the filter cake and against gravity. At the same time the danger of scouring is greatly increased by the attempt to get sufficient wash liquor onto the cake. This usually results in inefficient washing, although with easily washed materials the degree of wash obtained on disc filters often is sufficient for the needs.

Vacuum filters have a natural advantage in washing in that the pressure differential source is behind the filter medium; and this tends to distribute the wash evenly, no matter what the cake formation; and as vacuum is definitely limited to a low differential figure, uneven cake formation is rare and compression is avoided. All of these factors makes washing fairly easy.

This does not mean that washing is not a feature of filter presses. With solid, even though compact cakes, the wall-like passage of wash liquor will still hold good despite the higher differentials required.

Cake Drying. The degree of filter cake drying depends upon the individual requirements, but meeting the requirements depends upon the cake structure, assuming the filter construction and filter medium are correct. As in washing, a porous, uniform cake is the most desirable for drying if air or drying gas is to be passed through it, as in leaf and drum filters. On the other hand, in the filter press, where the cake is built by compression, a dense hard cake is necessary to give a dry cake discharge.

Whether cake drying is by air or some other gas, when once the filter cake is exposed, drying takes place largely by entrainment; thus the greater the quantity of drying agent passed through the cake, the dryer it will be. In this passage the higher the air or gas temperature, the more moisture will be picked up by it, for although it carries the moisture mechanically, the velocity impact at the higher temperature is on a reduced surface tension. This means that more liquor is removed from the filter cake per cubic foot of drying agent per unit of time.

The velocity of the drying agent through the cake, caused by pressure or vacuum, is economically determined by the filter cake, the filter medium and the drainage line resistance. A certain number of cubic feet of air or other gas can be sent through a square foot of the filter cake at a certain differential during the drying section of the filtering cycle. The volume is directly proportional to the differential, and the economical point is where further decreased moisture does not justify the increase in power or time to obtain this reduction.

This is most pronounced in very free-filtering material, *viz.*, crystals where a vacuum of 6 to 10 inches with an air passage of 30 to 60 cfm per square foot of filter area is common practice, with a resulting discharged cake of low moisture content. A higher vacuum would greatly increase the air volume as the resistance is low; but it would also greatly increase the horse power with only a small decrease in the final moisture content, and therefore probably would not be justifiable.

The assumption has been made in the above that the proper filter medium has been selected for least resistance to flow and also the proper filter design, with particular reference to restriction of drainage lines. This assumption is necessary, for otherwise a considerable proportion of the pressure differential would be expended before reaching the filter cake.

Other factors being considered, the cracking of a filter cake, due to shrinkage upon drying, usually determines the length of the drying cycle and excess air provisions. When cracks appear, the air immediately escapes through them rather than through the filter cake and little drying is accomplished thereafter.

In drum vacuum filters devices are available such as rolls, flappers, endless belts and pressure shoes for ironing out cracks if they occur. One of the most effective of these is the pressure roll used in handling of bicarbonate of soda, where very high pressures are used, often reducing the cake moisture from 22 per cent to 11 per cent. Bicarbonate of soda happens to be a free-filtering material, forms a firm crystalline cake, and readily responds to rolling for moisture release. Other materials may be too soft, have too weak a structure, or too low a coefficient of cohesion to make such devices practicable, so their use is distinctly limited.

Cake Discharge. The completeness of the cake discharge ranges from removal of the entire cake, as in the flushing discharge of pressure-leaf filters, to only partial removal, which leaves a permanent layer on the filter, as in fiber de-oiling with single-compartment vacuum-drum filters.

The degree of discharge with specific requirements is dependent upon the cake structure. If there is any tendency for the solids to become lodged in the interstices of filter medium, complete discharge is not only desirable but usually a necessity. This is most readily accomplished in a filter press in which the plates and frames are moved apart by hand and the filter cloth can be easily washed before re-use, if necessary.

With permanently fixed cloths in leaf or drum filters, cake loosening and cleaning require reverse pressure. This is readily accomplished by air blow-back if the cake is well formed and has a greater coefficient of cohesion than of adhesion.

In clean discharge the imprint of the filter cloth is left on the cake and the medium itself is open and free. A smooth surface, as on a metallic cloth, is likely to give the easiest clean discharge, although fabric cloths give excellent results, and because of their lower price are more generally used.

A rough surface or long nap used for clarity will be more difficult to discharge if the filter cake is tacky, thin, or sticky. Precoating is often used simply to aid in discharge, and its effect is protection of the cloth by making clean discharge possible.

With thin cakes and those difficult to remove, if dryness is not of consequence, sluicing by direct spray or jets against the cloth is resorted to. This may or may not be accompanied by blow-back of air, steam or water.

Discharge Medium. Air is the preferred blow-back medium since it is normally readily available, does not add moisture to the cake of itself, and is clean. Steam will add heat (although air can be heated) and also acts as a lubricant between the medium and the cake; but it is more easily dissipated than air, may wet the cake, and is usually more expensive. Water gives the most positive blow-back discharge, but wets the cake and strains a fabric medium.

Where dryness is important, vent pipes or blow-back baffles should be used with scraper discharge drum vacuum filters or strings may serve the purpose where air is not used for discharge. Again, the entire filter medium with adhering cake may be carried endlessly over or through a dryer.

Discharge is seldom so complete that a filter cloth is restored to its initial porosity, but in many cases after a short period of service an equilibrium is reached, where practically no further void reduction occurs.

Actually the replacement of filter cloths is as often due to gradual clogging as to cloth wear. Lack of complete cake removal may cause smearing or compression of the left-over solids into the medium voids, finally resulting in more or less complete clogging of the cloth.

The importance of a clean discharge is the condition in which the filter medium is left, since this will have a direct bearing upon the rate of flow, cake deposition, washing and drying in subsequent runs.

(3) Filtration for Both Solids and Liquor Recovery

Cake building, washing and drying for both liquor and solids recovery differs from filtration for solids recovery only in the care which must be exercised in operation. If the filtrate is valueless, excess wash liquor can be applied without regard to quantity, time permitting; but if it must be saved, maximum use must be made of the allowable wash liquor in its passage through the filter cake. There should be no uneven structure or variation in thickness, and clean-cut separation of mother liquor from wash liquor, and of the various wash liquors one from another, must be striven for. This goes back to cake formation for porosity and uniformity in depth, and equipment design and plant operation for clean separation.

If the liquor is valuable, progressive washing is generally resorted to, the final wash being used as a make-up liquor for first application.

Dryness is likewise important unless the washing has removed all solubles and repulping is to follow; even so, the dryer the cake is before washing the fewer are the wash liquor requirements.

(4) Leaching

Leaching, or the dissolving of some of the constituents of the solid particles by a solvent, is not in itself filtration, but the two are often combined in one operation. The use of false-bottomed tanks formerly was common practice where the residue was washed and dried after application of the solvent, as in straight filtration; and this procedure is still followed to some extent.

Occasionally a cake is built upon filter leaves or drums and the solvent applied as a leaching wash, followed by an ordinary liquor wash and drying.

Countercurrent decantation or agitating and settling with decantation, however, is largely used on this class of work, often followed by straight filtration for final separation.

(5) Facilitating Other Plant Operations

Filtration, like other steps in plant operation, bears most immediate relationship to the steps immediately preceding and following it. Before filtration, the step is largely one of preparation for filtration, if difficulty is anticipated in direct filtering, i.e., thickening, coagulating, heating, conditioning, etc. It may be a question of pH adjustment, or the production of an unstable floc, which must not be broken by rapid pumping or agitation prior to filtration. This preparation is primarily to obtain a more filtrable material, and thus to permit use of continuous filtration, smaller filter areas, or both.

There is naturally a certain flexibility in the various types of filters which gives an opportunity of meeting a set of conditions preceding filtration that cannot be changed, to which conditions the filter must be adapted.

The filter in turn is the preparatory factor in the step following filtration. This may be drying or incineration for the solids, and concentration or direct use for the filtrate. The filter then must be selected to deliver the best feed material to the next step, or if this is impossible, there must be modification to meet the limitations of the filter.

A dry, thin, porous, broken cake is best for drying where grinding is not used, as it is not likely to ball up, case-hardening is reduced, and quicker drying can be obtained, since the heat will come in direct contact with all sides of a small particle, and the insulating effect of the material itself is reduced.

A clear, concentrated filtrate usually aids further treatment following filtration, and the filter can often be so operated as to increase the efficiency of the following equipment without affecting its own efficiency.

In any case, the ideal arrangement is a smooth, continuous flow through the plant; provision should be made to avoid shutdown, which will hold up delivery of feed to the filter and cause shutdowns following the filter for lack of discharge from it, or filter shutdowns which will cause stoppage for lack of filter discharge. Extra filter area, feed storage supply tanks and discharge storage space are always desirable in a synchronized operation to prevent one piece of equipment from throwing all the others out of step.

Chapter 4

Preparation for Filtration

In the preparation for filtration three broad divisions are usually made:

    (1) Classifying, thickening, and settling.

    (2) Coagulation and conditioning.

    (3) Filter aids and precoating.

(1) Classifying, Thickening, and Settling

Classifying, as generally considered, is the separation of mixed suspended solids according to their size and specific gravity. This may be accomplished by water jets, as in coal grading; by plain settling tanks, as in the separation of sand and clay; in special classifiers, as in metallurgical work; or in centrifuges, as in some salts separation.

Thickening and classification are two different operations, although both may be accomplished in a thickener at the same time by overflow of the fines and bottom collection for thickener underflow. Basically, thickening is solids concentration, and classifying is the separation of the slow-settling from the rapid-settling particles. Settling also may be considered as classification and thickening, with the emphasis on concentration by gravitation.

Anable and Knowles state:[1] Thickening or concentrating is the gravitational settling of the solid particles that are suspended in a liquid, the removal of the bulk of the solids from the bulk of the liquid under the influence of gravity alone. Stokes Law for spherical grains, as given below, is of little practical value in thickening calculations, but is of interest because it shows what factors have an effect on the settling rate or terminal velocity of a particle and the relative magnitude of the various effects.

"The formula: $V = 3{,}246\ D^2(d_s - d_l)$, where V is terminal velocity in cm per min., D is diameter of the spherical grain in mm, d_s is density of solid as specific gravity, d_l is density of the liquid as specific gravity. Here 3,246 is a constant. The formula unfortunately deals only with free-settling particles, whereas in the process industries particles are often originally in physical contact with one another and this is always the case in the final or compression zone of sedimentation.

The actual test procedure in use today is based not on the work of Stokes, but on that of Coe and Clevenger and later of Deane, who showed that for any zone of settling between feed and discharge dilution the settling area required can be expressed as $A = 1.33(F - D)/R$, where $A =$ settling area in sq. ft. per ton per 24 hrs.; $F =$ feed dilution (*i.e.* ratio of liquid to solids by weight); $D =$ final dilution; and $R =$ settling rate, in ft. per hr.

To use this formula, tests must be made to determine the settling rate, R, in zones ranging from feed to discharge dilution and the maximum unit area, A, which, in turn, will determine the size of the thickener."

Settling occasionally is long enough to separate completely all the solids from all the liquids, except in the case of material like sewage solids which retain 8 to 10 per cent moisture indefinitely; on the other hand classifying, by its nature, never gives, and thickening seldom gives complete separation. Yet as an adjunct to filtration for complete separation, both are of great importance in making difficult materials filtrable, in cheapening the filtration process of others, and in separation of mixed solids allowing one type of filter to be used for overflow and another for under flow (from a thickener) and the filtering rate of both can be improved.

While there is a distinction between classifying, thickening and settling, in their relationship to filtration they all have the common factor of being the prior step. So considered, and as the first step in the separation of solids from liquids, with filtration the second step and drying the third, a hypothetical case would show that the first step might reduce the feed dilution from 20:1 to 1:1; the second step, filtration, might carry it from 1:1 to 20 per cent moisture (dry basis), and the third step, drying, from 20 per cent to the per cent dryness required.

Normally the costs of the three steps increase from the first to the last. Considering the first two, the costs are often given in the ratio of between four and eight. This is of considerable importance, particularly with dilute solutions, where it is usually cheaper to remove 95 per cent of the initial liquid by thickening, 4 per cent by filtration, and the remaining 1 per cent by drying.

Since the settling rate is governed by that of the slowest-settling particles, these must be considered first when deciding upon the thickener area; the area varies inversely with the settling rate.

In the division of solids by Zsigmondy, the mean diameter of the particle determines its classification; *i.e.*, suspensions are particles of mean diameter greater than 0.0001 mm, colloidal solutions are particles under 0.0001 mm and over 0.000005 mm, while true solutions are particles under 0.000001 mm in mean diameter. This is accepted generally, the metallurgical separation of particles coarser than 200 mesh being considered as sand and those finer than 200 mesh as slimes. Most slurries have variable particle sizes from fine to coarse, with only slight quantities of colloidal matter, except in trade wastes, sewage or clays.

The colloidal particles are of importance because of their effect on the settling rate. In the colloidal state, where the particles remain in suspension, the force of gravity is counterbalanced by surface energy and Brownian movement. According to many writers, the stability of colloidal particles is due to the adsorption of either the positive or negative ions from the dissociation of compounds, and to the mother liquor or solvents. Like charged particles mutually repel each other for continued dispersion and continued suspension.

Thickeners consisting of plain settling tanks have been used for many years, but classifiers had to wait for the machine age for their development. On the other hand, thickeners have been continually improved to aid gravitation. The standardized thickeners with their collection arms, the Boston tanks with their elaborated Pachuca system, inverted cones, Imhof tanks, and modified filters such as the tube and filter-press thickeners, all have contributed to thickening. Their function in most cases is to handle suspended solids which approach in specific gravity the liquid in which they are suspended.

In collecting arm thickeners, the settled solids are continuously raked to the center of a circular or end of a rectangular tank, for continuous or intermittent discharge, while the fines overflow the top and are carried off by an overflow launder. New designs have been introduced recently in thickeners, particularly those of large diameter. In one a hydraulic lifting device, operating automatically in response to load conditions, makes it possible to employ thickeners for temporary storage of settled solids, when operating on certain types of pulp. This should in many cases smooth out tonnage surges as well as enable operators to shut down the mechanism without the necessity of pumping out all settled solids. The arrangement of a large thickener with hydraulic lifting device is illustrated in Fig. 12.

In classifiers, the solids are raked by reciprocating or continuous rakes up an incline for top discharge with the fines falling back for overflow collection.

The filter-press thickener consists of a standard press with spiral-type plates and frames. Each frame contains a spiral groove which starts at one corner and spirals to the center, where it passes through the frame and spirals outward on the other side of the frame to a different corner. The press is not opened during operation, but operation is intermittent in that the slurry is circulated and recirculated by batches, until sufficient clear liquor has been removed through the filter medium to give the desired slurry thickness.

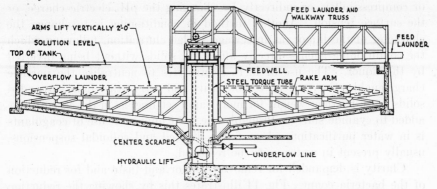

FIGURE 12. Thickener. (*Courtesy General American Process Equipment*)

FIGURE 13. Press thickener. (*Courtesy T. Shriver & Co.*)

(2) Coagulation and Conditioning

Coagulation and conditioning are used to make unfiltrable or poor filtering slurries relatively easy to handle; coagulation is almost always used in conjunction with thickening. It may be the result of temperature rise. An increase of 10°C in certain cases has changed the thickening and filtering capacity 100 per cent.

Mechanical or chemical coagulation or flocculation causes minute particles to coalesce, corrects pH, liberates the electrostatic charge, or by recirculation promotes increase in particle size, which will alter completely the settling and filtering characteristics of the suspended solids. Such other factors as increased temperature, elimination of convection currents, or the use of special devices as vertical fingers to release liquor occluded in a sludge, yield a denser, more compact sludge for easier filtration.

Conditioning is employed to coagulate by chemical action, either by directly changing the physical structure of the solid particles as to shape or compressibility, or indirectly by changing the pH, electric charge, or the surface tension. Another method of conditioning is to change the character of the liquor, as in sewage sludge elutriation, following which the conditioning agents directly affect the solids without being diverted by the liquor. The use of inert electrolytes to neutralize the particle charge enables the particles to floc easily and carry other light suspended solids down by their weight for more rapid settling, as in the case of lime added to cyanide slurry. Probably the most important use of coagulants is in water purification, where finely divided and colloidal suspensions, usually present in water, must be removed.

Clarity is demanded for removal of odor and taste and for reduction of the bacteria count. Fig. 14 illustrates this by showing the reduction

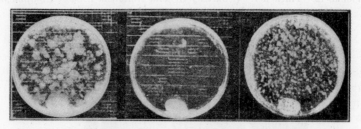

FIGURE 14.   Reduction in bacteria by filtration.

due to filtration with particular reference to typhoid fever. This does not mean that clear water is pure water. It does demonstrate that bacteria largely feed on suspended solids and that removal of the latter materially reduces the number of bacteria present.

The kind of coagulant to employ for water coagulations, while dependent upon local conditions, is normally either aluminum or iron sulfate; aluminum sulfate is most extensively used, as it is always safe. The use of aluminum compounds for water coagulation probably originated in China thousands of years ago, but up to the last thirty-five or forty years it was not looked upon with a great deal of favor because of the idea that coagulation produced an ill effect upon the health of communities using water so treated. At the present time, however, the use of coagulants is common practice in water purification and is endorsed by health authorities.

In the use of aluminum or iron sulfate [$Al_2(SO_4)_3 \cdot 18H_2O$ or $Fe_2(SO_4)_3 \cdot 18H_2O$] there is formed, on its addition to water containing colloids, positive trivalent Al or Fe, which precipitates the negative colloids. At the same time the negative divalent (SO_4) precipitates the positive colloids and the ferric and aluminum hydrates form a heavy floc. This heavy floc in its settlings carries colloidal suspension by entanglement and adsorption. At times lime is used with aluminum sulfate, giving the reaction $Al_2(SO_4)_3 + 3Ca(OH)_2 = 3CaSO_4 + Al_2(OH)_6$. Again, ammonium alum, black alum, or other combinations are favored.

The quantities of different coagulating chemicals depend upon local requirements and the percentage of available aluminum and iron present, if their sulfates are being considered. Very turbid or highly colored water frequently requires several grains of coagulating chemical per gallon. This quantity may be equal to 17 parts per million by weight, as one grain per gallon of aluminum sulfate requires for its decomposition about 7 parts per million of alkalinity. This means that 17 parts per million of carbonates and bicarbonates of calcium and magnesium, naturally present in the untreated water, are converted into sulfates.

When potash alum or aluminum sulfate is applied to water, the chemical is usually rapidly and completely decomposed by the alkaline compound naturally present in the water. Ordinarily this alkalinity is due to calcium and magnesium carbonates and bicarbonates. The sulfuric acid portion of the coagulating chemical displaces the weak carbonic acid of the alkaline compounds above mentioned. As a result the soluble sulfates of calcium and magnesium are formed, and equivalent amounts of carbonic acid and alumina are liberated. The latter unites with the water and forms the white gelatinous precipitate of aluminum hydrate. The carbonic acid is usually decomposed by the alkalinity naturally present in the surface water; if the natural alkalinity is low, the deficiency can be made up by adding lime or soda ash to the water.

When iron sulfate is used as a coagulant it is normally necessary to add lime, as copperas (iron sulfate) decomposes somewhat similarly to alum; but the resulting bicarbonate of iron is partly soluble and more or less granular. By adding lime, bicarbonate of iron is changed to gelatinous ferrous hydrate, which in turn is oxidized to insoluble ferric hydrate. Care must be taken in the addition of the lime, as too little causes incomplete precipitation of the iron and too much results in lime incrustations.

Where the amount of turbidity and suspended solids is small the coagulant may be applied to the liquid influent to the filter. If there is considerable turbidity, and with certain coagulants, time and often agitation are required for floc formation. The pH must be adjusted to obtain proper coagulation, and in order that the coagulant be effective throughout the mass of water, thorough mixing is often needed. Sometimes a final rolling mix is necessary to promote clumping and to prevent floc breaking.

In treating water, activated carbon is used for phenol, chlorine and off-taste adsorption. Clay is added to water having low suspended solids and high color to aid coagulation, and many other substances have special uses. These remain insoluble or produce insolubles which must be filtered out. Where considerable solubles are present, the excess floc should be settled before filtration and the filter used to polish the supernatant liquor, with another filter or sluicing for sludge handling.

In boiler feed water, one of two general methods is used, and sometimes both: (1) coagulants for precipitating scale-forming chemicals and (2) zeolite for removing water hardness by interchange of salts.

Coagulation is effective in removing silicon dioxide (with ferric sulfate or magnesium hydrate) or iron as an organic compound, denoted by the high color. Sodium aluminate is sometimes used advantageously for boiler water used for steaming purposes. Likewise phosphates, etc., are employed for coagulation where the requirements are effective economical removal with adequate floc formation, so that filtration may be efficiently accomplished.

In sewage filtration ferric chloride is the most common coagulating chemical, others being ferrous sulfate and alum. In their use the pH is important in that without the proper pH no floc will be formed. Lime is regularly used to raise the pH to the desired point, so that a ferric or aluminum hydrate floc will be formed, as in water treatment. With sewage sludge ferric chloride coagulates the sludge while the lime adjusts the pH (with elutriation lime is not required).

In many chemical slurries and trade wastes a coagulating agent is necessary for filtration. Aluminum and iron salts predominate, with or without such other agents as lime and soda ash, tri-sodium phosphate, magnesium hydrate, certain catalysts, etc. The interest from a filtration standpoint is the resultant filtrability; no matter how effective they may be in the removal of impurities, the coagulating agents are useless unless the product is filtrable.

(3) Filter-Aid and Precoating

As previously stated, one of the greatest aids to filtration is heat; this may be said to hold true with practically all slurries. Whenever it is economically possible to raise the temperature of a slurry prior to filtration, this should be done (unless it will affect the suspended solids), as a decided increase in the filtering rate will be obtained, with a corresponding increase in washing efficiency and ease of discharge.

The use of acids for lowering the pH often gives excellent flocculation, but the cost and difficulty of handling acid slurries is such that they are seldom used. One particular example of this type of handling is in the filtration of cachaza, or defecated raw sugar mud. In this case, after flocculation with lime, the filtrate is cloudy; but on being made slightly acid, filtration is easier and a brilliant filtrate is assured.

Occasionally, where heating is not practicable and the viscosity is high, water dilution may be used to lower the viscosity. While the total volume is increased, the diluted liquor may filter at a sufficiently faster rate to warrant this increased volume.

The use of a free-filtering foreign material, which is inert in the slurry to be filtered and which has approximately the same specific gravity, has made possible the filtering of a great number of finely divided or colloidal materials which otherwise could not be handled, and has greatly increased the efficiency in filtering numerous other materials.

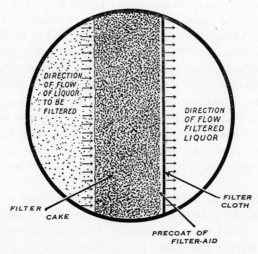

FIGURE 15. An enlarged sketch illustrating the manner in which a filter-aid prevents the passage of finely divided impurities through the filter cloth. (*Courtesy Johns-Manville Co.*)

Filter aids may be used as precoats solely for protecting the filter medium, or they may be mixed with the slurry to produce more open cake building, or both. Many materials are used as filter aids, *i.e.*, paper pulp in the clarification of sugar juices, salt in caustic filtration, carbons in decolorizing and deodorizing, asbestos in acid solutions, and miscellaneous uses for Fuller's earth, gypsum, sawdust, magnesia, zinc dust, etc. The most important of all from the volume standpoint is diatomaceous earth. This material is composed of porous silicious valves or shells, the remains of diatoms, or Infusoria, deposited widely and thriving wherever moisture, sunlight and food were available. This fossil sediment in the early ages of the earth (the Miocene Period) settled to the sea bottom. Later it was raised by earth upheavals so that now it is found in thick, easily available deposits.

Various grades of diatomaceous earths are produced and graded as to size and purity. These earths possess irregular shapes, minute size, are free-filtering, and of light weight. This, coupled with their inertness in most solutions, gives them wide application in filtering sugar juices, vegetable oils, petroleum products, beverages, varnishes, gelatin, gums, organic chemicals, etc.

There are three methods of application in precoating with a filter aid: (1) Mixing the precoat with clear liquor (water, clear filtrate, or other liquor) and sending it through the filter, and recirculating until the filtrate is clear, which shows that the precoat is built up as required. The filter is then emptied of excess precoat slurry before the slurry to be handled is admitted. (2) The same initial procedure is followed, but the precoat slurry may be followed directly with the material to be handled without emptying the filter. (3) The same original procedure, but with the precoat added to the first unfiltered slurry feed, or mixed with this slurry.

The first method gives a perfectly clean precoat; but, as most filters have no means of holding the precoat on the filter medium, a pressure drop caused by emptying the press may produce cracks or breaks in the precoat. The second method insures no pressure drop and is the safest. The third method should be used only where there is no danger of the filter cloth being clogged by the fine particles in the feed liquor getting into its voids.

In precoating with diatomaceous earth the volume of initial precoat should be from 25 to 50 per cent greater than that necessary to fill the filter and connecting lines; the amount of precoat material normally used is 5 to 10 pounds per 100 square feet of filter area.

No matter what the filter medium is made of (fabric, wire mesh, wire winding, or other material), the proper grade of filter aid should be selected to give the required clarity at the greatest flow rate. In building the precoat the mixture should be recirculated until the effluent is clear and the desired thickness of precoat is obtained.

Fabric filter cloths may show clarity quicker than wire mesh or rigid media because of fiber ends and quicker arching. In any case, clarity should be obtained in a short time with the recirculating process. Where paper pulp, salt, or similar material is used for precoats, the layer is relatively heavy, from ⅛ to ½ inch, whereas with diatomaceous earth the deposit is often so thin it can hardly be seen. Practically, the method of determining the amount and thickness of precoat is to make laboratory check-ups for any particular problem. Where cloths are used, considerable latitude is permissible in the precoat and in the relationship between it and the amount of filter aid; but with metallic cloths this latitude cannot be allowed. This is because of the medium voids, which are many times larger than the average filter-aid particle, the shape of the openings, the hard smooth surface, and the absence of fiber ends in metallic cloths, which demand a certain minimum concentration to arch or bridge the openings of the filter medium.

A most important point in the formation of a precoat is proper agitation of the mixture fed to the filter. This insures uniform dispersion of the aid throughout the liquor. A better precoat is formed by agitation within a filter, as in vacuum-drum and rotating-leaf filters, for here the filter medium moves through the precoat slurry during precoating. This also holds true in filters having wire-wound elements where the inlet to the filter is made to agitate the influent as it enters the filter. The speed of precoating, or rather of flow through the filter, is an important factor and is closely related to concentration, mesh, and type of filter aid. In general it may be said that the initial rate should be very low for the first formation, to insure a surface formation only.

The precoat protects the filter medium and in so doing very often makes possible filtration of otherwise unfiltrable materials. For these materials a filter aid added to the influent is commonly necessary; otherwise the precoat will become slimed over. The function of the filter aid is to form a porous cake and to deliver a clarified effluent. The quantity of filter aid depends upon the kind used and the nature and quantity of suspended solids, sufficient filter aid being used to obtain clarity and maintain a reasonable rate of flow.

The amount of diatomaceous earth added to the unfiltered slurry generally ranges from 0.1 to 0.5 per cent of the weight of the liquids. The filter aid may be added continuously or in batches. There are many different grades of diatomaceous filter aids, ten being usually listed, ranging from those for the handling of slimy or colloidal particles less than 0.1 micron, to coarser grades for high rates of flow. The coarsest filter aid that will yield a satisfactory clarity is the best, as it will give the greatest capacity.

If gelatinous or albuminous substances are to be filtered, the use of filter aids is especially valuable. Without a precoat of filter aid, the first filtrate to pass through the filter medium carries with it gelatinous particles which soon form a thin, almost impervious layer on and in the filter medium. Coatings of this nature are practically impossible to remove, as the clogging occurs in the interstices of the medium, and the solids are deformed in such a manner as to resist back-pressure and other methods of cleaning.

As previously stated, the precoat keeps the filter medium clean; but with materials of a gelatinous nature an impervious layer is quickly built up on the precoat, unless an appreciable amount of filter aid is added to the filter feed slurry.

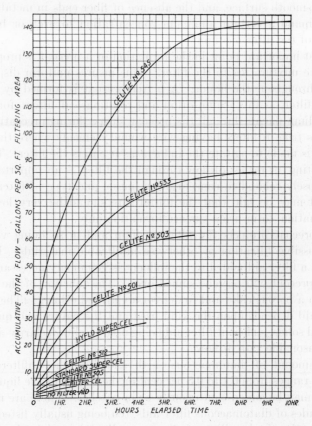

FIGURE 16. Relative rates of flow and filtering capacities obtained with filter-aids, and no filter-aid, in filtering a certain syrup; quantities of the filter-aids being the same. (*Courtesy Johns-Manville Co.*)

In the use of filter aids several general rules should be borne in mind. The filter aid should be selected on the basis of the clarity requirements, rate of flow, ease of handling, technical control necessary, and economics. The precoat tank should be of such a size as to precoat one filter at a time, and located as close to the filter as possible, preferably below the filter to permit circulation during precoating with the return circulating line discharging below the liquor level.

The average rate of precoating is usually considered as 20 gallons per hour per square foot of filter area, at a pressure of 5 to 10 pounds per square inch at the filter. Centrifugal pumps are best for most precoats, except that at times slow-moving diaphragms are preferred for delicate, easily broken flocs. Agitation at 20-30 rpm, with suitable baffles to prevent swirling, is preferred to air, and particular attention must be given to the prevention of breaking of unstable flocs and to keeping the line from clogging, where rapidly settling particles are handled.

Filter aids should be added uniformly, in proportion to the volume, assuming a uniform proportion of impurities in the feed liquor. Unless this can be done, batch preparation is preferred, with overdoses where unforeseen maximum impurities are likely to occur. If proper agitation is available, slightly higher efficiency is obtained by adding the filter aid in the dry form; without such agitation, the slurry form should be used.

Changing from precoating to filtering should be accompanied by the minimum of pressure fluctuation. If there is no restricted pressure in the liquid feed, the operator should watch the control valve closely to regulate pressure increase. From that point the pressure increase should be slow for the first 25 per cent of the cycle, after which it may be rapid to the maximum for the last 15 to 20 per cent. Owing to the character of the suspended impurities, slow pressure rise and long filter cycles, under otherwise comparable conditions, produce the largest proportion of well clarified filtrate at a minimum filter-aid expense.

When handling poor-filtering liquors there are three ways of obtaining the desired capacity. (1) Increase the filter-aid dosage. (2) Use a filter aid giving a faster rate of flow to which there is a limit from the filter operation standpoint; lowered filtrate clarity and increase in consumption of filter aid may possibly result. (3) Crowd the filter with short cycles and rapid pressure rises, which results in higher filter-aid consumption due to an increase in the number of precoats and possibly a reduction in the average clarity.

In the presence of different colloidal and suspended impurities the performance of each type of filter aid is radically altered, although each type will nearly always occupy the same relative position with respect to the others in the clarity-flow ratio. In the final analysis it is the character of the filter cake that is important.

Precoating should be applied at low pressures (up to five pounds), and at a speed short of washing or scouring the leaves in the filter. Turbulence adjacent to the inlets at high liquid flows, friction caused by rotating leaves revolving too rapidly, or an insufficiently large outlet gooseneck vent may retard precoating, or even prevent it. Fast rotors should be precoated while stationary, at the start, and then turned over only a few times at the end of the precoating period to smooth out irregularities and liquidate any turbid filtrate inside the filter assembly.

It is very difficult to precoat the conventional bottom-corner discharge plate-and-frame press evenly over the entire filtering surface. Installation of top-corner outlets on a bottom-inlet filter will permit an approach to the same degree of uniformity as on the stationary leaf filter. If once used filter cake is re-used in the filtering of lower-grade liquids it should always be as an aid mixed with the unfiltered liquor, and never as a precoat.

Adsorbents

Many adsorbents, as distinct from inert filter aids, are used in the industries: clays such as Fuller's earth, bauxite, and chemically treated substances of this nature; carbons such as bone char, bone black, and activated carbons; silica gels, activated alumina, magnesia and similar materials all have their particular applications. The actual adsorption properties of such agents is not clearly understood. In some cases the actions are similar to chemical reactions; in others they appear to be physical. It is presumed that the action takes place on the surface of the adsorbent through some forces between molecules, electrons and atoms.

There are no apparent adsorption or absorption properties with the ordinary filter cake, the structure of which is controlled by the gravity and kind of filter aid used. Where coagulation occurs, the character of the suspended solids is changed and the use of coarser filter aids to obtain the desired clarity is often possible.

The function of adsorbents is to remove taste, color, odor, and troublesome solids in a fine state of subdivision. Adsorbents do not add any ingredients that would require further processing to remove; they may also function as filter aids, or in connection with filter aids, as well as acting as decolorizers, deodorants, and eliminators of off-tastes.

They are extensively used in recovery of dry-cleaning solvents such as carbon tetrachloride, Stoddard solvent, etc. Here they act as decolorizers and deodorants in their adsorbent capacity and as filter aids in preventing the fats, oils, grease, dirt, etc., from clogging the filter medium.

References

1. Anable, Anthony, and Knowles, "Technique of Settling Separations," *Chem. Met. Eng.,* **45,** No. 5 (May, 1938).

Chapter 5

Filter Media

The filter medium is the porous mass which holds back the suspended solids and allows the carrying body to pass through. As such, it may have a variety of forms.

Although nature and the arts have produced a very large number of porous media, those employed to any extent in filtering are comparatively few. They generally consist of sand and gravel, paper pulp, vegetable fiber, precipitates, fabrics of cotton, wool, silk, hair, linen, hemp, or synthetic materials, rubber, asbestos, woven materials, wire, perforated plates or plate edges, porous stones, charcoal, bagasse, sawdust, infusorial earth, coal, zinc dust, straw, coke, etc.

The filter medium selected is chosen because of its cost, the separation to be made, the particular requirements, and the type of filter to be employed. In making a selection of the proper medium to use the decision is first made as to the group and then the individual material, in a classification of which the following groups of materials are typical:

- A. RIGID media
  - I. Fixed (agglomerated or fused)
    - a. Alumina
      - 1. Alundum (electrically fused)
      - 2. Aloxite (fused, refined)
    - b. Carbon
    - c. Metallic
      - 1. Perforated
      - 2. Plain (edge filters)
      - 3. Porous metal
      - 4. Wire windings
    - d. Wood, perforated
    - e. Silicious materials
      - 1. Diatomaceous earths (molded)
      - 2. Bonded silicas
      - 3. Stone, porous
  - II. Movable (loose, simply in contact)
    - a. Coal and coke
    - b. Charcoal, animal and vegetable
    - c. Diatomaceous earths
    - d. Precipitates or salts
    - e. Sand and gravel
    - f. Stones and brick
- B. FLEXIBLE media
  - I. Metallic (woven fabrics)
    - a. Bronze
    - b. Lead

            c. Monel
            d. Nickel
            e. Silver
            f. Stainless steel
            g. Steel, plain
        II. Metallic and Non-metallic (woven fabrics)
            a. Asbestos and metallic
            b. Metal cloth (copper-sulfated fabric cotton)
       III. Non-Metallic (woven, perforated or loose)
            a. Asbestos
            b. Cotton
            c. Glass
            d. Linen
            e. Hair
            f. Hemp and cocoa matting
            g. Paper (pulp sheet)
            h. Rubber
            i. Silk
            j. Synthetic fabric
                1. Nylon
                2. Vinyl acetate
            k. Wool
            l. Plastic windings

The Fixed Rigid Media

A filter medium composed of rigid particles in rigid contact has the advantage of easy portability as a unit and the ability to be set and used in any desired position. It may be gauged as to its porosity with the greatest accuracy, and in most cases it permits easy cake removal. Such media have long life and resistance to corrosion.

Their disadvantage, despite the ease of cake removal of many materials, is the danger of medium clogging. Although a cake is easily removed from the surface, particles which penetrate the mass are hard to get out and, when the medium is once clogged, thorough cleaning is extremely difficult. This is combined with the rigid setting, which does not permit easy shifting for scrubbing or changing.

Alumina. Alumina is fused by two methods to form different media, in the rigid contact of rigid particles, known as Alundum and Aloxite. Alumina used as a filter medium has a high porosity (25 to 38 per cent) and withstands considerable temperature variation, although sudden violent changes and severe shocks should be avoided. The common method of grading such media is by their air permeability (permeability is differentiated from porosity), which for convenience has been specified as, "that quantity of free air, in cubic feet per minute, which will pass through 1 square foot of area of the plate or tube, when tested dry at 70°F, under a pressure equivalent to two (2) inches of water." Since the porosity is relatively high, and there is a definite capillary attraction when in contact with liquid, careful washing of media is necessary in changing from one liquid to another.

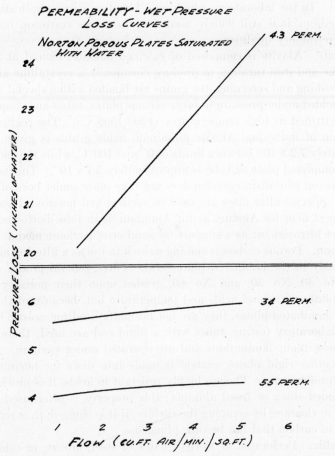

FIGURE 17. Air flow—wet pressure loss. (*Courtesy Norton Co.*)

Alundum. Alundum media are composed of electrically fused alumina grains bonded with a high temperature alumina glass and fired to a high temperature. Permeable media of different physical characteristics are obtained by varying the particle size of the fused alumina grains and by controlling the volume percentage of alundum grain, bond and pores. The physical characteristics of primary importance are permeability, porosity, pore size, pressure loss, uniformity, chemical stability, strength, and resistance to heat.

The coefficient of expansion is given as approximately ¼ of an inch in 10 feet; between 20°C and 900°C the coefficient is 0.000007. While used for gravity, vacuum and pressure filters, Alundum's greatest use is in false-bottomed tanks, as a direct medium or as a support for sand or other material. In the laboratory, which was Alundum's first application as a filter medium, it is still widely used, because of its corrosion resistance and its refractory qualities.

Aloxite. Aloxite is composed of calcined bauxite, melted at 2000°C with coke and iron turnings to produce chemically a crystalline alumina. After crushing and screening, the grains are bonded with a special ceramic bond, molded under pressure to form various plates, tubes and shapes, and finally vitrified at high temperatures (1200-1500°C). The coefficient of expansion of individual Aloxite aluminum oxide grains is given as approximately 7.2×10^{-6} between limits of 0° and 100°C, while the coefficient of the completed plate or tube is approximately 5.7×10^{-6}. This is stated as the reason why disintegration does not take place under normal conditions. Special filter discs are used in vertical and horizontal positions. The largest field for Aloxite, as for Alundum, is in false-bottomed tanks for direct filtration, or as a support for sand or other loose media.

Carbon. Porous carbon is coming more into use as a filtering medium, particularly in the laminated plate form. Three general grades are offered, No. 40, No. 50, and No. 60, graded upon their porosity. The carbon plates withstand acids and temperature but, because of the bond used for laminated plates, they are not normally used for caustic liquids.

For laboratory testing, tubes with a blind end are used; these are in one piece without laminations and are operated under vacuum.

Like other rigid plates, carbon is made into discs for horizontal or vertical pressure use. Though highly resistant to acids, it is much softer than bonded silica or fused alumina; this property is often used to advantage in cleaning by scraping the surface, if it is clogged, thus removing the film of carbon that has become plugged.

Metallic. Perforated or slotted plates of steel, bronze, or other material have been used for many years for filtering coarse particles and as loose rigid grain supports. Smaller perforations can be made in metal plates than in wood or plastics; round perforations are often cone-shaped or slotted surfaces bevelled, to present the smaller opening for actual filtration and the larger for backwash in cleaning. Sewage screens are examples of both slotted and round openings. In the industrial filtration of cachaza various perforated plates are used as filter media on drum vacuum filters.

The smooth surface presented by a perforated plate permits brush cleaning or scrubbing in addition to the naturally easier discharge from such surfaces. The hard metallic material has a long life, not being subject to abrasion or flexing. The size of particles filtered on such plates must be relatively large; normally the plates are confined to free-filtering materials where there is little danger of clogging.

Solid plates in thin sheet are used in close laminations for edge filtration. The spacing between the laminations, which is variable, determines the porosity, the plates being stacked in a vertical position.

Powdered metal is made up as a porous medium. The physical characteristics, chemical composition, structure, porosity, strength, ductility, shape, and size can be varied to meet special requirements. The porosity ranges up to 50 per cent void by volume, tensile strength up to 10,000 psi, varying inversely with porosity, and ductility between 3 and 5 per cent in tension, and higher in compression. Powdered metal cannot be ground or machined readily. It is made in discs, sheets, cones or special shapes for filtering fuel oil, refrigerants, solvents, etc.

Silica. Another class of rigid particles in fixed contact is the silicas, both artificial (diatomaceous earths) and natural (porous stone). Diatomaceous earths are graded and molded into tubes or plates for use as filter media. The properties of resistance are governed by the type of earth used and the binder employed. The greatest use of diatomaceous earths, however, is as filter aids or precoats in the loose form; they are described more fully in the preceding chapter.

Filtros. Filtros is composed of natural sand averaging 99.6 per cent SiO_2, bonded with a synthetic silicate fused at temperatures above 2000°F. A white, porous material is thus produced with a porosity from 25 to 40 per cent. Filtros is not affected by sudden changes of temperature from 60-212°F; above this, gradual temperature changes are recommended. On the low temperature side, even freezing does not damage the plate form. Being composed of silica, it is chemically inert to organic and inorganic acids and the general corrosive liquids requiring filtration in commercial processes. It is affected by soluble fluorides, hydrofluoric acid, and the stronger solutions of sodium or potassium hydroxide.

Filtros is made in various grades and shapes, but as with the other rigid particles in rigid contact, filtration is largely confined to crystalline bodies of the larger size, because of pore size, danger of particle penetration, and subsequent cleaning difficulty. Burning out or strong acid treatment may be resorted to; but these are rarely successful in cleaning a clogged medium. The fact that the medium is usually cemented in place makes removal of obstructions difficult, as the medium cannot be removed for thorough cleaning. False-bottomed tanks are again the type of filters most generally employing this medium.

Unglazed porcelain is a bonded silica and is porous, but it is rarely used as a filter medium except in the laboratory because of its brittleness. Here it has a decided place, as careful handling is ordinary laboratory procedure.

Natural porous stones were used by the ancients as water filters. To a limited extent they are in use today in tubular form for such work as household filters. Being detachable, they can be cleaned periodically and assure a clear water supply.

The Rigid Movable Media

A filter medium composed of particles of rigid structure, in which the particles are loose, *i.e.*, merely in contact with each other, has the advantage of being cheap and easy to keep clean by rearrangement of the particles. When the proper size and shape of particles is selected, the section of passage may be regulated through extremely wide limits. The drawbacks of a rigid medium in simple contact are that it can be used conveniently only in a horizontal position and that it does not permit removal of thick deposits or surface cleaning except back washing, without disturbing the filter bed.

Coal and Coke. Materials in simple contact must be supported by a porous medium, usually of the rigid fixed type, such as the porous plate supports for anthracite in water clarification. Coal (hard) and coke are used in water filtration, primarily for the removal of coarse suspensions, care being taken to prevent them from scouring or washing away, because of their relative lightness and fine division.

Being composed principally of carbon, coal is inert to acids and alkalies and its irregular shapes are advantages at times over silica sand. Though inert to acids, sand is affected by alkalies, and its spherical particle shape allows deeper solids penetration and quicker clogging than coal. With the lighter weight of coal, normally 50 pounds per cubic foot compared with 100 pounds per cubic foot for sand, a greater area of surface is exposed for solids entrapment.

Charcoal. Charcoal, whether animal or vegetable, where used as a filter medium, is commonly required to perform a dual service decolorizing or adsorbing, as well as filtering. The char filters of the sugar industry are largely decolorizing agents and the activated carbons, in water clarification, are for deodorizing and removal of taste. There are many kinds of charcoal in use as filter media, ranging from ordinary wood char to specially prepared carbons.

Diatomaceous Earths. The function of diatomaceous earths is usually like that of the charcoals, for some special purpose besides acting as a filter medium. The earths are primarily filter aids, precoats or adsorbents, the function of the filter medium being secondary. Fuller's earth and clays are for decolorizing, diatomaceous earths for clarification, etc.

Precipitates or Salts. Very often a corrosive liquor must be filtered, and there is no available medium of sufficient fineness, that is corrosion-resistant and will not contaminate the cake. In these cases, precipitates or salts are used on porous supports. In the filtration of caustic liquors, ordinary salt (sodium chloride) is often used as the filter medium in the form of a precoat over metallic cloth. This procedure has the advantage that the salt medium will not be detrimental to either the cake or the filtrate if inadvertently mixed with it. Moreover, it is inexpensive.

Sand and Gravel. Sand is the most widely used of the rigid media in simple contact. Most of the sand being used this way is for the clarification of water for drinking or industrial uses. Washed, screened silica sand is sold in standard grades for this work and is used in depths ranging from a few inches to several feet, depending upon the type of filter and clarification requirements. Heavy, irregular grains, such as magnetite, give high rates of flow, low penetration by the solid particles, and are easily cleaned. They are, however, considerably more expensive than silica sand so that their actual use has been quite limited. Sand beds are often gravel supported but gravel alone is seldom used as the filter medium.

Stones and Brick. Occasionally stones (not contact beds) or bricks are used for coarse filtration of particularly corrosive liquors. Their use, however, is extremely limited and they are not an important factor as filter media.

The Flexible Metallic Media

Metallic filter media have greater strength than fabric and have been used for the past twenty-five years or more for the handling of corrosive liquors, or for high-temperature filtration. A large variety of metals can be wire-drawn and thus can be used for metallic media, *viz*, bronze, copper, lead, Monel, nickel, silver, stainless steel, steel, or special alloys. Their uses depend upon their resistance to the particular liquor or temperature to which they are to be exposed.

The construction of metallic media is in the form of screens, wire windings or woven fabric, the last being termed filter cloth, since its method of fabrication is similar to that of cloth. Wire screens are used for coarse separations or as supports for filter cloths or filter aids, and are manufactured in the standard screen sizes and wire diameters. One of the largest filtration fields for these screens is in the pulp and paper industry. In some cases the screens are made with oblong slots instead of standard meshes, to minimize blinding and increase the open area in the handling of round particles, as in salt manufacture.

Metallic filter cloths are woven in two weaves and three types to cover most projects. These are plain and twill weaves and plain dutch (corduroy), in twill and stranded types. The weaves are used to make up cloths in a wide variety of meshes and wire sizes, as from 10 x 50 to 400 x 20 mesh, and of various wire thicknesses.

The plain dutch or corduroy weave (as illustrated) is the fabric "over one under one" construction, with the warp straight and the fillings pushed closely together, so that multiple warp wires may be laid side by side for strength. In the twill weave there is the "over two and under two" weave with the resulting diagonal pattern. The twills may be of single wires, of multiple wires to give the basket-weave type weave, or of dutch weave (Fig. 18), whereas in the plain dutch weave the warp wires are not crimped. The "over two and under two" is followed only by the filler wire, giving a dense weave. As in the plain dutch, multiple-warp wires can be used for extra strength.

The warp wires run the length of the cloth and the filler, or shute, across the cloth both may be crimped or corrugated to prevent slippage. When it is to be used as a supporting medium, the crimped cloth is often rolled or calendered to produce a flattened surface and reduce the abrasion on the finer wires it supports.

Mesh in filter cloth is now commonly indicated by the number of wires per linear inch in either direction, the warp being given first, as differentiated from screens, where mesh is the number of openings per inch. The openings between the wires vary with the wire diameter and therefore are smaller with larger diameter wires, even though the mesh is the same.

Metallic filter cloths are in use in the pulp and paper industry for stock washers, deckers, thickeners and savealls; in the chemical industry for caustic lime mud, salt, acids, and dyes; in the food industry for sugar, coffee, yeast and vinegar; in the petroleum industry for clay, crude oil, etc. In these cases mechanical strength, corrosion, and heat resistance are more important than first cost; relatively large openings are permissible, or filter aids can be used.

In their resistance, the cloths are subjected to more severe conditions than metallic plates or castings in that the fine wires can stand much less attack from the standpoint of actual tensile strength loss. There is also the danger of cloth blinding due to the products of corrosion, which may accumulate in the cloth voids.

Wire windings as the filter medium may be made by winding a wire of definite diameter on a filter element threaded to a definite pitch, thus producing the desired openings between the windings.

Metallic and Non-Metallic Cloths

Metallic wires are sometimes woven with weaker threads to give the threads more mechanical strength. This is particularly true of asbestos which, though resistant to high temperatures, mildew and acids, is quite

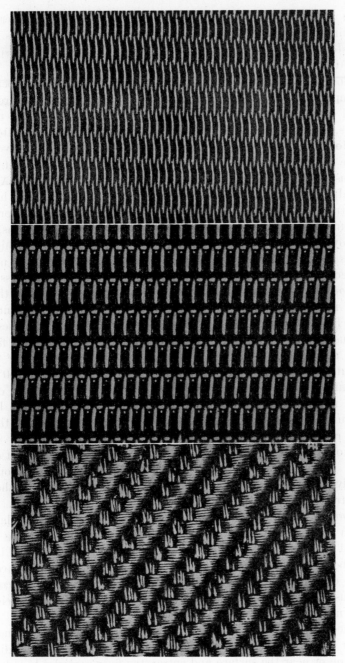

FIGURE 18.　Various metallic weaves.　Top, dutch or corduroy; Center, twilled dutch; Bottom, stranded.　(*Courtesy Cambridge Wire Cloth Co.*)

weak when woven into cloth by itself. There is difficulty, however, in such weaving in maintaining uniformity between the metallic wires and the asbestos, and considerable trouble has been experienced with such construction on this account.

Cotton cloths may be treated with such metallic salts as copper sulfate to improve their corrosion-resistant qualities. Such cloths are in the usual cotton filter cloth grades; and while they are not equal to metal cloths, the treatment does materially prolong the life of the cotton fiber.

Non-Metallic. Asbestos as a non-metallic cloth is extensively used in the loose form as a precoat in the laboratory and in beverage filtration, because of its chemical inertness and its resistance to heat. As above stated, it has not been found possible to spin asbestos yarn with high tensile strength. Combining metallic wires with asbestos tends to produce a non-uniform cloth; and cotton, while blending well with asbestos, is soon destroyed by the corrosive liquor or high temperatures to which such cloths are usually subjected. Therefore, the use of asbestos is normally limited to cases where there is no mechanical stress or high pressures.

Cotton Filter Cloth. More cotton is used as filter medium than any other material and its annual volume for this purpose runs into quite large figures. Cotton is mechanically strong and the fiber possesses numerous hair-like ends that are of great assistance in entrapping fine particles at the start of filtration, to give an initial clarity prior to cake formation. The use of cotton is limited by temperature (max. 350°F) and high and low pH, although cotton will withstand slight acidity or causticity remarkably well. At times trouble is encountered from bacteria and fungus growths which are fostered in cotton; prevention of this difficulty requires special care.

Most of the cotton for filter media goes into woven fabric of duck or twill. Within the past few years, however, the use of unwoven cotton has greatly increased, particularly for "one use" clarification in the dairy industry.

Unwoven Cotton. This material is made from successive layers of cotton from a number of carding machines, built up until the desired weight is obtained. The cotton is next treated to produce a bond between the fibers of the surface layers, and then it may or may not be faced with gauze or other backing for strength. By this means, pads of cotton of various weights and in several grades of retentiveness per unit weight can be formed, in either absorbent or non-absorbent material.

Sheets of this carded cotton, generally used in weights totaling 2 to 6 oz per square yard, filter out the coarser particles (over 0.003″ dia) in a layer on or near the surface and entrap the finer particles by adsorption or adherence to the relatively rough surfaces of the hair-like fibers. The

latter action takes place throughout the depth of the medium and therefore does not greatly retard the filtration rate.

FIGURE 19.

a. Unwoven cotton medium.

b. Flannel medium.

(*Courtesy Johnson & Johnson Co.*)

The unwoven cotton is sometimes used in front of paper in filter
presses; with the low pressure drop through the cotton the initial rate of
flow is not appreciably reduced, while the rate at which the paper medium
is plugged is considerably retarded. This results in longer filtration
cycles.

The dairy industry is the largest user of these media in the form of
discs for milk filtering where their low cost, high rate of flow and complete
dirt removal have caused them to replace, to a large extent, the flannel
formerly used.

In the filtering of viscous liquids, unsized cotton is frequently obtained
in rolls, from which the user cuts the lengths required and assembles the
cotton with the backing cloth desired. These cloths may be gauze, flannel,
muslin, nainsook, etc., their function being to support the cotton or to
protect it from the impact of the feed liquor.

In the filtration of air, cotton web filters, sized on one side or on both,
are increasingly used for air-conditioning installations. At times the

cotton webbing is cut and placed in fluted cardboard cartridges. When they have reached their dirt-holding capacity the cartridges are discarded and replaced. In some cases cotton has been flameproofed. Cotton thicknesses of an inch or more are used for filtering outside air, giving efficiencies comparable with those obtained with electrostatic precipitators.

Because of their low cost unwoven cotton media are also used in certain filter-cake filtrations, such as on wood gums, where cleaning is so difficult as to make the discard of the medium and solids the more desirable. Paints and varnishes and other gravity clarifying work is often handled by these cotton media. Their use also extends to filter presses, where a number of layers are used for the removal of minute dirt particles, as in viscous liquor clarification.

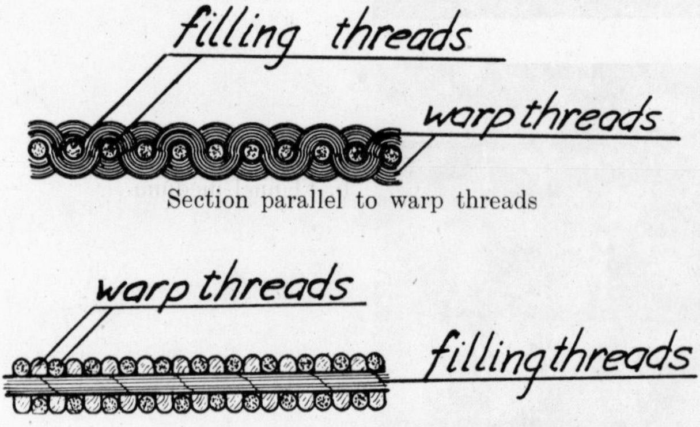
filling threads
warp threads
Section parallel to warp threads
warp threads
filling threads
Section parallel to filling threads

FIGURE 20

Woven Cotton Media. Woven cotton filter cloths are made up in ducks and twills, in some cases with three hundred variations, including drills, chain weaves, canton flannel and unbleached muslins. The cotton duck, like the metallic cloth, is a fabric weave, a plain cloth with threads equal in thickness and texture in the "over one and under one" of the warp and woof, or filling. The twill weave is over two and under two with the next filling splitting the warp strands and giving a diagonal rib at 45 degrees, if the number of warp and filling threads are equal. Differences in the number or in the weave alter the rib angle; more mechanical force is required to weave duck than twill or chain.

Ducks may be more closely woven by putting tension on both warp and filling and driving them tightly together during weaving. Hose duck is a loosely woven duck and is somewhat more open in texture than ordinary duck. Canton flannel is a twill weave in which one surface has been brushed up to give a nap finish. A drill in a twill in which one surface only is ribbed, whereas a true twill has both top and bottom ribbed. A muslin cloth is a very thin duck weave which, for filtering, is unbleached.

In the chain weave one filling goes over two warp threads and under two, the next reversing this; the third is a true twill sequence, and the next repeats the cycle. Less weaving force is here required than for twill or duck, giving a looser fabric.

With each weave there are numerous modifications depending upon the weight of the yarn and the number of strands per inch.

In duck the filter cloth is sold either by weight or number, *i.e.*, #42 is about the same as 16-oz. Twill and chain weaves are designated by the number of warp and filling members per inch; thus #1842 means 18 warp threads per inch and 42 filling threads per inch, although not all sellers follow these rules. A single ply has a single thread to form each warp or filling, while a double ply has two threads twilled together to form each warp or filling, the increased ply giving a closer texture.

Insofar as filtering is concerned there are certain characteristics of each weave which may be generalized in comparison one with the other, as follows:

Weave	Tensile Strength	Clarity Filtrate	Rate Flow	Cake Discharge	Tendency Keep from Blinding	Shrinkage
Canton flannel	Fair	High	Fair	Poor	Good	Even
Chain	Low	High	High	Fair	Fair	Uneven
Duck	High	Fair	Poor	Good	Poor	Even
Muslin	Low	Poor	High	Good	Good	Even
Twill	Fair	Fair	High	Fair	Fair	Uneven

The yarns of cotton cloth are affected by the liquids with which they are wetted. Water causes shrinkage more in duck and chain than in twill. Aluminum sulfate has a contracting action; ammonium salts may give distortion, etc.

Drills seem to be little used, as they are usually somewhat more expensive than twill, yet have about the same filtering characteristics.

In selecting the most desirable fabric, all the above factors must be considered in addition to initial cost.

A duck may be preferable to a twill with more porosity, because the hard surface of the duck permits a freer cake discharge. Under high increasing pressure a strong, durable cloth (duck) is required, since the first resistance is small as compared with that during cake building. Certain types of machines, such as drum filters, cannot stand uneven shrinkage and, in some cases, cloths must be pre-shrunk to insure fitting during the life of the cloth. The amount of shrinkage is in the warp threads and can be taken care of by cutting and installing the cloth for such shrinkage. This warp thread shrinkage is probably due to the fact that in weaving greater tension is on the filling threads, causing them to be practically straight when woven, whereas the warp threads have a "wavy" appearance.

It is often possible to use an open cloth giving a cloudy filtrate and recirculate the latter until clear, thus enabling a higher rate of flow to be obtained even though some time is lost in recirculating. In some cases clarity of filtrate is not required at any stage of the filtering operation and recirculating is not necessary. Precoating also will allow the use of a more open fabric with the higher flow rates. The cloth weave therefore should be only sufficiently close to secure the necessary results.

The whole range of filtration engineering, with the variety of materials to be filtered in the many types of filtration apparatus, affords a wide field of cooperation between filtration and textile engineers. Slight changes in fabric construction, such as the amount of twist in the yarn, distribution of weight, or tightness of weave, may result in a considerable difference in the efficiency of the filtration.

Nitrated Cotton Cloth. Nitrated cotton cloths were first utilized for the filtration of acid solutions about 1892, and a few years later they were in quite general use in European dye and chemical plants. It was not, however, until rather recently that they were manufactured and sold in America.

Nitro-filter cloths are about the same thickness and texture as ordinary cotton filtration cloths, but they have a harder surface and it is claimed that the cake is easily detached and that clogging is rare. Their tensile strength is from 70 to 80 per cent of that of the specially manufactured cotton cloths from which they are prepared, and they are resistant to the corrosive action of sulfuric, nitric and mixed nitration acids and even hydrochloric acid. They are recommended for filtering sulfuric acid solutions to 40 per cent and at temperatures as high as 90°C, with the advantage of removing finely divided amorphous particles, which would quickly clog most ceramic media.

Nitro-filter cloths are composed of cellulose nitrate, which is an ester of cellulose, and any chemical compound which will saponify the ester will obviously destroy the cloth. Caustic soda or potash in strengths of 2 per cent at 70°C or over, and alkali sulfides, polysulfides, sulfohydrates, or mixtures of ethyl alcohol and ether, ethyl, amyl, and butyl acetates, pyridine, ferrous sulfates and other reducing agents are detrimental to the cloth.

The cellulose nitrate, of which the cloth is composed, is inflammable and explosive when dry, but when soaked in water it is considered entirely safe if reasonable care is taken in handling. For this reason it is colored red and packed in special containers; users are cautioned to keep the cloths wet and to handle them carefully.

Glass Media. Glass filter media are woven on practically standard textile machinery, from glass yarns, and the glass can be hemmed or seamed with glass thread and fabricated into bags or blankets as desired.

The glass yarns are made from a resistant hard glass, essentially alkali-free, and are not affected by the pH of any solution. The average fiber diameter is under 0.00025″ and the fibers range from 10 to 12 inches in length. It is rare that more than 23 per cent of the fibers vary more than 20 per cent from the average. According to A. A. Griffith[1] the tensile strength of 0.00025 inch fiber is 15,000 pounds per square inch.

Glass yarns differ from those made of organic materials in that the specific weights of glass products are somewhat greater and the range of size is more limited. For this reason, an individual size-measuring system has been adopted, wherein the counts represent the number of 100-yard lengths per pound of glass yarn, compared to cotton, which represents the number of 840-yard lengths per pound of cotton yarn.

Glass cloth is one of the most stable and inert forms of filter media for acids, alkalies, high temperatures and resistance to rot, mold, etc. It gives comparatively high rates of flow, has high thermal resistance, high corrosion resistance, a high tensile strength, is easily handled, and the composition and diameter of the fibers can be altered as desired.

FIGURE 21. Glass filter cloth. (*Courtesy Corning Glass Works*)

The weakness of glass cloth is the lack of flexibility of the individual fibers, causing splits and fractures, and its low resistance to abrasion. In plate-and-frame presses fiber crushing is marked; but both this and flexing wear can be reduced by impregnating the fibers with latex, which also is used to reinforce edges, prevent unravelling, and arrest failure of damaged spots on the cloth. Perforated plates, lead, or rubber mats or other backing is desirable whenever using glass cloth in plate-and-frame presses. Tests with the rigid backing of the glass cloth by plates gave a 100 per cent greater life, while backing of cotton or rubber gave 50 per cent greater life, than in cases where no backing was used.

Often glass cloth is covered with paper to facilitate discharge, as care must be taken to prevent abrasive damage, particularly with wet cloths. There is some abrasive wear by fine suspended solids, but this stops as the cake forms.

The resistance of glass to heat is especially advantageous in high-temperature gas filtration, although care must be taken if discharge is by bag shaking to avoid flexing failures.

Linen Cloth. Filter cloths of linen are occasionally used for replacement of unbleached muslin. The linen, while much more expensive, has a considerably longer life and will stand more abuse than muslin.

Hair, Hemp and Cocoa Matting. Filter media made of various forms of hair, hemp, or cocoa matting are used primarily with hydraulic presses. The cloths are sufficiently elastic to withstand high pressures without cracking or bursting, and they have considerable resistance to acidity and temperature. In order to obtain any degree of clarity, it is necessary to have cloths of considerable thickness, up to an inch or more in some cases.

Paper Pulp and Fiber. Paper pulp is an excellent material for precoat and a filter aid, and was extensively used at one time in sugar-juice clarification, although now it has been largely replaced by diatomaceous earths. Paper pulp gives a high rate of flow, is easily discharged and shows little tendency to clog.

The objection to it is mainly that of preparation. Soda or sulfate pulp, most commonly used, must be disintegrated and kept in suspension by agitation before precoating, making considerable auxiliary equipment necessary. Diatomaceous earths, while they should be kept in suspension, are very light, easy to handle, and do not need to be disintegrated.

Paper pulp compressed into pads is used to a large extent in pressure filters for beverage clarification filtration. After becoming dirty, as evidenced by decrease in the rate of flow, the paper may be repulped, water-washed, and reformed into pads. This makes considerable work, but excellent clarity and a high rate of flow are obtained. The impurities do not form a cake as such, but penetrate into the pad and can only be removed by repulping and washing the disintegrated pad.

Pads of a mixture of paper pulp and asbestos fiber are used in bacteriological filtrations.

Paper in the form of sheets has long been standard in the laboratory for all kinds of filtration. Filter papers are made in many grades of porosity for use in porcelain and glass funnels. Industrially, paper in the form of sheets is used directly or as a precoat in filter presses.

Used directly in lubricating-oil clarifications, in a "blotter press," it acts in much the same manner as the paper pads, but is much thinner and is not reused.

As a precoat, paper protects the filter medium from slimy fines; it may be pealed off and discarded after clogging, leaving the medium underneath clean.

Rubber Media. The use of rubber as a filter medium is a development of the past few years, although it was suggested by Charles Goodyear decades ago. A porous, flexible rubber sheet and a microporous hard rubber sheet for inflexible media are now available.

The commercial types of rubber media have 1100 to 6400 holes per square inch and pore diameters of 0.012 to 0.004 inch; they are manufactured out of soft rubber, hard rubber, flexible hard rubber and soft neoprene.

The process of manufacturing is interesting: the medium is made upon a master form, consisting of a heavy fabric belt, surfaced on one side with a layer of rubber filled with small round pits uniformly spaced. These pits are 0.020 inch deep, and the number per unit area and their surface diameter determines the porosity of the sheet. A thin layer of latex is fed to the moving belt by a spreader bar so that the latex completely covers the pits, yet does not run into them, thus trapping air in each. The application of heat to the under surface of the blanket by a steam plate causes the air to expand, blowing little bubbles in the film of latex; when these burst, small holes are left, corresponding to the pits. The blown rubber film, after drying, is cooled and the process repeated until the desired thickness of sheet is obtained, when the sheet is stripped off the master blanket and vulcanized.

About 95 per cent of the pits are reproduced as holes in the rubber sheet. The holes are not truly cylindrical in shape but are reinforced by slight constrictions which contribute to strength and tear resistance. This type is called "plain," and can be made with fabric backing on one or both sides, to control the stretching characteristics. If the unvulcanized material is first stretched, in either one or two directions, and then vulcanized under stretch it is called "expanded." The resulting holes are oval with a higher porosity, sometimes up to 30 per cent. Special compounds have been developed for resistance to specific chemicals under high concentration at elevated temperatures, such as 25 per cent sulfuric acid at 180°F.

It is claimed that the smooth surface allows removal of a thinner cake than cotton or wool fabrics. Rubber does not show progressive binding;

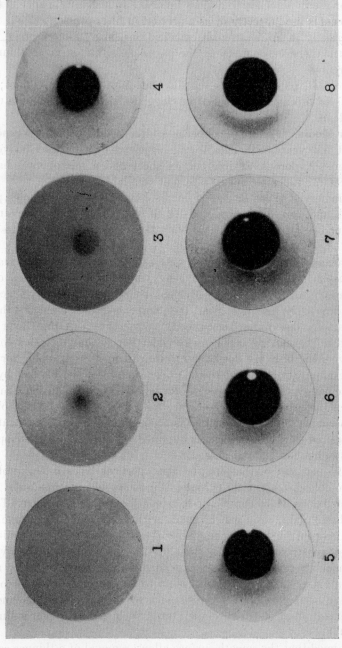

FIGURE 22. Microphotographs of stages in blowing of multipore. 1. Wet latex film immediately after spreading. 2-6. The growth of the pore caused by the entrapped air expanding as it is heated. 7. The latex film is drying out and the bubble is about to break. 8. The bubble has broken and the latex is "set." (*Courtesy U. S. Rubber Co.*)

it can be readily cleaned and can be used in temperatures up to 180°F. On the other hand, because a clear filtrate is difficult to obtain, when filtering finely divided solids, a precoat becomes necessary.

FIGURE 23. Cross section multipore openings. (*Courtesy U. S. Rubber Co.*)

Silk Cloths. Silk filter cloths were a carryover from the bolting cloths used in screening. For a period, several years ago, silk cloths had considerable vogue, but at the present time they are seldom used because of the development of cheaper and more suitable materials, aside from the scarcity of silks due to war conditions.

Silk is resistant to some conditions that cotton will not withstand; it is strong, and usually gives a clear filtrate and high rate of flow. It is, however, expensive, and being without hair-like fibers it gives a cloudy filtrate with finely divided suspensions.

Vinyon. A rather recent development in filter-cloth manufacture is synthetic fabric made of a special grade of unplasticized synthetic resin, the copolymer of vinyl chloride and vinyl acetate. These Vinyon fabrics were developed for specific filtering operations because of their resistance to mineral acids, alkalies, and oxidizing agents. It is stated that the yarn at room temperature is not attacked by 70 per cent nitric acid, aqua regia, hydrochloric or hydrofluoric acids of maximum concentrations, by 30 per cent sodium hydroxide or 28 per cent ammonium hydroxide, by salt solutions of all types, by cuprammonium solutions, by alcohol, glycol and higher aliphatic hydrocarbons. The yarn is water-repellent, but it may be surface-wetted by the use of commercial wetting-out agents. It will not support combustion, bacteria, or fungus growths. It is dissolved by ketones and softened and partly dissolved by esters, certain halogenated hydrocarbons, ethers, certain amines and lower aliphatic hydrocarbons. As Vinyon yarn is thermoplastic, a temperature in excess of 65°C will cause shrinkage. This shrinkage is given as definite for the temperature to which it may be subjected; for example at 75°C there is a shrinkage of about 12 per cent; at 80°C the individual filaments of the threads will shrink very materially and will cohere; and at 135°-140°C definite tackiness in the thread will develop.

The tenacity may be controlled within the range of 1.00 to 4.00 grams per denier[2] and the elongation within the range of 120 to 10 per cent, an increase in tenacity having a concomitant effect of reduction in elongation.

The tensile strength of Vinyon is the same in the wet as in the dry state; comparison with real silk and commercial rayon is given as follows:

	Dry (R.H. 65%)		Wet	
Yarn	Tenacity (g/dm)	Elongation (%)	Tenacity (g/dm)	Elongation (%)
Silk-degummed	4.22	15.7	3.4	26.3
Viscose	2.00	19.0	1.00	28.0
Acetate	1.40	27.0	.85	36.0
Vinyon (1)	—	—	4.00	18.0
" (2)	—	—	2.30	25.0
" (3)	—	—	1.00	120.0

The yarn can be woven easily, but high relative humidities are desirable to preclude static developments. As there is no strength impairment under any conditions of wetting, the Vinyon yarn may be run while surface-wetted.

As a filter fabric, the cloth is being successfully used in such industries as dyestuffs, plating, bleacheries, pharmaceuticals, caustics, phosphoric acids, etc. Being a synthetic filter medium, it has a smooth surface; and though the cake discharges well, it becomes clogged more easily than wool or cotton and does not give as clear a filtrate, as it has no hairlike fibers for entangling the fines.

Disc Medium. Laminated plates, while not strictly a filter medium, are used in edge filters as means of solids separation. A series of discs is placed with their spacing close enough to retain rather minute solids at the edges, the liquor passing between the plates. Such a method of separation is discussed at greater length in Chapter 7.

Wool. Wool cloth, as a filtering medium, has been used for many, many years. In the handling of acid solutions, up to 5 or 6 per cent, it has a life comparable to cotton on neutral liquors.

Wool is woven in the duck-like square cloth weave, or with a raised nap; or it may be formed as a felt. Originally the smooth cloth weave was used for filtering electrolytic slimes and similar slurries. The hair-like fibers as in cotton cloth, insure a good clarity of filtrate.

With the development of sewage sludge dewatering and in cases where ferric chloride only is used for conditioning, with the resulting acid sludge, a long-nap wool cloth has come into use. The wool has a long life and it does not clog easily. Wool cloths are sold by weight, usually ranging from 10 to 22 oz per square yard with the majority at 12 oz. The clarity through wool cloths is considerably less than through cotton cloths, and their high cost, 4 to 5 times that of cotton, limits their use.

Depth Media. A method has recently been devised for the mounting of low tensile strength filter media, such as asbestos, etc., whereby the fibers are so arranged as to be on edge. The resulting effect is as if the coarsely woven materials were mounted in a folded manner with an over-all depth of from 1 to 3 inches, thereby giving depth filtration. With depth media, the initial bridging of particles is more readily accomplished, that is, a greater depth is allowed for the initial formation and thus greater permeability can be maintained in continuous operation.

References

1. Griffith, A. A., Phil. Trans. 221, 1920.
2. New International denier = numerically to number of grams per 10,000 meters.

Chapter 6
Gravity Filters

General

Filtration by gravity is the oldest method of separating solids from liquids and is the way by which nature accomplishes its many clarifications. As the pressure differential required is furnished by gravity, it is definitely limited, thereby confining the application of gravity filters to those materials which can be handled by low differentials. This low pressure has one distinct advantage, namely, production of a clear filtrate. With the gentle flow impact the solids are not driven through the filter medium, but work their way through gradually if the voids in the medium are too large.

Bag filters, false-bottomed tanks, fixed beds and rotary screens of the gravity type are primarily drainage or clarifying filters at the present time. Before the practical development of continuous and modern intermittent leaf filters, filtration by gravity filters with fixed beds was extensively used for solids recovery. These filters were clumsy to operate, required extensive labor and gave poor drying of cake, but did give a clear filtrate.

Bag Filters

Relatively few gravity bag filters are employed today and these are principally units which have been in use for many years. The exception to this statement is in pharmaceuticals, paints and varnishes where a type of bag filter, or "hat," is rather widely employed. The bag filters formerly used in the sugar industry have been largely replaced by presses of the leaf type. The few regular gravity bag filters still employed are of the Taylor or similar design (the Danek and Philippe filters are considered as leaf filters because of their rigid frames).

Taylor Bag Filters. The regular Taylor filter construction is usually rectangular in form. It consists of a frame-supported pan or head into which the liquor to be clarified is run. In this head are numerous openings, to which drainage nipples are connected. The filter bags, closed at one end, by being woven or tied with string, are slipped over the nipples and tied in place. The unfiltered liquor finds its way by gravity down through the nipples and bags and the clarified filtrate is collected in channels beneath the bags. The head is divided into two bag sections. When a bag section becomes clogged that section is removed, and the bags are disconnected, cleaned and later replaced. This may be accomplished without interruption in filter operation by alternating changes of bag sections.

Cylindrical Bag Filter Type. In another of the types of bag filters a cylindrical frame support is used with a center bottom collection outlet. In cleaning, the entire head with the bags is removed and replaced by a new head and set of bags. Provision is made to prevent a fallen bag (bags often drop off the header) from closing the discharge opening. Otherwise operation is the same as with the Taylor filter.

Bag filters are expensive to operate because of the excessive labor costs and bag replacements. The cleaning and replacement of cloth in the elevated temperatures of a sugar refinery, where they were chiefly used, is hard, disagreeable work, and good operators are difficult to keep. While the filtrate is clear and the filter cheap to install, the disadvantages normally more than overbalance these features. As previously stated, their use has practically died out and they are found only in older plants.

"Hat" Filters. Gravity bag or "hat" filters for paint, varnish, and pharmaceutical clarification are still used extensively by the smaller manufacturers. Bags like inverted hats are tied to frames, and a collection vessel placed beneath. The hat is filled with the paint or varnish, or other material, and the liquor drips through slowly, leaving the dirt, specks and other solid material inside the hats. The hats are made of felt, canton flannel and unwoven cotton, and the setup is usually home-made. The rate of flow is low; but the filter is extremely simple, cheap and requires no attention. Often the medium is thrown away after one or two filtrations with no attempt at cleaning. This is always the case with unwoven cotton media which are not designed for cleaning.

Round, flat-bottomed gravity filters, similar to sieves, with cotton or paper medium inserts, are also used in paint or varnish clarification. At times these filters are set upon shakers or connected to vibrators to increase the filtering rate. The agitation prevents the fines from quickly sliming over to form a more or less impervious layer, if such fines are present, although there is some tendency for the vibration to cause the particles to work their way through the medium and show up as a cloud or specks in the filtrate.

Both the gravity "hat" and the gravity flat-bottom sieve-like filters are small in size, a diameter of thirty inches being large. The quantity of filtrate produced is likewise small; but the fact that expensive materials are handled and the utmost clarity is obtained makes these filters of considerable importance.

Stationary Filters

Stationary gravity filters and gravity false-bottomed tanks are the same in general principle and construction, with the former consisting of relatively small cylindrical vessels and the latter of large round or rectangular tanks. Their action, like that of all gravity filters, is one of low differential filtering.

Stationary Ceramic Filters. A large number of the stationary filters are of ceramic construction; these are called stoneware filters, and may be of either gravity or suction design. The false-bottom is usually from ¼ to ½ the way down the vertical sides of the vessel. The bottom is of permanent construction, cast with the sides or resting upon ledges so cast. The false bottom itself is rarely the filter medium. It usually acts as perforated support for porous plates cemented into place upon it.

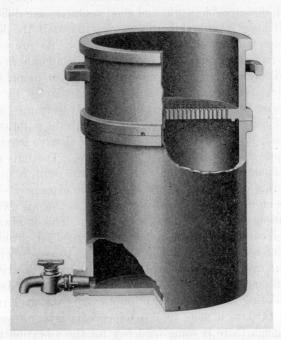

FIGURE 24. Gravity ceramic filter. (*Courtesy General Ceramics and Steatite Corp., N. J.*)

The stoneware filters have a normal holding capacity of from five gallons (two gallons above the filter medium and three gallons below) to 200 gallons (100 gallons above the filter medium and 100 gallons below).

As the porous plates used with stoneware filters have average dimensions of 12 inches square by 1½ inches thick, considerable caulking is required. The plates usually fit with close clearance, ¼ inch grooves being left for open caulking, which is often done with a marine caulking compound, applied with an ordinary caulking gun.

Where metal is permissible, a simple arrangement is to insert ¼ inch round or square bars in the seams, letting them cross and rest upon the main supports. If metal is not permissible, asbestos rope, sulfur, asphalt, paraffin or special cement may be used for caulking. The greatest use of ceramic gravity filters is in corrosive filtration, where small quantities of liquor are involved.

Filtration is slow and no materials should be handled which will get into the interstices of the medium, for the latter is permanently fixed in place. Precoating is used at times, but care must be taken to prevent any colloids from getting through to the plates. The filters normally assure a clear filtrate and are convenient to handle. As there is storage space above and below the filter medium no attention is needed for a complete batch filtration. The corrosion-resistant structure throughout means that no replacements are needed, except in case of accident.

Occasionally cast iron, steel, bronze, special metals, wood or lined stationary vessels are used rather than ceramic material. This depends upon the liquor to be handled and the filter medium permissible.

False-Bottom Tank Filters

False-bottomed tanks, formerly employed widely in the chemical industry, have been replaced by more modern filters, except for special projects. They are, however, still used in water clarification where sand or coal is often employed as the filter medium (Chapter 12), and in sugar and oil refineries for decolorization, where carbons, Fullers earth, etc., are used as filter media.

In water clarification the tanks are round or rectangular, of wood, steel or concrete structure, with porous ceramic plates, screens or other materials as the medium support. Large volumes of water are handled, with special back washing for cleaning and periodic renewal of filter medium.

Drainage Filters

The simplest type of drainage filter is a fabric spread loosely over the top of a tank and held by hooking over the sides. The slurry to be filtered is then poured onto the fabric, which has been given sufficient slack to hold a batch of material. This is similar to a hat gravity filter. Filtration is by straining through the fabric, and collection is in the bottom of the tank. After the run the filter medium can be quickly taken out for washing or for cake removal. The filter cake often is washed by

FIGURE 25. Water gravity filter beds. (*Courtesy Norwood Engineering Co.*)

applying a wash solvent, which is simply poured over the formed cake
as the mother liquor begins to disappear from sight on this cake; the wash
follows the mother liquor through the cake. As a rule batch lots of quick-
filtering materials are the kind of slurries handled on drainage filters of
this design, because of the low cost of handling.

Char Filters

In sugar refineries cylindrical tanks about 6 feet in diameter by 22
feet high are provided with false bottoms for supporting vegetable char,
bone char or other carbon; these are called char filters. Their function
is really one of decolorizing rather than of filtration, although they are
known in the trade as filters.

These decolorizers are nearly filled with char and then the feed liquor
is allowed to percolate through the entire depth. After a given time, just
before the carbon has begun to lose its effect, filtering is stopped, the old
char is removed and sent for revivifying, and a fresh charge is put in the
cylinder.

Similar filters for decolorizing lubricating oils are used in petroleum
refining (Chapter 11).

Fixed Beds. Fixed filter beds are considered to be those which have replaceable sand or gravel media in a fixed bed support, such as slow sand filters or gravel beds (Chapter 12). Such filters in water and sewage filtration are for clarification as there is no provision for dry cake removal. Back-washing for medium cleaning will remove the accumulated solids as a slurry but can only handle a limited quantity of such solids. Usually, after varying periods of time, the medium must be replaced, as cleaning is never complete and eventually the back-washing becomes ineffectual.

Sand beds also are used for sewage sludge dewatering. Here the sludge is run out onto gravity filters of sand and allowed to drain by gravity until dry enough to shovel. A good deal of the moisture is lost by evaporation to aid in the total reduction of moisture.

Sand beds are used also in gasoline clarification for the removal of mechanical dirt, etc., and in paper mills as savealls and in other processes.

Fixed beds for clarification have large capacities, and rather elaborate systems of underground drains are provided to collect the clarified effluent.

Floating Beds

One interesting design of gravity filter is an upward flow type, wherein the liquor to be clarified is made to pass through a floating mass, or layer, of its own or other solids, which act as the filter medium. The unfiltered solids are retained by this medium and clarified effluent flows up to exit at the top of the tank. Periodically the floating mass is changed, or some is taken away continuously and fresh material added or accumulated. The particular application of this type of filter has been in the sewage field.

Rotary Screens. Rotary screens of the flat, inclined disc, or drum design, for gravity separation are rather extensively used for sewage and water screening and in paper mills as knotters, thickeners, savealls, deckers, etc. While many of the gravity rotary screens have been replaced by vacuum filters there are still a large number in use.

The rotating, inclined-disc gravity screen or filter is constructed with flat, slotted plates as the filtering surface. It has a low vertical circular center for the drive connections, giving the whole the appearance of a broad-brimmed hat. The disc is set at a low angle so as to give it about 50 per cent submergence and still retain the solids and allow for counter brush removal of them. The rotating brushes, two or three in number, turn against the rotating disc to brush the solids back, up and off the disc in a rolling movement.

In the rotating-cylinder gravity filter the cylinder consists of spiders upon which are mounted perforated or slotted plates or wire screens rolled to shape; or the spider may mount wire windings or horizontal slats upon which wire screen is mounted.

In any case the cylinder is generally suspended in a vat, usually through stuffing boxes, as high submergence is most often desired, or with internal feed the vat or pan is for filtrate collection.

Discharge may be by brushes, couch roll, doctor blade or back-washing. The filtrate passes to the interior of the cylinder and is continuously drawn off.

In one design, inclined staves 1¼ inches thick by 6 inches wide are bolted to integral vanes which are cast in spiders. There is thus a space of 6 inches between the outer edges of the staves. A 3 to 4 mesh copper backing wire is stapled to the staves and a 40 to 60 mesh screen is placed over this with the ends soldered directly over a stave. On top of this soldering a 2 inch by 1 inch thick board is screwed down across the face of the cylinder. The boards serve both as agitators and to elevate the thickened stock over the discharge baffle. The inclined staves raise a small quantity of waste water as they revolve and cause it to wash off the screen from the inside out. The machine is used as a paper pulp thickener, increasing thin pulp to a 4½ to 5 per cent consistency, or as a pre-thickener to increase the capacity of the wet machine, vacuum filters and screw presses.

Rotary screens with external pockets sometimes are used for the removal and washing of knots in paper manufacturing. Open cylinder machines are often used as pulp pre-thickeners, with or without vats, for installation in troughs. Countercurrent open cylinder washers may be set in series with repulpers between, so that the paper fibers can be separated and scrubbed for ink and clay removal, etc.

Chapter 7

Pressure Filters

General

Pressure filtration by the action of relatively unlimited direct liquid pressure, as differentiated from gravity or vacuum filtration employing limited pressure differentials, covers a wide variety of applications. There are three general designs of such filters: plate filter presses, pressure leaf filters and pressure cylinder or drum filters. Of these, the filter press (plate-and-frame press, including recessed plate) is the most common and most extensively used. Of the other two designs, the pressure leaf filter, in a variety of types, has the wider range of use, the pressure cylinder or drum filters being employed in specialized fields.

A general classification would list the various pressure filters as follows:

- I. Plate Filter Presses
  - A. Standard Plate and Frame
  - B. Recessed Plate
- II. Leaf Pressure Filters
  - A. Rotating
    - 1. Continuous
    - 2. Intermittent
  - B. Stationary
    - 1. Vertical
    - 2. Horizontal
- III. Cylinder or Drum
  - A. Rotating
    - 1. Vertical
    - 2. Horizontal
  - B. Stationary
    - 1. Cylinder
    - 2. Edge

Plate-and-Frame Presses

The common filter press may be described as a frame on which there are a number of indented loose plates with filtering surfaces. These plates are clamped together, to form a series of hollow chambers and are capable of withstanding internal pressure. The filter surfaces are ribbed or grooved and covered with cloths of filtering material.

The regular plate-and-frame filter press consists of a filter press frame made of two end supports, rigidly held together by two horizontal steel

101

bars. Upon these horizontal bars are placed a varying number of flush plates and frames, clamped together, thereby forming the hollow chambers. The faces of these plates are grooved, pyramided or ribbed, as the case may be, except at the edges, which are machined to form a joint surface. The whole plate is covered with cloth, forming a filtering surface which is grooved, pyramided or ribbed, and acting as a gasket on the machined surfaces of the plates and frames.

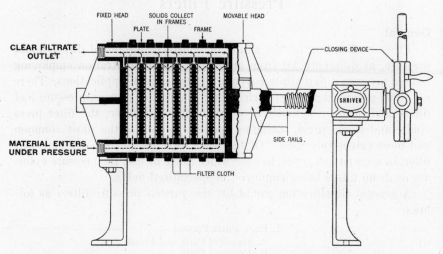

FIGURE 26. Sectional view of a fully assembled, corner feed, closed delivery filter press, showing plates, filter cloth and frames in place on filter press skeleton and indicating flow of material. (*Courtesy T. Shriver & Co., Inc.*)

Normally a screw or hydraulic ram, fitted with a closing device for pressing the plates or plates and filter press frames together, is situated on one end of the filter press and operated against a movable head. On the other end of the filter press the head is fixed, although in some special designs both heads are movable. In the smaller presses, the press is normally opened and closed by hand but, in the larger sizes automatic devices are often used. The plates and frames are pushed along the horizontal bars by hand, or ratchet-shifted (Fig. 26) when putting on or taking off cloths, or when discharging the filter cake.

There are two forms of plate presses in general use: flush plate-and-frame presses (or chamber presses) and recessed-plate presses. Either may be made circular, triangular or square.

In the plate-and-frame press, the filter chamber is formed by a frame and the adjacent plates. Thus, a 20-chamber press will be equipped with 20 frames and 19 plates, one less than the number of frames, because the filter press head and follower castings act as a half plate each.

The plate-and-frame presses are classified according to the method of feeding. In the internal feed, press eyes are cast in the plates and frames inside the joint surfaces (Fig. 27). When the plates and frames are

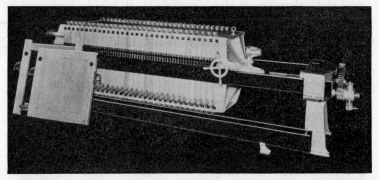

FIGURE 27. Corner feed, open delivery wood filter press. (*Courtesy T. Shriver & Co., Inc.*)

pressed together these eyes form a continuous channel, which is the passage for the material to be filtered and connects to the interior of the frames by cored inlet ports. A square-corner feed, two-eyed, open delivery, washing, flush plate-and-frame press is shown in Fig. 27. Here an eye or hole in one corner of the plates and frames forms a channel for the introduction of material to be filtered, the other being for wash water. In Fig. 28 is illustrated a four-eyed closed delivery press; the plates and frames are standing by the press, showing the eyes.

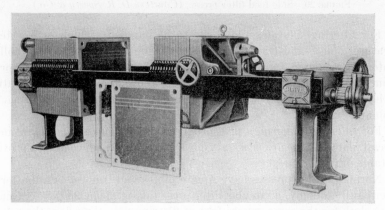

FIGURE 28. Corner feed, closed delivery washing press with plates and frames of laminated phenolic plastic material. (*Courtesy T. Shriver & Co., Inc.*)

One of the most widely used flush plate-and-frame presses is the square-shaped, external or side feed, open delivery, washing filter press.

The feed entrance is through a channel formed by external lugs at the side of the press made tight by rubber collars inserted in the holes of each plate and frame. The design makes it unnecessary to cut holes in the cloth, and cloth changing is thus simplified. It is only necessary to cut the cloths to the proper lengths and fold them over each plate. In washing, the wash liquor is pumped through a channel in the side of the press opposite the feed channel and similarly provided with rubber collars, and the wash can escape only through the filter cake, the feed connections being shut off.

FIGURE 29. Side feed filter press. (*Courtesy D. R. Sperry & Co.*)

For filtering solutions that have to be handled at high or low temperatures, plate-and-frame presses are made of plates having hollow centers. A channel, formed by eyes running the entire length of the press connecting in multiple all hollow interiors, allows the desired temperature to be maintained with steam, hot water, hot oil, electric heating, or coolant.

For filtering under high pressure, up to 1000 pounds per square inch, special plate designs are necessary for structural resistance and to provide suitable drainage surfaces.

Normally filter presses have square plates and frames, as a matter of filter cloth economy, a circular filter press taking about 25 per cent more filter cloth for the same square foot of filtering area than does the square press. Many circular and triangular presses have been made, however, the triangular press particularly for metallurgical work and the circular press for beverages. In the latter case, as formed paper pads frequently are used as the filter medium, the shape is not detrimental.

There formerly was a triangular plate-and-frame press with the discharge cocks at the top. This press was designed for ore slimes and was used in conjunction with zinc dust for precipitation of silver, and with carbon for the precipitation of gold. The press was triangular in section and the feed pipes were so arranged that the solution and precipitant en-

FIGURE 30. Corner feed press with hollow plates for steam circulation. (*Courtesy T. Shriver & Co., Inc.*)

FIGURE 30A. Sluicing filter press, cake discharge by horizontal sluicing tube passing through center of press and equipped with nozzles positioned at center each frame, periodic cake discharge without press opening. (*Courtesy The Merrill Co.*)

tered from the bottom of the apex of each filter compartment. In this way the solids, gradually accumulating in the frames, were kept constantly agitated. This provided a layer of precipitant through which the solution must pass, thereby insuring better contact.

Recessed-Plate Press. The recessed-plate press is simpler in construction than the plate-and-frame, consisting as it does of hollow chambers formed between two recessed plates, the thicker edge of the plate forming the joint surface. The feed passage is taken through the body of the plate, side or center, and the filter cloths are laid over each side of the plate, forming a pressure-tight joint at the rims when clamped up, and having holes for feed passage. The cloths are either sewed or clipped to make a joint at the corresponding holes in the plate.

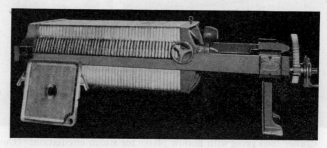

FIGURE 31. Recessed-plate filter press. (*Courtesy T. Shriver & Co., Inc.*)

According to Spooner and Kriegel, (consultants) "the recessed plate press imposes a severe strain on the filter cloth at the edges of the plate joint surfaces and at the feed channels; cake thickness is limited; filter paper and wire mesh cloth cannot be used to an advantage; a soft core is often formed in the cake around the center feed channel, making a non-uniform cake difficult to wash; and the filter cloths must be fastened at the feed openings on each plate by clip nuts or sewing. Against these disadvantages, as compared to a plate-and-frame press, the recessed-plate press feeds directly to the filter chamber without the use of ports to connect the feed channels with the chambers; the feed openings do not clog on thick materials, as will happen in the plate-and-frame press; and also there are only half the joint surfaces to keep tight and a lower initial cost in the recessed plate."

Filter Press Capacity. The size of plates, thickness of frames or depth of recess in plates and number of chambers govern holding capacity. Of these factors, the frame thickness or recess depth is the most important in providing for an economical filtration cycle. If the frames are too thin, the filter cake will fill them rapidly and the filter press will have to be opened frequently for cleaning. If, on the other hand, the frames are too thick, a firm cake will not be formed before the filtering action has ceased, resulting in a soft cake that is impossible to wash properly. In selecting the number of chambers, it is preferable to go to the next larger size of filter press rather than have too large a number of chambers.

Dummy plates or solid frames are used to reduce the capacity of a press. A thirty-chamber filter press thus can be reduced to 1, 6, 12, 14, or any other number of chambers. Webbed or solid frames cut with a web of metal in the middle are used to cut down cake thickness when required for additional flexibility.

Leakage. Because of high pressures, worn surfaces, and the leakage hazard through the filter-cloth gaskets when handling thin fluids, a number of plate designs have been offered as "leak proof." The filter cloth

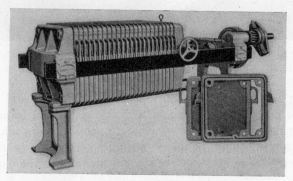

FIGURE 32. Four-eyed filter press with leakage drainage grooves. (*Courtesy T. Shriver & Co., Inc.*)

may be caulked into a groove inside the packing and a gasket placed between plates, or the grooves may be connected with the filtrate delivery outlets of the plates in open delivery plates or in closed delivery with openings, forming a channel which discharges through the head of the press; this channel may be connected to suction. Again, retaining rings are provided to hold the filter cloth and the joint packing in place. The filter cloths do not extend into the joints, but a packing does extend through the joint, or rubber gaskets are placed in special plate grooves and extended ⅛″ to 3⁄16″ above the joint surfaces.

Closing. The closing device, which presses the plates or plates and frames together, is usually a large steel screw located at one end of the filter press which forms the follower toward the head, squeezing the plate-and-frame assembly together. The screw is hand-operated by means of a simple ratchet and lever. In large-size filter presses and for all high-pressure work, gear-and-pinion or hydraulic closing devices are used.

These usually actuate the movable head backward and forward, or may move the empty plates back in a body.

FIGURE 33. Wood filter press with electric hydraulic closing device. (*Courtesy D. R. Sperry & Co.*)

Venting. At times, holes are tapped in each frame and fitted with petcocks; or ported vents to channels in the plates and frames may be used to vent the filter chambers to avoid air pockets. This may be to aid in quick chamber filling, to insure a proper precoat or cake, or if the pump capacity is too low, to force the air out through the cloth quickly enough.

Filter presses are commonly made of cast iron because of its cheapness, durability and strength. However, filter presses readily lend themselves to various materials of construction, such as galvanized, enameled, or rubber-coated cast iron or lead, bronze, Monel metal, aluminum, stainless steel, or wooden plates and frames.

Wood and to a lesser extent rubber filter presses are extensively used under corrosive conditions.

Operation. The filtration cycle consists of the following steps:

(1) Forming the filter cake (the clarifying period).

(2) Washing the cake to eliminate mother liquor, or washing for recovery of soluble values (if required).

(3) Cleaning and preparing for the next cycle.

First the filter press is closed and locked with the cloths or medium carefully in place. The outlet cocks or valves are closed. The main feed line valve is opened and the pump, or pressure, is started. Presses are normally pump-fed, although gravity head and air pressure on closed chambers or blow cases are sometimes used. The unfiltered liquor passes through the feed opening in the various plates to the filter medium. The solids are left in the chambers after clarifying or in cake building, the pressure being low at the start and increasing with the cake resistance. This continues until the high pressure, or low rate of flow, indicates the end of the filtering period.

FIGURE 34. Combination square and disc filter. (*Courtesy Ertel Engineering Co.*)

The press may be air- or steam-blown before "thorough" washing (complete soluble content removal), or "simple" washing (partial soluble content removal); or, if washing or blowing is not required, the press is opened directly after the filtering period for cake discharge and cleaning or changing the filter cloth.

Plate Surface. The filter plate surface forms the drainage surface as well as supporting the filter medium, and therefore its design is of great importance in filter-press operation. The cloth must be well supported to withstand the relatively high filtering pressure (up to 1000 pounds). For such a high pressure perforated plates and screens are sometimes used. Pyramid surfaces are commonly used on metal plates, on both center and corner feed types radial grooves for corner feed, circular grooves on circular plates, and corrugated surfaces on wood or rubber plates.

Filter Medium. Cotton is used for filter cloths more than any other material because of its low cost and excellent filtering qualities, although wools, hair, asbestos, paper, metals, and other materials also are used. Paper may be used in sheets alone (blotter presses) over filter cloth for the protection of the cloth and in pad form particularly, for beverage filtration.

Advantages. The filter press has found wider application than any other type of filter. It is structurally simple and without complicated auxiliaries, making for low initial cost, low installation cost and low power requirements. It can be operated with unskilled labor and provides large filter areas in a compact space. Presses may be jacketed, operation may be with filtrate enclosed or exposed, and corrosion-resistant construction is not difficult. High pressures are obtainable, capacities can be quickly varied by the use of dummy plates or shutting of cocks or valves, and clarity of effluent is easily obtainable.

Disadvantages. The greatest disadvantage of the filter press is its intermittent operation and the labor involved therein. Almost as great is wear of the filter cloths from the squeezing and the rough scraping in cake removal, when the cake does not fall off. There may be difficulty in efficient washing due to compression in cake formation and the danger of channeling, with by-passing of wash water through the line of least resistance. There is also the necessity of filling the frames for dry discharge of cake for, with partly filled frames, the excess feed would be discharged with the cake. With highly compressible or weak structure solids, complete frame filling is difficult. Finally, there are certain hazards: filtering corrosive liquors; leaks, as the pressure is outward, and from handling cake discharge; also there is loss of volatile solvents through leaks and in opening the press at the end of cycle.

Application. In clarification work, with or without precoats, filter presses are extensively used, particularly in small or batch handling. They are excellent polishing filters for which filter aids are often employed, *viz*, beverages, shellacs, and varnishes, soaps and vegetable oils, or with filter paper, as blotter presses for lubricating oils, or paper pads for beer. They will handle hot liquors, since separation is by direct pressure; as they are easily made of corrosion-resistant materials, the chemical and allied industries, such as dye and color manufacturers, employ them widely, as do decolorizing, bleaching and deodorizing concerns. Again, for materials that require a relatively high pressure for separation, as certain clays and slimes, the filter press has proved best adapted.

Standard sizes of plate-and-frame presses are square 4″, 18″, 20″, 24″, 30″, 32″, 48″ and 56″; of recessed-plate presses square 7″ to 48″; wood presses, 12″ to 56″, with up to 42 chambers and possible cake formations from ½″ to 2″.

Leaf Pressure Filters

Leaf pressure filters are made in both the rotating leaf and the stationary leaf design. In the former the leaves are circular or eccentric, while in the latter they are circular, square or rectangular.

The rotating design may be of the continuous type, for particles which form cakes rapidly, or of the intermittent type, for clarification or cake formation in long cycles. The continuous type, one of the newer designs, is a combination of the intermittent rotary leaf pressure filter and the continuous rotary disc vacuum filter, with special controls and discharge arrangement.

Continuous Rotary Vertical Leaf Pressure Filter. In the continuous rotary vertical leaf pressure filter, one or more sectionalized leaves of the disc type are mounted upon a central shaft, and each sector connects to a valve on the end of the shaft. The valve is of the standard, automatic, disc vacuum, blowback type, but used for two different pressures, one for filtering under regulated pressure and the other for higher pressure discharge.

A casing encloses the discs and their shaft, and the lower portion of the casing is fitted with an overflow and float control for keeping the slurry level at a predetermined height, up to 50 per cent submergence. Scrapers guide the cake into separate hoppers for each disc, for discharge onto common screw-blade conveyors. There are a number of special controls for the discharge valve, the inert gas pressure, the slurry level, and to prevent overload on the screw conveyors, at the same time maintaining the whole in balance for continuous, automatic operation.

Operation. In operation the feed or slurry is supplied by a montejus or by a pressure pump, automatically controlled by the slurry height float. At the same time, a gas, such as air, nitrogen, or carbon dioxide, is maintained at the desired pressure in that portion of the casing above the slurry. The pressure causes the liquor to pass through the filter medium, sectors, pipe lines, and valve, to the collection chamber, while the solids form a cake on the surface of the discs.

As the discs emerge from the slurry their cake may be spray-washed as they revolve. The spray is admitted at a higher pressure than that within the casing, to supply the proper differential for spraying. The excess wash is collected in a gutter as it runs from the cake surface, and is carried off for re-use or discard. After washing, the cake is dried as it passes through the gas zone prior to discharge. The cake is dropped or discharged from the sectors by inert gas blowback from within the sectors, this pressure also being higher than that within the casing. The falling cake is guided to the conveyors and discharged as previously described.

Materials Handled. Rotary vertical leaf pressure filters are designed to handle slurries having sufficient cake-forming solids to enable a cake $\frac{1}{8}$ inch or more in thickness to be built up within 15 minutes' time, under pressures up to 100 pounds.

Advantages. Continuous, automatic pressure operation is the great advantage of this filter. It is specially suitable where volatile solvents are used; where the pressures will give a sufficiently dryer cake than a continuous vacuum filter to warrant its more expensive installation and operation; in filtering materials at temperatures which are not applicable to vacuum filtration; or in handling materials requiring higher than vacuum differentials for filtration.

Disadvantages. In order to obtain the above advantages, it has been necessary to make the equipment quite expensive and a rather elaborate set of controls is necessary, which must be kept in synchronized operation.

Intermittent Rotary Vertical Leaf Pressure Filters. The intermittent, rotary vertical leaf pressure filter consists of a casing containing the rotatable filter element, the discharge scroll or flushing device, and the frame support. The casing is generally made of welded steel with a movable head or with a lower stationary section and an upper movable section (Fig. 35).

The filter element consists of a number of filter discs or leaves, covered with filter fabric or metal cloth mounted upon a rotatable hollow shaft. Multiple inlet connections are used and space is provided below the element for the incoming liquor to reach all parts of the filter element at nearly the same pressure. In the hub of each single disc, or in each

FIGURE 35. Intermittent rotary verticle leaf pressure filter leaves with separate leaf pipe lines, each with sight glass and shut-off cock. (*Courtesy Turl Iron and Car Co.*)

sector of each sectionalized leaf, apex pipes are located for draining the filtrate to the central hollow shaft and through this shaft to the filtrate outlet at the end of the filter. Each filter leaf may be an assembled piece and the entire element may be removed as a unit, or the leaf may be sectionalized for individual sector or disc removal. Scrolls may be situated in the bottom of the filter, usually at the right and left of the center, to convey the discharged cake out of the bottom of the filter casing. For slurry or sluice discharge a perforated pipe may be used instead of the scrolls, or the hollow shaft of the scrolls may be perforated to serve the same purpose, in addition to the leaf sluicing sprays located in the upper casing section. Inspection or leaf sector removing doors may be placed in the upper section of the casing.

The filter leaves often have self-draining guides and, with an effective scroll, a dry cake discharge can be obtained. The filter leaves have filter media in disc form on each side, held by a screwed or bolted center clamping ring and an outer clamping ring or caulking grooves, or the leaves may be divided into pie-shaped sectors over which the filter medium is fitted.

Operation. The operation of the intermittent rotary leaf pressure type filter is, in general, as follows: All valves on the filter are closed except the inlet and overflow valves, and the leaves are started rotating. The slurry is fed to the filter by pump or pressure until it appears at the overflow valve. The valve is then closed and the forcing of the slurry into the filter is continued; this causes the filtrate to pass through the filter medium on the leaves and out through the leaf drainage and central hollow shaft to the desired collection point. The solids are deposited upon the leaf surfaces in a uniform layer due to the rotation of the leaves. When the predetermined cake thickness is built up, or the rate of flow of filtrate falls off too greatly, the inlet valve is closed, compressed air is admitted, the excess sludge valve in the bottom of the filter is opened and the excess sludge forced back to the supply tank. When the pressure drops quickly the filter is empty and the outlet and air valves are closed. At this point, it is necessary to be careful not to allow the pressure to drop to zero; if it does, the cake may fall off the filter leaves.

If the cake is to be washed, wash solution is forced into the filter; when it appears at the overflow, the overflow valve is closed and wash solution fed to the filter until the desired results are obtained. To empty the filter of excess wash, the wash outlet valve is opened, and compressed air again is admitted to force the excess wash liquor back to the wash solution supply, or to waste. When the wash solution is entirely out of the filter, the inlet valve is closed and compressed air allowed to blow through the cake, if drying is desired.

When the cake is ready to discharge, the screw conveyors are started, the air pressure is released, and the cake discharge on the bottom of the filter is opened. If the cake does not fall off of its own accord, air is applied to spray pipe to drop cake onto the screw conveyors. If the cake can be discharged by flushing the leaves are kept revolving, and water is turned on through the spray pipes, one on each side of each filter leaf. Air or steam enters through the perforated pipe in the bottom of the filter and the cake is washed from the leaves and out of the filter.

Applications. The field of application of this type of filter is the clarification of liquors with precoats or filter aids; liquids containing small percentages of solids that are slow settling; or small quantities of free-filtering solids, where an hour or so is required for 1 inch or less of cake formation; or where high temperatures or high altitudes are encountered. Some slow-filtering materials form very compact filter cakes and require higher filtering pressure than can be obtained by a vacuum type filter. A wide range of industrial products is handled, such as cane and beet sugars, syrups, beverages, caustic liquors, chemicals, oils, metallurgical slimes, and other products of the process industries. These filters also are used to handle volatile liquids, sub-zero or high temperature liquids, and poisonous gases or liquids.

Advantages. The filter is labor-saving, as it need not be opened during operation, valve manipulation being all that is required. It uses a small amount of wash solution, saves filter media, as they do not need to be touched, has a low maintenance cost, is easily insulated, produces a very uniform cake, due to the rotation of the filter leaves, and gives rapid, easy discharge of the cake and quick cleaning of the cloths.

Disadvantages. The filter has the disadvantage of being cyclic; cycles less than two hours are seldom economical. Its use is thus limited to clarification and to those slurries which cannot be continuously filtered.

The filter may be made of steel, cast iron, and corrosion-resistant materials.

Sizes. Sizes of filters range from 1½ sq ft (laboratory size) to about 1800 sq ft of filter area. Capacities of cake and filtrate vary according to the material being filtered.

A modification of the intermittent rotary vertical leaf pressure filter is one in which the leaves are rotated only for cleaning or discharge, rotation being by hand or power. Such filters are used in beverage or water clarification. Another type does not rotate the leaves at all; for cleaning, the cover is opened and the leaves are washed down by hosing or other means.

Still another type employs leaves constructed of rigid media rigidly in contact, somewhat similar to the old "filtros wheel." The leaves are enclosed in a horizontal cylinder and cleaning is by back washing and internal sprays so that the filter need not be opened for this operation

(Fig. 36). All these types normally employ a precoat for filter medium protection.

FIGURE 36. Rotary disc pressure filter with rigid media. (*Courtesy LeVal Filter Co.*)

Intermittent Vertical Stationary Leaf Pressure Filters. Intermittent vertical stationary leaf pressure filters may be constructed with discs or in irregularly shaped leaves. The disc form usually consists of a split shell or casing, the upper, stationary section and the hinged bottom section. Inside the shell there are suspended a number of stationary circular leaves or discs, which drain through individual outlets (often sight glasses) into a common discharge manifold. The feed connection may be at either end of the filter shell. Some units are equipped with a sluicing mechanism. The filter cake is removed either with the bottom of the filter shell opened (Fig. 37), or by sluicing down through the bottom drains, with the bottom section of the shell closed. The smaller units are opened and closed by hand, using a lever and counterweights. The larger units are equipped with a handwheel and a hydraulic hoist for opening and closing.

The leaf type may use various designs of discs, top and bottom drainage, with fabric or metallic media. The top drainage leaf, with a smooth rim, is shown in Fig. 37a and is the standard type for most filtration requirements. The bottom drainage leaf (Fig. 37b) is used where thorough washing of the cake and a dry finished cake is desired. The filtrate and wash drain to the bottom of the leaf and thence into the opening of a flat tube (extending upward and sealed into the outlet nipple), the liquor being forced to the outlet by the pressure. In the case of the top drainage leaf, some liquor is likely to remain in the lower portion of the cake.

FIGURE 37. Stationary verticle leaf pressure filter. (*Courtesy Oliver United Filters*)

There are two methods of applying cotton and wool fabric cloths to the leaves: (1) with the smooth rim leaves the cloths in the form of bags slip over the leaves and are sewn tight; (2) with the grooved-rim leaves, the cloths are cut in circular disc forms and caulked into the grooves. When metal cloths are used they are caulked into the grooves, as shown in Fig. 37c. This figure also shows the construction of a filter leaf with wire cloth cover.

Operation. In operation the filter is first closed and locked by fastening the two sections of the shell together with the swing bolts and nuts (see Fig. 37). To fill the filter, the valve on the supply line and the inlet valve are opened and the pump from the supply started. If the first filtrate is turbid it is recirculated to the supply until clear. When the filtrate is clear, filtering is continued until the proper thickness of cake is obtained. The cakes should never be allowed to build together. When the cake is built up, it may be washed by turning on the wash solution and shutting off the slurry inlet simultaneously and washing until desired results are obtained; or, if desired, the filter may be drained of excess slurry before washing, but some pressure is held so that the cake will not slough off the leaves. The wash solution is then admitted; at the same time the air pressure is gradually released through the valve on top of the filter.

FIGURE 37a. Filter leaf with top drainage. (*Courtesy Oliver United Filters*)

When washing is finished, the inlet valve is closed, the compressed air valve on the filter and the excess wash solution valve are opened and the filter emptied of excess wash solution. When the filter is empty, the excess wash solution and air is released, the filter is opened and the cake dropped.

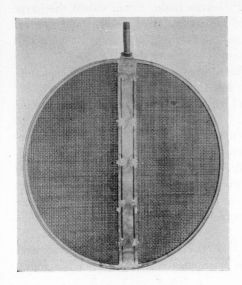

FIGURE 37b. Filter leaf with bottom drainage. (*Courtesy Oliver United Filters*)

If there is only a thin deposit, or if a precoat has been used, it may be sluiced off the leaves and through the outlets in the bottom.

Advantages. The advantages of such a filter are economy of floor space, since the leaves do not need to be removed or drawn out; accessibility; inspection of filtrate; and flood washing.

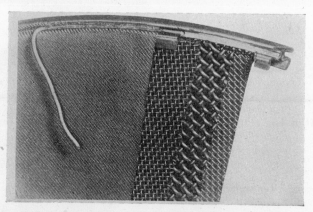

Figure 37c.   Filter leaf with caulked metal cloth.   (*Courtesy Oliver United Filters*)

Disadvantages. There are disadvantages due to the difficulty of maintaining proper agitation and at times the consequent formation of uneven cakes, which make for poor washing and drying; there is the tendency for the cake to fall off the leaves, if the filter is carelessly handled as the leaves are in vertical position; the bottom opening often causes spillage of unfiltered material; the stationary leaves make clean, closed discharge difficult, and opening means loss of time, labor, heat, solvent and wearing of the filter cloths by scraping.   Locking of the filter is sometimes difficult and considerable labor and attention is necessary.

Materials of Construction. The filter can be made of steel, cast iron, cast bronze, stainless steel, etc., or lined with any desirable non-corrosive metal and equipped with cloth and leaves of the usual corrosion-resisting materials.

Sizes. Filters of this type are made with filtering areas ranging from laboratory sizes to over 1000 square feet.   Capacity will vary widely depending upon the product handled.   The filters are generally constructed for a maximum operating pressure of 50 pounds.   Special designs are made for particular purposes, such as the all-stainless steel filter for edible juices, made with 15 leaves, 24 inches in diameter, and operated with a precoat for clear filtrate.

Square or Rectangular Leaves in Vertical Containers. Square or rectangular leaves may be suspended or supported in vertical or horizontal cylinders. In filters of the vertical cylinder type the leaf header is generally welded in position in the lower section of the cylinder and acts as a filtrate discharge outlet. The leaves are connected to the header nozzles by gaskets and adapters, being held down by gravity in the larger sizes and by "holddown" bars in the smaller.

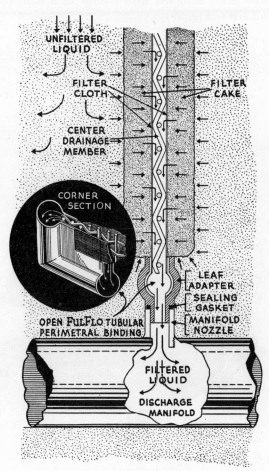

FIGURE 38. Section through pressure leaf in verticle container. (*Courtesy Niagara Filter Co.*)

On the other hand, the leaves may be suspended from a common header (Fig. 39). Leaves are made of varying widths to conform to the contour of the tank, but are of the same length. Each leaf generally consists of a center drainage member supporting the filter medium on each side. An open tubular perimetral member serves to bind the three pieces together. A bag of cotton, wool, Vinyon, etc., sewed or zippered, may be used as the filter medium.

These filters are generally precoated for use in clarification and are not used where the cake is to be saved. Individual leaf connections may be made with sight glasses and shutoff valves.

Often the filters are assembled with pumps as a movable unit since they are of small sizes (Fig. 39).

FIGURE 39. Assembly rectangular leaves in verticle container. (*Courtesy Industrial Filter & Pump Co.*)

Special units are used for such processes as solvent clarification in dry cleaning. Here the medium may be metal or fabric and clarification is continuous during each batch cycle. With metallic cloths there is usually back-washing, at times aided by hand-operated metallic scrapers machined to prevent cloth damage. With fabric cloth the filter is usually opened for cleaning.

Stationary Vertical Leaf Pressure Filter with Leaves on Movable Carriage. The stationary vertical leaf pressure filter with leaves on a movable carriage has a frame upon which the filter leaves are mounted, so that the whole may be drawn out of the filter shell for discharging the cake.

Construction. The filter (Fig. 40) consists essentially of a fixed cylindrical horizontal shell enclosing a removable carriage on which the filter

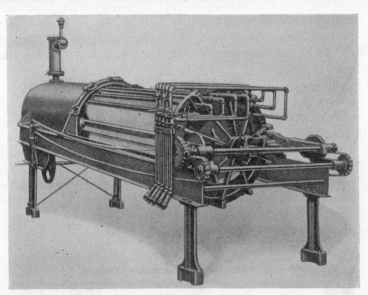

FIGURE 40. Stationary verticle leaf pressure filter with leaves on moveable carriage. (*Courtesy Oliver United Filters*)

frame or leaves are mounted in a vertical position. The shell has a closed head at one end and is open at the other and is mounted horizontally on I-beams. A heavy cast-iron ring is fastened to the open end of the shell and provided with U-bolts, by means of which the cast-iron head is locked in place against the shell. On the under side of the ring there is a flanged inlet connection through which the solution to be filtered is pumped.

The filter carriage provides a support for the filter frames, or leaves, and for the closing head, and a means of moving the frames in and out of the shell to discharge the cake. The ends of the carriage rest on wheels, the front wheels running on rails resting on the I-beam supports, while the rear wheels travel on rails supported inside the shell.

The filter frames or leaves (Fig. 40a), are rectangular in shape and extend longitudinally in the shell. The lengths are the same, but the widths normally allow for the curvature of the shell. Each frame, or leaf consists of a heavy wire screen bound on the four edges by a steel shape, which not only gives the frame the necessary rigidity but protects the filter cloth from the edge of the screen and also serves as a channel for the filtrate. The filtrate outlet can be at either the upper or lower corner of the leaf. Any suitable cloth may be used—cotton, wool, metallic, or glass. The cotton and wool cloths are usually applied in the form of a bag closed on three sides and slipped over the frame or leaf. The remaining side is sewed together in place on the frame. Metallic cloth covers are usually held by caulking grooves around the periphery of the leaf. An automatic air-regulating valve is mounted on the shell of the filter.

As with all vertical leaf filters, allowable cake thickness depends upon the leaf spacing; filtering should be stopped before the surface of two adjacent cakes touch.

Operation. When the carriage is run into the shell, the closing head bears against a gasket in the end ring on the shell and a tight joint is secured by a locking mechanism. This consists simply of radial arms mounted on the head and arranged so as to engage the U-bolts on the end ring of the shell. The locking mechanism, as well as the mechanism for running the carriage in and out of the shell, is operated by a hand crank on small filters and by an air motor on large ones.

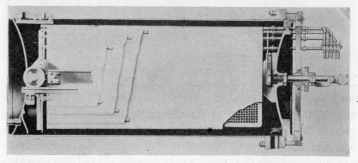

FIGURE 40a. Filter frame or leaf. (*Courtesy Oliver United Filters*)

When the carriage is run into place and the head makes contact with the shell, the operating mechanism causes the ends of the arms to slide into the U-bolts to engage them, thus pulling the head up tight against the gasket. A safety pawl, which drops into the teeth of the driving gear when the mechanism is on dead center, prevents accidental opening.

The filter operation, up to the point of discharge, is similar to that of other pressure leaf filters, but the discharge of the cake differs. To accomplish this the shell is opened, by releasing the locking mechanism, and the carriage is drawn out. The cake is dropped from the leaves either by shaking or by applying air pressure in the reverse direction to the filtrate flow. Sometimes the leaves are scraped with a wooden paddle to obtain complete cake removal.

Advantages. This type of filter can be built for pressures ranging up to 250 pounds per square inch, which is higher than usual for other types of pressure leaf filters. The shell can be readily insulated or jacketed to hold subnormal or high temperatures during filtration, and all parts are made accessible by drawing out the carriage. This also allows the operator to inspect the cake before discharge.

FIGURE 41. Leaves at right angles to shell. (*Courtesy Blackburn-Smith Co.*)

Disadvantages. There is a tendency for the solids to settle, as agitation is possible only through a valve on top of the shell and circulation back to source of supply. The filters are cumbersome, and considerable floor space is required for drawing out the leaves. If the cake builds too rapidly, constant labor is required for opening and closing the shell. Vertical leaves require careful attention so that they will hold the cake until the carriage can be drawn out and a clean discharge obtained; if paddle scraping is resorted to, the filter cloths become worn.

Materials of Construction. This filter is generally of iron and steel construction, but it may be built of non-corrosive material, as copper, stainless steel and Monel metal, and the shell may be lined and the leaves covered with non-corrosive substances such as rubber, lead, and carbon.

Size. The filter is made in various sizes from laboratory and pilot plant units to filter areas of 650 square feet. Double units are built with as large as 1300 square feet of filter surface; these have two filters facing each other, so that one can be discharging while the other is filtering, thus saving floor space.

FIGURE 42. Horizontal pressure disc filter. (*Courtesy Infilco Inc.*)

Leaves at Right Angles to Shell. In a variation of the above design the filter leaves are hung at right angles to the shell (Fig. 41). This enables the leaves to be of a uniform size for interchangeability, rather than with varying widths, as above. The leaves are top-supported and the cylinder head is moved to one side of the shell upon a frame support rather than being supported upon a leaf carriage. In general, such filters are made only in small sizes (1 to 200 square feet), as they are used most often in the clarification of relatively small batch lots of beverages, perfumes, etc., or in steam deoiling.

Stationary Horizontal Pressure Disc Filters. The stationary, horizontal, pressure disc filter is built primarily for fine or polishing filtration, for removing the last trace of suspended matter from liquor that already is comparatively clean.

Construction. The filter body may consist of two circular plates between which the filter discs are held. The top plate is placed over the discs and the discs are locked around the outer edges by means of quick-operating hinged hand bolts, which are attached to the lower plate and engage slotted lugs on the upper plate, as shown in Fig. 42. Or the filter may consist of a vertical cylinder in which horizontal flexible pads, or rigid media are layered, or a vertical shaft may be used.

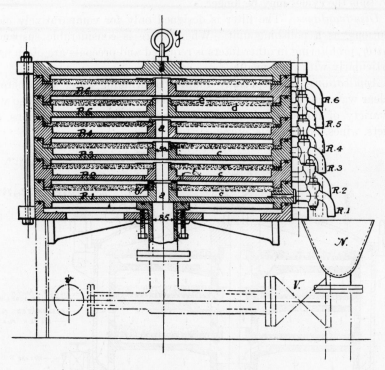

FIGURE 43. Perrin wood pulp filter.

The inlet in this filter may be in the lower portion of the cylinder and the outlet in the upper portion, so that upward filtration is employed. The filter medium is generally compressed cotton fiber, although paper pads and other media are also used, according to the particular problem at hand.

Operation. In operation with either type of construction, the filter medium is placed in the filter, which is then closed and locked. The unfiltered material is passed through the filter either by gravity or pump pressure. When the filter medium becomes too dirty for economical filtration, the feed is turned off, the excess unfiltered material drawn off, the filter opened, the dirty filter medium replaced by a clean one, the filter closed and locked, and the operation started again. Operating pressures are from ½ to 50 pounds per square inch.

Advantages. The filter is simple in construction. It occupies very little space and all portions are easily accessible. In the type where the flow is upward, the heavy particles in the unfiltered material tend to fall away from the filter medium, instead of lying on top of and clogging it, and thus the cycles may be longer.

Disadvantages. The filter is designed only for comparatively clean solutions, as a polishing unit. Where there is considerable suspended matter, prefiltering in other filters is required and precoats are often used, particularly with rigid media.

Applications. It is specially adapted to drinking water and wherever a clear water is required in industrial plants. The filter is used also with a variety of liquids, such as chemical and medicinal preparations, extracts, wines, liquors, oils, etc.

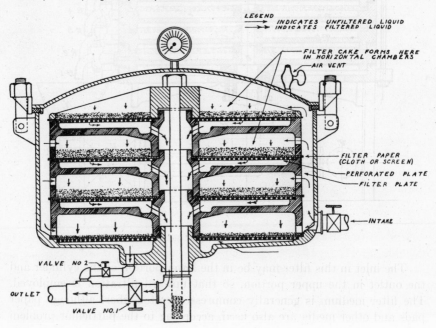

FIGURE 44. Submerged plate filter with extra chamber. (*Courtesy Sparkler Mfg. Co.*)

Horizontal Stationary Submerged Plate Pressure Filters. The horizontal stationary submerged plate pressure filter is similar to the wood pulp filter developed many years ago for sugar refining. (Fig. 43), where the plates were nested one above another in a horizontal position and entirely closed in a container.

Construction. The construction and operation of these filters is shown in Fig. 44. The arrows show the direction of travel. When filter aids are used these are deposited on the flat surface and the flow of filtrate is downward. For cleaning, the top is lifted off, exposing the whole assembly.

In one design an extra chamber is used for filtering the residue left in the filter at the end of the run (Fig. 44). Here the auxiliary filtrate valve is opened only during precoating, or at the end of the run. The excess feed liquor is sent through the auxiliary chamber by means of air or gas pressure admitted through the feed inlet valve.

In a variation of this construction there is a filter consisting of a fixed lower plate with an upper plate moving on rods so that filter frames can be placed between. The ends are hollow, and also act as frames; with alternating eyelets, a flow passage is obtained. In another type the feed is between two pads of filter medium.

Horizontal filters are used most often in the clarification of such materials as beverages, soaps and oils, and are built in relatively small sizes. At times they may be used for cake-forming slurries, where cycles are long and area requirements not excessive. Operating pressures are normally 5 to 40 pounds per square inch.

Advantages. The filters have the advantage of positive flow through the filter medium because of their horizontal position. Precoats are readily formed and the cake will not fall off with interrupted operation, for this reason. There is also the ability to filter completely all, or practically all, of the feed liquor in each cycle. Space economy, ready accessibility, quick filter medium replacements or cleaning, and simple dismantling are worthwhile features of these filters.

Disadvantages. For disadvantages, the filters are intermittent, must be taken apart for cleaning and are designed for rather small capacities.

Intermittent Revolving Cylinder Pressure Filter. An intermittent revolving cylinder pressure filter is shown in Fig. 45. This filter is used for wet discharge only, principally in the metallurgical industries, in the manufacture of electrolytic zinc, and in the filtering of residues from leaching solutions, pigments or paints, etc.

Construction. An average filter cylinder is five feet inside diameter and 40 feet long, made up in ½-inch welded steel plate, with welded flanged ends. Sixteen holes in a row are drilled circumferentially in the cylinder. Ten of these holes are spaced longitudinally for fastening the triangular filter boards to the inside of the shell by means of bolts and specially shaped angles (Fig. 45). These sets of filter boards are divided into two sections and extend from the ends to the midsection of the cylinder. At the midsection two rows of sixteen holes, drilled circumferentially in the cylinder, serve as ports for the outlet pipes and nipples from each triangular filter board.

The filter boards are channelled longitudinally on their two sloping sides and covered with filter cloth, made in the form of a stocking and sewed on the triangular forms. At the point of filtrate discharge the outside of the cylinder is covered with a channel-shaped apron of non-ferrous metal, around which is placed a hopper or launder, to receive the filtrate. The cylinder is revolved by means of gearings at the inlet end and is supported about nine feet from the discharge end by a steel riding ring and a rolled steel replacable tire.

FIGURE 45. Intermittent revolving cylinder pressure filter. (*Courtesy The Joshua Hendy Iron Works*)

Four discharge valves are located in the filter discharge head. These are opened and closed by the operation of a single handwheel, without stopping the rotation of the filter. The inlet valve, which is of the quick-opening, lever-operated type, is located in the trunnion liner of the feed head (Fig. 46). A pipe, through which air and sometimes steam, water or reagent is admitted, is located on the axis of the feed head and extends through it into the filter drum. The pipe forms the stem for the quick-opening feed valve. There is also a five-inch plug valve, located in the sludge feed line, which may be used to control the feed.

Operation. In operation, the four discharge valves are closed, the cylinder started, and the inlet valve opened to fill the cylinder. When it is full of feed liquor, the feed valve is closed and air under pressure is admitted into the cylinder, to build up a cake on the filter cloth-covered triangular filter boards. The pressure at the start of filtration is usually about 10 or 15 pounds per square inch and gradually increases to 40 pounds. It is held at that pressure until all the cake is on the filter cloths and the carrying liquor is removed. This is indicated by air blowing from the filtrate outlets. The filtrate passes through the filter cloths and along the filtrate channels in the filter boards to the outlets in the mid-section of the cylinder. When air blows from the outlets it is then turned off, wash solution forced in to the required amount, and air pressure again applied to force the wash through the cake. When this wash is completed, as indicated by air blowing from the filter, the operation is repeated until the cake is washed as clean of mother liquor as possible. After washing, the cake is sluice-discharged with water as a waste slurry. Another method is to reslurry the cake in the wash and refilter.

FIGURE 46. Feed end of intermittent revolving cylinder pressure filter. (*Courtesy The Joshua Hendy Iron Works*)

During filtration, the cylinder revolves slowly. When disintegrating the cake to a slurry and washing, and when discharging the waste slurry, the revolutions of the cylinder are increased, and at the same time a slight vacuum is induced within it. This speeds up loosening of the cake and cleaning of the cloths.

Advantages. The filter normally has the advantage of building a uniform cake by the revolving of the cylinder; this cake is readily washed with a relatively small amount of wash water. If steam or hot water is used in the operation, the cylinder can be easily insulated and temperatures maintained. Practically all the slurry in each batch is filtered during each cycle.

Disadvantages. The fact that operation is intermittent, with several steps in washing and discharge, is a considerable disadvantage; moreover, since a dry cake cannot be discharged, the use of the filter is limited to cases where such a cake is not required. The machine is comparatively expensive and takes up considerable room.

Materials of Construction. The revolving filter cylinder may be lined with copper, lead or other corrosion-resistant materials and the filter boards also may be constructed of similar materials and covered with cotton, wool or other filter media.

Continuous Drum Pressure Filters. Drum pressure filters of the continuous type are usually similar to continuous drum vacuum filters, except that the drum is enclosed in a pressure-tight housing and direct pressure is used for filter operation. Because of the structural difficulties in enclosing a drum in a pressure vessel, particularly in the larger sizes, the normal operating pressures are seldom over 20 to 25 pounds per square inch, and are often much lower. Such filters are used with volatile solvents, elevated temperatures or inert gases.

FIGURE 47. Pressure precoat filter. (*Courtesy Oliver United Filters*)

The various devices for maintaining the proper balance between slurry level and inert gas level, discharge, etc., make a rather complicated setup; considerable room is required, and the filter construction is expensive.

Stationary, Cylinder Pressure Filters. Stationary, cylinder pressure filters may have rigid media in several materials or fabric media supported by porous plates or wires. The filters usually have a central filtrate removal pipe and a pressure casing enclosing one or more cylinders (Fig. 48). Operation is intermittent, and is normally clarification of batch lots of materials involving the use of a precoat.

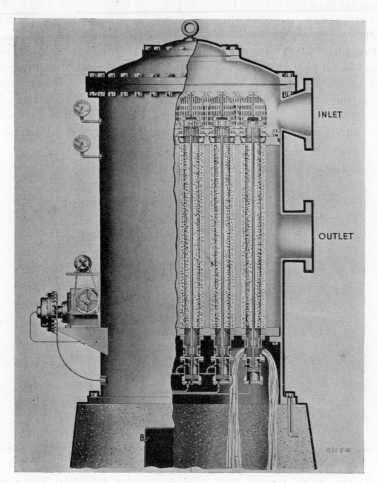

FIGURE 48. Verticle pressure cylinder filter. (*Courtesy R. P. Adams Co., Inc.*)

In the rigid medium filter, cleaning often can be accomplished by backwashing, thus avoiding the necessity of opening the filter. Where fabric is used as a filter medium, a perforated plate, screen, or wires support the media; these are constructed for ready cloth replacement. The cloths may be strip-wrapped, woven as stockings, wire wound, or sewed as bags.

The greatest use of vertical cylinder pressure filters is in water clarification, although they are used for chemical work and for oil filtration.

Corrosion-resistant construction is readily provided, especially with the rigid medium, which in itself is usually resistant.

Filters are constructed also in a design in which the cylinders are in horizontal banks; otherwise they function like vertical-tube filters. Thus head room may be saved although batch lots are somewhat harder to handle.

Pressure False Bottom Tank. Pressure false bottom tanks are made in both small and large sizes. The small filters are most often of ceramic construction and are used for batch lots of corrosive or volatile solutions, etc., in the pharmaceutical, beverage and essential oil industries. The large filters, on the other hand, are generally confined to the filtration of water through sand, charcoal, zeolite or similar material (Chapter 12).

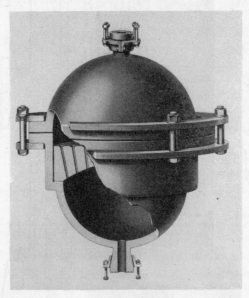

FIGURE 49. Ceramic pressure false bottom tank. (*Courtesy General Ceramics and Steatite Corp.*)

Construction. A typical small-sized, pressure, false-bottomed tank or vessel is shown in Fig. 49. It will be noted that the construction is similar to vacuum or gravity ceramic vessels, with the addition of a removable pressure hood. High pressures are not resorted to, filter aids are customary and the work is batch clarification. Another type called the Pot Filter, of metallic construction, is used most often in grinding-oil clarification.

Magnetic Filter. Several types of magnetic filters have been developed for the removal of fine particles of iron from oils, clay slips, etc. Essentially these filters consist of magnetized screens which may be a single vertical element (Fig. 51) or a stack of screens (Fig. 50). The screens are normally magnetized by a direct current coil surrounding, but insulated from them. The magnetized screens are enclosed in a pressure-tight casing with a direction of flow for direct contact between the liquor and the screen, yet without marked retardation of flow.

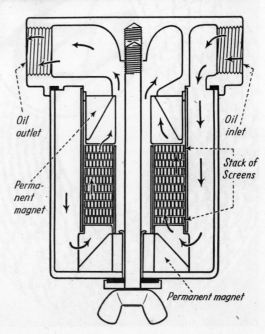

FIGURE 50. Magnetic filter. (*Courtesy S. G. Frantz Co.*)

The filters remove iron and steel particles as fine as $\frac{1}{25,000}$ inch diameter, and are readily cleaned by demagnetizing and flushing; or the screens may be removed for cleaning. An automatic valve, magnetically operated, usually cuts out the feed, in case of electric current failure.

The particular function of these filters is to remove very fine iron particles, which would cause black specks in ceramics, and to clarify oil for internal combustion engines.

Edge Filters. Surface or edge filters in a number of types and designs are distinctive in their use of laminated sheets, placed in the stream flow. The spacing between the sheets determines the solids retention, as the liquor passes through these spaces. The permeability can be controlled by adjusting the end compression of the sheets or by special spacers.

In the design employing metallic sheets cleaning is by wiper segments, either rotated between the sheets or stationary with the sheets rotating about them. Rotation is by hand ratchet or motor. Fine particles cannot be removed by these filters, as in order to secure passage of any volume of liquor it is necessary to maintain a distance between consecutive sheets which unavoidably permits the passage of some fine particles.

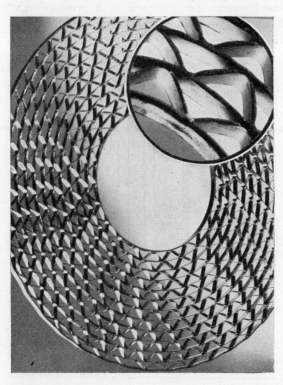

FIGURE 51. Magnified insert showing collected magnetic particles at screen edges. (*Courtesy S. G. Frantz Co., Inc.*)

In one type of filter the filter cartridge consists of two elements alternately assembled, one on top of the other, on a common shaft. These cartridge elements are termed *discs* and *spacers*. The disc consists of a wheel-shaped piece of metal, with hub, spokes and rim; the discs are separated by the spacers, which are flat pieces of metal with hub and spokes but without rim. The hub and spokes of the two elements are the same shape and size, so that when they are placed together the same free area is available. A stack of these discs of varying lengths and diameters mounted on a rotatable shaft constitutes the filter cartridge.

Cleaning is accomplished by rotating the filter element or stack of discs and spacers past a stationary assembly of cleaner blades, which consists of flat, wedge-shaped, knife-like metal pieces that extend into the cartridge between the discs sufficiently to clear the rim; they are shaped so as to wipe the material outward, whichever direction the cartridge may be rotated. When the cartridge is given one complete revolution the solids larger than the size spacer are combed from the cartridge and the original free area restored. The extracted solids collect in the sump provided and may be removed as required.

This type of filter is used on lubricating oils, fuel oils, greases, inks, glues, syrups, water, etc., and is usually made with filter spacing from 0.0035 inch in the self-cleaning types and from 0.0015 inch in the "non-clogging" types.

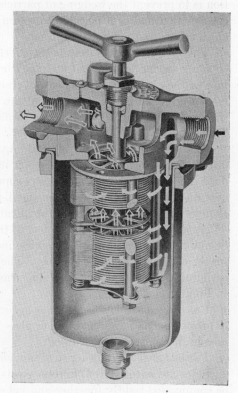

FIGURE 52. Edge filter. (*Courtesy Cuno Filter Co.*)

There is another filter of the backwash type wherein a wire is wound around a cage. This wire-wound cage is the filter element and is made up in diameters ranging from 4 to 16 inches and from 8 to 48 inches long on a single shaft which is rotated slowly. Inside this cage is a stationary pump which backwashes the cage as it slowly revolves. The backwash pump obtains its supply from a portion of the cleaned liquid as it passes through the wire-wound cage; thus no special backwash source of supply is necessary. As the path of the liquid is straight and the only restriction is a fine wire, the pressure drop is low. Filter openings are usually from 0.0025 to 0.020 inch, which corresponds to a mesh ranging from 230 to 35.

In another type, a metallic ribbon is wound edgewise on a perforated frame. The ribbon has a flat front edge and tapers in cross-section. It is provided, at definite intervals, with projections of uniform height, which support the front edge of the ribbon parallel to the frame on which it is wound. The height of the projections determines the degree of filtration which takes place and can be made as small as 0.001 inch, thus preventing the passage of particles of this size. The effect of the tapered cross-section is to prevent the wedging of particles behind the front edges, and the construction makes it possible to retain the desired spacing permanently at all points on the filtering surface.

The metal elements may be provided with externally operated knife-cleaning mechanisms, to cut underneath the solid material adhering to the face of the element and lift it away from the element surface. The solid matter either falls to the bottom of the filter or remains in suspension in the fluid. In either case the cake formed must be removed through the drain.

Another type of element is made up of a number of perforated metal discs. Each perforated disc is 0.002 inch thick, so that in placing the discs the perforations in one disc are superimposed on the open slots of the next disc. The spacings between the discs are 0.002 inch, and continuous channels are formed for flow of the filtrate.

Applications. Very small filters of this type are used in filtering gasoline on average-sized marine engines, industrial units, trucks, buses, passenger cars and outboard motors. They may be installed either at the carburetor or fuel pump and, in some cases, between the fuel tank and the fuel pump.

Construction. The small sizes are made with the elements in an iron or brass head and an iron, brass or glass bowl, held in place with a bail for ease in dismantling for cleaning.

Fibrous Sheets. In order to obtain clarity with Edge Filters where fine particles are encountered, fibrous sheets are used, *e.g.*, paper, which may be compressed tightly together and yet will present an edgewise porosity. In addition, the unsupported fibers of the sheet edges become matted together at the filtering surface, insuring excellent clarity without flow regardation. For this reason the filter normally is used for the clarification of relatively small quantities of valuable liquors where practically all traces of suspended solids must be removed. The packs of paper rings are held together by springs in the inner tube formed by the paper rings. The metal shell forms a container for the filter elements; and by bolting down the head against the filter rings and the springs, the filter rings can be held as close together as desired. The inlet for the unfiltered liquor may be near the bottom of the shell and the outlet through the head, or *vice versa*.

Operation. In operation the unfiltered liquor enters the inlet under pressure, and when the shell is filled, it is forced by the pressure through the pack between the rings. The solids are retained on the surface formed by the outer edge of the rings and the clarified liquor passes to the inner tube formed by the rings, and then through the head and outlet.

When the rate of flow drops off materially, the filter is cleaned by either backwashing, air blow-back, removing the element for brushing, or pack replacement.

Precoat Edge Filters. In the precoat design, filtration is through a removable layer of filter aid supported by a rigid metal backing of strips or rings. The performance depends upon the functioning of the precoat layer. Usually the pack of metallic rings forming the filter element is not over one inch in diameter with about thirty rings for a pack and spaces between rings of 0.001 to 0.008 inch. This spacing retains the filter aid normally required and which must be replaced after each cycle.

Chapter 8
Vacuum Filters

Vacuum Filtration. Vacuum filtration is akin to gravity filtering in that atmospheric pressure is the force by which filtration is accomplished. This limits the maximum pressure to the maximum vacuum at the altitude of the installation. In the mining industry, where filtration is frequently carried on at high altitudes, the low maximum vacuum may seriously affect filtration rates.

Vacuum filters have two inherent advantages over pressure filters, *i.e.*, safety and cake formation. "Inward" pressure leaks are not dangerous to workmen—an important point when handling corrosive liquors, where "outward" leaks are hazardous. As for cake formation, the creation of a vacuum behind the filter medium tends to produce a cake of uniform density (assuming a uniform slurry), since the vacuum is equal at all points behind the medium. Combined with this is the fact that the limited pressure differential obtainable by vacuum does not pack the cake as would higher differentials, and a more porous deposit is normally built up.

The production of a porous, uniform cake insures efficient washing and drying of the cake. The same vacuum factor, or low differential, which helps to produce this kind of cake limits vacuum filter applications to those materials which do not require high pressure differential for filtration.

Vacuum filters, as such, may be classified as continuous and intermittent. These types may be subdivided as follows:

Continuous Filters	Intermittent Filters
1. Belt	1. Leaf and Cylinder
2. Circular Leaf or Disc	2. False Bottom Tanks
3. Drum	3. Drum
4. Hopper	
5. Rectangular Leaf or Cylinder	

Continuous vacuum filters are not classed as clarifying filters but as filters for removing a substantial quantity of solids. This is necessitated by their design, wherein the rate of flow is maintained by continuous cyclic cake removal and consequent cleaning of the filter medium, which is impossible without the presence of sufficient solids in the unfiltered liquor to form a dischargeable cake within a reasonable time. A total cycle of more than twenty minutes is usually impractical, because of the large filter surface areas required to obtain capacities.

Continuous Belt Vacuum Filters. The belt vacuum filter is an adaptation of the paper mill drainage screen. It consists of an endless belt filter medium carried on rolls over vacuum boxes, with provision made at the discharge end for scraping off the cake. The scraper is affixed to the head roll and sprays are used for washing the filter medium, on the return of the belt, before loading. The slurry to be filtered is fed onto the belt at the opposite end from the scraper, before it passes over the vacuum boxes. Water may be applied for cake washing, after cake formation and the disappearance of surface water.

Filtering, drying and washing may be accomplished by separate vacuum boxes. Discharge is by scraping. No agitation or vat (except the vacuum boxes) is required, but the space occupied by such an arrangement, the wear on the belt as it passes over the vacuum boxes, the danger of vacuum leaks, and the difficulty in cleaning the medium are handicaps of this design of filter.

Continuous Disc Vacuum Filters. The continuous circular leaf or disc vacuum filter is composed of one or more filter leaves or discs mounted vertically upon or about a horizontal central shaft and suspended in a filter tank (Fig. 53).

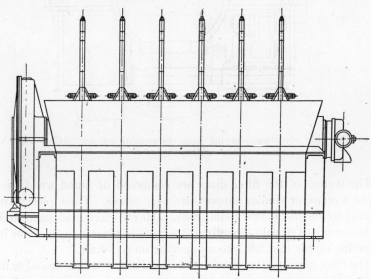

FIGURE 53. Continuous disc vacuum filter. (*Courtesy Conkey Filter Co.*)

Construction. The filter discs are uniformly spaced upon the horizontal supporting shaft, suspended in a filter tank, the discharge side of which is divided by partitions into chambers. On the top of each of the partitions, discharge scrapers or discharge rolls are mounted one on each side of each filter disc. The spaces between the divisions are utilized for discharge of the cake as it is freed from the discs, to direct it to a hopper or conveyor placed beneath the filter. The filter may be supplied with washing sprays located on each side of each disc.

Each disc is divided into a number of separate sectors, independently connected through the central axis shaft to the multiple valve. Each of these separate connections serves as a filtrate and wash channel for all sectors along the shaft on that line. The sectors are interchangeable and readily removable for filter cloth changes.

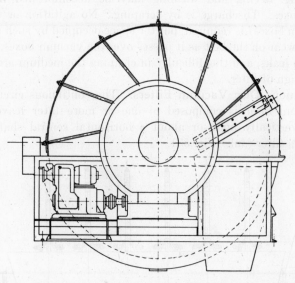

FIGURE 54. Side elevation showing disc trapezoidal sectors. (*Courtesy Conkey Filter Co.*)

The sectors of the filter discs are composed of fluted wood, iron or bronze screens, or similar support drainage pieces. These pieces are assembled by means of two radial rods, each rod having a clamp and nut on the outer end to hold the adjacent sectors in place. Each sector has a projecting nipple that fits into an opening on the shaft.

The filter medium, if of fabric, consists of a bag cut and sewed to fit the sector. The peripheral edge and the lower end of the small sleeve, through which the nipple passes, are left unsewed. When the bag is drawn over the frame and smoothed down it is tied with a cord around the nipple and the outer end closed by lapping the extending cloth edges over the end of the sectors and clamping them in place. Metallic filter cloths are welded or soldered to the backing screens, as they are expected to have a long life.

The center shaft usually consists of a metal tube, drilled to take the sector nipples in a "leak proof," easily removable connection. The shaft also is drilled to take the radial sector rods and carries the multiple valve at one or both ends. The shaft carries the drive worm gear, which meshes with the worm mounted on the filter tank. The actual rpm is low, averaging one revolution in six minutes, with a range of from one to one-twentieth of a revolution per minute.

Operation. When operating a disc vacuum filter, vacuum is automatically applied to the disc sectors through a multiple valve, as the sectors become submerged in the unfiltered material in the filter tank, and is kept on the sectors and their adhering cake (filter cake being formed on each side of each disc), as they emerge into the air, continuously to the point of discharge. The vacuum, in drawing the filtrate through the filter medium, causes the solids to deposit on the filter medium surface, where they are held on by vacuum, as the discs revolve to point of discharge. The filtrate is drawn down the internal sector drainage into the hollow drainage caps and out through the individual sector lines in the central shaft to the multiple valve. This valve is similar to the multiple-compartment drum vacuum filter valve construction. Here the filtrate may be collected separately from the wash that follows, should washing be employed and separation of wash be desired. Wash is applied, as a spray, to the cake on the sides of the discs as they emerge into the air. Air drying either follows the washing or, without washing, continues from emergence of the solids on the discs to vacuum cutoff for discharge.

At the point of discharge, blow-back pressure, often pulsating, is applied for filter cloth inflation and cake discharge. The inflated cloth is thus pressed against adjustable metal- or rubber-tipped scrapers for discharge of cake, or discharge may be over rolls of the rotating type. The discharged cake drops into the discharge chutes between the slurry containers, to be removed by belt or conveyor.

Materials Handled. Disc vacuum filters are generally used for handling large volumes of free-filtering solids (40 to 200 mesh normally) in a relatively small space; for, with discs mounted about a horizontal shaft, large square foot areas are obtainable in a compact machine. Cement slurries, concentrates and metallurgical slimes are the types of material most often handled with these machines.

Advantages. The disc vacuum filter economizes space, is light to ship, is cheaper than the drum vacuum filter per square foot of filter area, and allows separate sector changes, thus economizing on filter cloth. If the feed is homogeneous and rapid settling does not easily occur, a homogeneous, uniform cake is built up. Large capacities can be handled in disc filters and the operation is continuous and automatic, always an advantage in filtering. The ability to handle different slurries simultaneously upon the same filter is often a considerable advantage.

Disadvantages. In continuous disc vacuum filters, because of the right-angle application, washing is difficult and the results are never equal to those of a drum, hopper, or submerged leaf vaccum filter. This is likewise true of the drying, the moisture content of the discharged cake being higher than that of the drum filter, usually higher than the hopper filter, and often higher than the rectangular leaf filter. Agitation is difficult in the slurry container if the solids settle rapidly, and any cake which tends to slough off on emergence is more likely to do so on the vertical disc than upon the drum type machine. While individual sector cloth changes save cloths, they also make complete changing tedious, and the lack of wire-wound cloth protection causes considerable frictional cloth wear. With cakes of any thickness, where cracking occurs, it is difficult to keep pieces from falling off and breaking the vacuum, reducing its effect upon the balance of the exposed cake. These difficulties become more pronounced in the large machines.

Materials of Construction. These filters are usually of wood and iron construction, although the sectors may be made of bronze, aluminum, or other materials. The medium for filtering is normally cotton cloth, though metal cloths and special weaves are sometimes used. The center shaft is of cast iron or cast chrome alloy, and the tank, pipe lines and valves are usually of iron and steel.

Sizes. The size range of the discs is from four feet to twelve feet six inches in diameter, and one to twelve discs per unit, with eight to fifteen sectors per disc, providing from 22 to 2400 square feet of filter area per machine.

Continuous Drum Vacuum Filters. Drum vacuum filters, like disc filters, are continuous automatic machines for the handling of relatively free-filtering solids. The Hart filter patent of 1872 still covers the essentials of drum filters.

Like disc filters, drum filters must form their cake during the submerged portion of the cycle and the washing and drying of this cake are accomplished through their respective portions of the total cycle. Therefore, lengthy periods of cake forming, cake washing, or drying greatly lengthen the cycle or minutes per revolution, which in turn reduces the capacity of the filter and, if extended, reaches the point of economic impracticability.

The more rapidly a filter revolves the greater will be its capacity, providing that during each revolution a sufficient cake is built up for adequate discharge. The various modifications and changes in drum vacuum filter construction from the simple hollow cylinder type have been for the purpose of improving washing and drying of the filter cake, for separation of the wash water from the filtrate, or for increased capacity by insuring clean, complete cake discharge.

Continuous Rotary Single-Compartment Vaccuum Drum Filters. Although the multiple-compartment continuous drum vacuum filter has been known, as a design, for the past seventy years, most of the early drum filters were single-compartment machines. Here the entire interior of the cylinder, or drum, is under vacuum at all times. In the simplest design, a layer of filter cake of a predetermined thickness, regulated by the setting of the scraper, is sometimes left permanently upon the drum surface. This is to prevent a clean filter medium from being exposed to the air below the scraper and before resubmergence, which would cause loss of vacuum. Other designs provide for blocking off the exposed filter surface from vacuum.

Construction. The filter drum, in the single-compartment design, must necessarily be of heavy construction to withstand the total interior vacuum, and rather limited in size for the same reason. In one form, where no reverse blow is used for discharge, the filter drum consists of a rolled perforated plate closed at the ends by head plates. The perforated plate is usually welded to the heads and, if a center supporting ring is necessary, it is welded to this also. Through the heads and connected together to form a U, a pipe is used to remove filtrate and to act as a central trunnion. The bottom of the U just clears the perforated plate and the pipe is perforated at this point for filtrate intake. Exterior filtrate connections are made by means of a swivel joint. A coarse cloth is usually placed over the perforated plate and the filter cloth placed on top of this, with wire winding to hold both in place. The coarse cloth is to prevent the filter cloth from being partially blanked off between perforations, which would cause some reduction in vacuum effectiveness.

In the reverse-blow type of vacuum compartmentized drum filter, the heads are connected by and support separate surface sections, which have common drainage openings to the interior of the drum. These sections consist of grid drainage inserts in shoulders and spiders, with sloping drainage bottom sections.

The sections are kept separate and distinct, one from the other, by longitudinal division strip bars, which are placed across the drum surface The sections terminate in a machined ring open to the interior of the drum. Upon the rings a discharge shoe either rides or just clears, depending upon the application. The shoe has a blank extension on the leading end to block off the compartment following the blow, so that it will not be exposed to vacuum before submergence. In cases where the cake is scraped off, with the blow for cloth cleaning only after discharge, the blank extension is put on the lagging end of the shoe, if it is desired to shut off the vacuum without blow during discharge.

In this reverse-blow construction, an ell-shaped pipe line, with an open bell end as the suction pipe extends into interior of the drum; or the filtrate is allowed to fill the drum to the point of a center outlet pipe drainage connection line before discharging. This outlet pipe supports the worm gear and connects directly to a barometric leg through separating chamber of air and liquid. The air pressure connection is on the opposite side through a bearing-supported pipe trunnion.

In another modification of the surface-sectionalized compartment vacuum drum filter, a non-sloping deck is used and screen-supported slots form the compartment filter medium supports. The section drain consists of short pipe nipples to which are attached gravity pendulum valves accentuated by counterweights. These valves close at the discharge point, to break the vacuum, by the rotation of the drum. The seats slide across the valve shoes, which are kept upright at all times. Breaking of the vacuum allows cake discharge. This particular type of drum filter is used in paper mills as a washer or saveall-decker.

In these compartment vacuum drum filters a wire screen, expanded metal, or perforated plate is placed over the surface of the grid compartment, either in separate sections or continuously, as the service demands. Coarse cloth under the filter medium is normally used where expanded metal or perforated plate forms the medium support. Wire winding holds the medium in place, protects it from the scraper and keeps it from inflating appreciably at the time of blow-back for cake release.

On the vat there is a knife-type scraper for cake discharge. This scraper may ride the wire winding or clear it, to leave a permanent layer of cake on the drum at all times.

In the surface-sectionalized design, cake rollers may be used which exert pressure up to 1100 pounds. These, combined with cake sprays or washing boxes, are used to give a dry, washed cake, as in filtration of sodium bicarbonate.

In both the blow-back and the non blow-back designs, the filter drum is suspended in a filter vat, which may or may not be equipped with mechanical agitation of the rocker or the paddle type. If the vat allows for more than 50 per cent submergence of the filter drum, stuffing boxes are required for the pipe trunnions, and the vat is usually equipped with a combined feed and drain connection and with an overflow connection.

Operation. In operation the material to be filtered is fed to the filter vat, where the agitator prevents settling, if there is this tendency. Vacuum, applied through the pipe line to the interior of the drum, causes the liquor to be drawn through the filter medium to the drum interior. From here, the liquor is removed by the suction pipe or by rising to the overflow point at the vacuum pipe inlet to the drum. The solids are deposited upon the surface of the filter medium in the form of a layer or cake. As this cake emerges into the air with the drum rotation, it is air-dried by the action of the vacuum drawing air through it, or it may be washed by drawing water through it in the same manner, the wash water being applied by sprays or wash boxes, and the cake then air-dried prior to discharge.

At the point of discharge, the cake may be scraped off, with the vacuum either on or blocked off; or it may be loosened or lifted by blow-back for guidance or deflection on the scraper.

From the point of discharge to the point of resubmergence the section is "dead." The blow back may be applied here for cloth cleaning; or this section may be blocked off, or left with a layer of cake on it and not blocked off. Sometimes it is simply exposed to the air, extra vacuum pump capacity being provided to take care of the vacuum loss through the exposed medium.

Materials Handled. While formerly single-compartment filters were used to handle nearly all free-filtering solids, today their use is confined largely to bicarbonate of soda, caustic lime mud, salts, or dewatering of paper pulp.

Advantages. These filters have the big advantage of simplicity of construction in a continuous automatic machine. There is no multiple valve, and internal pipe lines are eliminated, except for the one combined filtrate and trunnion line. As operation is on very free-filtering solids, high vacuum is not needed; thus a pipe type filtrate receiver with a barometric leg can often be used without a moisture trap. The heavy construction of some types allows for the use of adjustable pressure rolls up to 1100 pounds, together with wash-water boxes for flood washing. This gives an exceptionally dry, clean cake.

Disadvantages. On the other hand, the elimination of separate compartments means that there can be no separation of wash water and filtrate, often a decided disadvantage.

Also, because the entire interior of the filter drum is subjected to vacuum, heavy construction is often necessary, even though high vacuum is not resorted to; and there must be sufficient vacuum pump capacity to take care of this entire interior exhaustion. A machine larger than six feet in diameter usually becomes excessively expensive.

Generally the filter-drum heads and filter vat are cast, except in the smallest sizes. Cast iron or nickel cast iron is commonly used, with cotton, Monel or nickel cloth as the filter medium.

Continuous Rotary Multiple-Compartment Drum Vacuum Filters.
In the continuous multiple-compartment drum vacuum filter, the periphery of the drum is divided longitudinally into a number of independent uniform compartments by means of cross or division strips.

Construction. Each of the compartments is connected separately to a central value hub, designed to receive these connections. Generally the valve hub, faced with a removable wear plate, rotates with the filter drum.

FIGURE 55. Multiple-compartment drum vacuum filter. (*Courtesy Conkey Filter Co.*)

The rotation is against a stationary valve cap which has exterior outlets to separate vacuum and pressure lines. The interior of the valve cap is recessed behind the exterior outlets and has bridge separations, often movable, to divide the recess into zones corresponding to the exterior outlets The valve cap is movable, so that its setting may be readily shifted, and often the internal bridges are externally adjustable.

A stud bolt passing through the valve cap to the hub supports the cap, and a spring or springs, adjustable by lock nuts, holds the cap with the desired pressure against the wear plate, in the simplest valve cap design. Other designs have a cone-shaped cap and valve for self-alignment, or there may be an annular wear plate with the valve cap to match. In all cases, however, the cap is held in place by means of an adjustable connection which allows for setting the cap in the desired position for vacuum and blow back.

The individual compartments must have means of supporting the filter medium; and while the supporting screen, plate or expanded metal occasionally is continuous, passing over the division strips, each compartment normally has its own individual supports.

There are several different methods of supporting the filter medium; but unless this medium is rigid, as in the case of porous plates or perforated sheets, all have the common function of supporting a porous, rigid body which in turn supports the filter medium. This is to present a medium for filtering which is as free as possible from backing obstructions and which offers a smooth surface for ease of cake discharge.

There must be adequate room for free drainage between the filter medium and the drum deck if operating efficiency is to be obtained. Also, after reaching the drum deck, there should be adequate drainage connections and elimination of pockets where filtrate might accumulate, full advantage should be taken of the force of gravity to remove the filtrate and to avoid frictional consumption of pressure differential.

FIGURE 56. Endflow filter for sugar juices. (*Courtesy International Combustion Ltd.*)

The filter medium backing supports are sometimes compartment grids spanning a deep sloping drainage deck; or each may be cast complete with a sloping drain to the filtrate outlet connection at one end and the segments bolted as separate units to the end spiders in order to make the drum face. In any case the compartments are kept separate by solid horizontal division strips. With the flat deck, the supports are often notched strips, called bridging strips; or they may be crimped flat strips or rods, or linked mesh wire inserts. Again the supports may be heavy crimped wire die-formed screens, or leg-supported expanded metal inserts simply placed in the compartments without fastening. These inserts may be held down by circumferential end strips and various cross seals placed in the division strips. The filter medium is placed over the compartments and held in the division strip grooves by caulking, the filter medium being wire-wound in the usual manner.

The filter medium, if flexible, is placed around the drum on top of the rigid screen or plate backing. Because of their more open surface and absence of flat spaces for filtration obstruction, screens are preferred for this purpose.

Generally the filter medium is held in place by wire under tension, helically wound about the drum. Wire spacing across the face of the drum averages 1½ inches, with several close windings at the ends of the drum for sealing. The individual compartments may be kept separate on the surface by placing cross rods, wires, ropes, or caulking into division-strip grooves over the filter medium and under the spiral wire winding (Fig. 57). The cross rods or bars are usually held down by countersunk

FIGURE 57. Continuous rotary drum vacuum filter showing cross wires, wiring winding and washing sprays. (*Courtesy Conkey Filter Co.*)

screws; the wires or ropes are simply laid over the medium and forced into the division-strip groove by the wire windings. The ropes may be caulked in the grooves by having the grooves dove-tailed. This separation, particularly in the larger drum sizes, prevents filter cloth creepage as well as intercompartment leakage.

Where wire winding is not used, as in the string discharge filters, end grooves in addition to compartment grooves are used for caulking the filter medium to prevent end leakage. The same type of end groove is often used with wire-wound drums where there is metal decking, but they are seldom employed with wood deck drums.

The cross strip design makes for panel medium construction, should this be desired, as here pieces of filter medium can be overlapped from the two adjacent compartments, or individually wrapped and held down tight without danger of leaking, by the positive fastening down of the panels.

The majority of continuous multiple-compartment drum vacuum filters have pipe-line connections to the drum deck entering each compartment on the leading, or on the leading and lagging sides. For very free-filtering solids, when a large volume of drying air must be drawn through the filter cake, as open a drainage as possible should be maintained. This is often accomplished by sloping drum decks, with large pipe drainage connections at the drum edge, and by the use of a large valve hub.

In other designs, the arms of one of the supporting spiders, either end or center, are hollow and act as compartment drainage lines.

In one type of filter, where brass or copper or other perforated plate is used as the filter medium, very shallow drainage is used and the pipe lines are proportionately small. This construction is often used for cachaza filtration in the sugar industry.

In most of the multiple-compartment drum vacuum filters, the blow back for cake discharge is through the same lines that the filtrate and wash traverse; therefore, unless these are completely drained, some filtrate or wash will be blown back into the filter cake at the time of discharge. This danger may be avoided by having ample drainage connections as well as baffles to deflect any water which may be blown back and prevent it from entering the cake, while allowing the air to pass around the baffle for cake discharge.

Sloping drum decks and unobstructed compartment drainage also tend to obviate the blow back of water. One particularly effective method, especially with compact cakes which allow little air to pass through, is the use of a separate air pressure connection at the valve. This bleeds some air into the compartments or allows the upper compartment drainage line to become an equallizing line, to drain out the compartment and carry away accumulated water by entrainment.

In multiple-compartment continuous drum vacuum filters the drum heads may be open or closed, depending upon the material being handled, metallurgical slime filters often having open heads while chemical and sewage filters normally have closed heads. The filter tank or vat, in which the filter drum is suspended, follows the contour of the drum, particularly where no agitation or where the rocker type of agitator is used. In the case of paddle agitators, the filter vat is V-shaped with a half round at the bottom to hold the agitator. The height of the vat is dependent upon the drum submergence desired, ranging from that which will give 15 per cent submergence, as in salts handling, to that which will give 75 per cent submergence, as in some paper mill work.

The rocker type of agitator consists of crescent-shaped channels, straps or pipes connected by channel or angle rakes which are set at right angles to the face of the drum. The rakes oscillate only a short distance (2 to 4 inches) in each direction with an over-lapping movement, and often are equipped with extension fingers which break through the surface of the sludge to prevent stratifying. The rocker agitator is suspended from the sides of the vat or from the drum trunnions, and is moved by pushing arms actuated through eccentrics.

In the paddle design, the agitator consists of paddles or blades mounted upon a horizontal shaft located in the extension at the bottom of the vat. The shaft passes through the tank stuffing boxes to a miter-gear drive from the drum drive or, to a separate connection for direct drive.

The filter vat has inlet connections at the bottom, at the side, or over the top, depending upon the material to be handled, with bottom connections for rapidly settling solids. Where the bottom inlet connection is used it also may serve as a drain. Most vats are equipped with overflow boxes which often contain floats for intake control of the feed pumps or feed valves.

Top Feed Filters. For quick-draining products of not too high specific gravity a top feed may be used. Here the vat is dispensed with and the feed is distributed over the top of the drum surface, where the vacuum causes cake formation as the drum revolves. Baffles prevent the feed from running off the ends of the drum.

Drainage areas and pipe lines in top feed filters are large in order to carry a large volume of air under low vacuum (2 to 4 inches) and up to 200 cfm per square foot of filter area. The vacuum holds the cake in place as the drum revolves, and allows discharge at an angle as near the point of feed as possible in view of the specific gravity of the particles. The charge hopper and the filter drum may be enclosed, so that heated air can be drawn through the cake for better drying (Fig. 58).

Wash water may be applied as in the vat type filters. This is followed by drying with room-temperature air or with heated air, sent to the filter by a fan. This fan draws a volume of air equal to the capacity of the vacuum pump either past heating coils or directly mixed with the products of combustion. The former gives a lower thermal efficiency (65-70 per cent) but clean air; the latter has a high efficiency (90-95 per cent), but gives air that is contaminated.

FIGURE 58. Top feed filter with hot air dryer. (*Courtesy International Combustion Ltd.*)

Uniform feed distribution is important for uniform wash and drying; this is at times difficult to accomplish with quick-settling solids, even with spreader aprons, dams, and baffles. If the heated drying air case-hardens the cake, one or two preliminary scrapers may be needed. The scrapers are set to remove the outer case-hardened layer of cake. At times it is desirable to wash the filter medium, after discharge and before reloading, to prevent clogging from saturated liquor crystallization. This is accomplished by spray application between the point of discharge and the point of loading.

Cake thicknesses average about 1 inch, drum speeds 1 rpm, and cake capacities 500 pounds per square foot per hour, all varying considerably with the size and shape of crystals, the dryness desired, etc.

Operation. The operation of the multiple-compartment drum vacuum filter is initially the same as that of the single-compartment type. However, the drainage of each individual compartment is kept separate up to the valve cap, where it may be either removed or united with that of several other compartments. The filtrate drainage of any one compartment may be separated from its wash drainage with little overlapping or from subdivisions of several stages of filtrate or wash drainage. Blank areas and blow-back areas for one or more compartments are also automatically taken care of in the valve cap.

It may be desirable to separate the filtrate from any one compartment into various stages in order to keep suspended solids which may have come through the filter medium at one stage from contaminating the clear subsequent filtrate. The separation of washes is to take advantage of the high percentage of mother liquor in the first washing stages.

As it emerges into the air upon the filter drum with the rotation of the drum, the filter cake may be subjected to washing from perforated pipes, sprays, pans, nets, or belt washers, either immediately or after it has been rolled, slapped by flappers or squeezed by rollers or shoes. These attachments are an attempt to iron out any cracks that may be present, or to squeeze out excess filtrate before the wash is applied, in order to obtain more effective washing and drying. Combinations of belts, rollers and washing may be used.

With the scraper discharge the vacuum is automatically cut off and blow back applied at, or just before, the discharge point. This blow back tends to free the cake from the filter medium for removal by the scraper; at the same time it cleans the medium for the next cycle. Occasionally blow back is used after the scraper is passed, before or after resubmergence of the filter drum, as a means of cleaning the filter cloth; or occasionally it is omitted entirely with free-filtering materials, discharge being by scraping only.

The filter cake is sometimes lifted off by a series of individual endless strings, usually arranged on $\frac{1}{2}$-inch centers over the filter medium. The strings pass around the filter drum and over a discharge roll, where they make an abrupt bend in order to dislodge the cake. An aligning comb then guides the strings to a return roll and thence to the drum (Fig. 59). The object of the strings is to lift off the cake and eliminate the blow-back requirement. This is effective with such materials as paper pulp, where there is no tendency for the strings to pull through the cake and where the filter medium does not require the blow back to keep it free and open.

Sometimes a pulsating blow back is used to help dry the cake before discharge. A low-pulsating blow is applied just before the zenith so that the filter cake is shaken up and down without losing its position. A second pulsating blow back may be applied about half way between the zenith and the horizontal for further moisture freeing by particle rearrangement.

Starch filtration is a particular application of this method of treatment, since it readily rearranges itself, expelling excess moisture in so doing.

FIGURE 59. String discharge filters. (*Courtesy Filtration Engineers, Inc.*)

In another design the entire filter medium is removed from the drum for passage to a dryer or for discharge over a roll, followed by special cleaning.

Materials Handled. Multiple-compartment drum vacuum filters handle a great variety of materials—clays, chemicals, food products, metallurgical slimes, oils, reclaimed rubber, sewage, etc., when the solids are in a fairly concentrated slurry. These slurries are concentrated only insofar as the material itself is concerned, since "concentrated" for one material may be "diluted" for another, *i.e.*, 2 to 3 per cent solids is concentrated for activated sewage sludge, or paper stock, whereas 30 to 40 per cent solids is concentrated for caustic calcium carbonate or copper sulfate. As stated in Chapter 2, temperature and concentration followed by pH adjustment are the first essentials in attempting to handle materials on a continuous drum filter when they could not otherwise be so filtered.

Advantages. The ability to handle materials quickly, cleanly, continuously and automatically, and at such a slow drum speed as to require a minimum of upkeep, makes the multiple-compartment drum vacuum filter a most desirable machine for efficient and economical filtration. In addition, there is the important advantage of a thin, uniform, and porous cake, easily washed and dried, and the often advantageous ability to separate the filtrate, the wash water, and the drying sections of the cycle.

Large capacities can be handled on small filter areas, as the accumulated solids are constantly removed and the filter medium cleaned on each drum revolution. Finally, there is considerable flexibility in operation to meet unforeseen or changing conditions: variation of drum submergence, vacuum variations, rotation variations, shifting of discharge position and variation in the filter cloths used.

Disadvantages. The material to be handled naturally dictates the type of continuous filter to use; for area alone, the drum vacuum filter is at a disadvantage compared with the disc vacuum filter. The former utilizes only one surface, either exterior or interior, in standard designs. Filter drums in which both surfaces are covered with filter cloth have been designed and occasionally used, but because of complicated construction and operation, there have been few installations.

Like other vacuum-operated machines, multiple-compartment drum vacuum filters cannot be used for boiling temperatures, and even near this point the available vacuum is relatively low. The pressure differential, in any case, is limited to the vacuum equivalent, thus restricting such filtration to maximum pressures of 12 to 14 pounds per square inch at sea level, and less at higher elevations.

Volatile solvents can be handled by hooding the filter drum, but this often necessitates the use of an inert gas under a slight pressure, and a rather elaborate system of recirculation and control (See Chapter 11). Even this, however, may be preferable to intermittent operation, if there are no other complications.

Materials of Construction. Multiple-compartment drum vacuum filters are constructed of a wide variety of materials, depending upon the service required. They may have wood decks with steel or cast-iron headers and steel vats; or they may be completely constructed of wood, cast iron, bronze, nickel, Monel, stainless steel, Duriron, rubber, plastics or any other materials which have the necessary physical characteristics. This likewise holds true for the filter medium employed, *e.g.*, cotton, wool, Monel, plastic, glass, carbon, woven metals, perforated plate, etc., are used.

Inside Filter Medium. In the drum vacuum filter in which the filter medium is on the inside, the surface of the drum is solid and is supported by tire and roller bearings at the feed end, with the trunnion and worm-gear driving mechanism at the other end (Fig. 60). The inside of this drum shell is divided, as in other drum filters, into compartments running parallel to the axis of the drum. A heavy screen within each compartment supports the filter cloth and is so arranged that a space for drainage is allowed between the screen and the drum shell. The filter cloth is fastened by straps or wires into grooves at the ends of the drum and along the compartment partitions. The drum is closed at the drive end and has a circular baffle at the feed end for retention of slurry to be filtered within the drum.

Operation. In operation, the feed is to the interior of the drum, the bottom of which retains a quantity of unfiltered material, as determined by the circular baffle. Vacuum is applied to each compartment as it be-

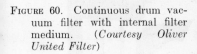
FIGURE 60. Continuous drum vacuum filter with internal filter medium. (*Courtesy Oliver United Filter*)

comes submerged in passing through the zone of unfiltered material. The cake is then formed by a combination of gravity and vacuum as the drum revolves. Vacuum holds the cake on against gravity. At the zenith, vacuum is cut off and air pressure, often pulsating, is applied to release the cake; this is aided by gravity. The cake falls into a chute in the case of short drums, or onto a conveyor in larger filters.

Materials Handled. The interior-medium filter handles rapidly settling solids, which would slough off the surface of an exterior-medium drum but are retained on the surface of the interior medium.

Advantages. The advantages of this type of filter are elimination of the filter vat and agitator and the ability to handle solids that are not adapted to an exterior-medium drum. The filter occupies a minimum of head room, as feed and discharge are within the drum.

Disadvantages. The interior-medium filter has the disadvantage of wash difficulties, since the wash is against gravity. Care must be taken in feeding to prevent overflow. Materials of high specific gravity, thick cakes or cake cracking may cause the cake to drop off. Changing the filter cloth is somewhat difficult, and the "dead" area, from discharge at the zenith to submergence, is a considerable percentage of the total area.

Syncro-Drum Filter. Syncro-drum filters are continuous rotary vacuum filters which have two synchronized drums rotating in opposite directions with cheek-plate dams to provide an "over-drum" feed reservoir or pool entirely above the horizontal center line of the filtering surface.

Construction. Though similar to other multiple compartment drum vacuum filters, the double-drum arrangement requires greater accuracy in construction. Synchronization of the two drums is obtained through opposite-hand worm wheel drives from a common worm shaft.

FIGURE 61. Syncro-drum multiple-compartment filter. (*Courtesy Peterson Filters & Engineering Co.*)

Maintenance of the "over-drum" reservoir requires a seal at the ends of the drums and at the point of tangency of the drums. The end seal is obtained by using cheek plates that bear against shoes built into the drum heads. Cheek-plate pressure is adjustable, and is set by noting the reading of an ammeter connected to indicate the load on the filter drive motor. An absolute seal is not desired because a slight leakage acts as a lubricant for the Micarta cheek plates.

The tangential seal at the center of the drums is obtained by providing a back pressure at that point in each drum, so that the filter cloths are forced together. Leakage, which may occur from the center or ends, is returned through drip pans to the feed pump. A special scraper is used which involves a double-fulcrum adjustment rather than the common single-fulcrum. The scraper is set at "3:30 on the clock," as it is claimed that no difference has been found in cake value between this scraper setting and a "6:00 o'clock" setting.

The valve arrangement is totally inclosed, and provides a means of collecting filtrate without use of any flexible connections. A counter-thrust is provided in the valve to compensate automatically for the pressure that tends to disturb the seal at the wearing surface.

Operation. Fig. 62 shows the elements of the Syncro-drum filter. The reservoir is set above the two drums, but a control overflow back into the preceding circuit accommodates any surges in feed and automatically compensates for increasing resistance in the filter medium. The medium enters the slime zone last, and the cake of coarser particles that first forms on the medium tends to keep the slime away from the cloth. The result is a much more permeable cake than would be obtained if the slime were next to the medium and the coarser particles above it.

The reservoir or pool between the two drums (Fig. 62) receives the feed liquor and acts as a surge tank, a well, or a classifier, so that the

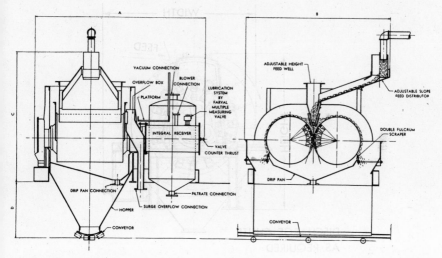

FIGURE 62. Diagrammatic sketch of syncro-drum filter. (*Courtesy Peterson Filters & Engineering Co.*)

vacuum, which is applied to the filter drums just as each compartment enters the pool, acts with gravity to produce a graded cake with the coarser particles next to the filter medium. As the drums revolve and the compartments emerge from the pool, the cake may be washed and air-dried prior to scraper discharge, as in other drum vacuum filters.

The pool overflow and the leakage may be recirculated to the pool or to the feed tank.

Materials Handled. The Syncro-drum filter is designed primarily for high specific gravity or coarse solids in mixtures up to 0.4″ x 0 down to all minus 48 mesh, in pulp densities of from 30-70 per cent solids, as in ores, coal, etc.

Advantages. The filter has the advantage of being able to handle mixed feeds and to give classifications in the pool with an overflow for rejections or recirculations. The use of a depth filter medium, such as cocoa matting, and dead area from discharge to loading allows thorough medium washing in this arc, while the squeezing action of the drums as they come together aids in keeping the medium open. The filter also has the advantage of scraper discharge for the solids.

Disadvantages. The initial cost of the Synchro-drum is higher than other drum vacuum filters per square foot area, although this may be compensated for by the increased tonnage handled. There is considerable "dead" portion of the cycle, and accurate construction is necessary for economical operation.

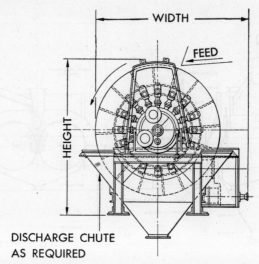

VALVE END ELEVATION

FIGURE 63. Rotary hopper vacuum dewaterer. (*Courtesy Conkey Filter Co.*)

Rotary Hopper Vacuum Dewaterers. The rotary hopper vacuum dewaterer is a multiple-compartment continuous drum vacuum filter of the top-feed type with radial fin extensions (Fig. 63). Actually it is similar to a series of false-bottom tanks arranged about a central shaft.

Construction. The heads of the drum extend beyond the filter medium to form two ends of the hoppers, with radial fins forming the other two sides. In some designs the fins are withdrawn automatically, as that section of the drum becomes inverted, to allow cake discharge from the scraper. In other cases, the fins are movable in end slots, in order to cover the drum with one continuous filter medium.

Again, the hoppers may be entirely separate units fastened together, through outer and inner rings, with the pipe lines and connected to the central multiple-valve hub. The compartment drainage may be through pipes from a flat deck or a pipe taking off at the drum head from a sloping deck. The latter is the design most used since large air passages and ample drainage lines are necssary with the granular material usually handled.

The drum trunnions are pedestal-supported, with the filter valve at one end of the dewaterer and the worm drive at the other, as in some multiple-compartment drum vacuum filters.

A spray- or drip-washing attachment may be set above the hoppers for cake washing; and belt and rollers with automatically removable fins may be used for cake ironing. The dewaterer may be equipped with a complete hood or one just above the hoppers for solvents; or heated air may be used for drying. A discharge chute may be located beneath the machine for cake guidance in discharge.

Operation. The material to be dewatered is fed to the hoppers from an overhead chute, approximately 20 degrees, before the individual hopper reaches its zenith, and vacuum is automatically applied at this point. Where washing is desired, the wash is applied as soon as the surface liquor disappears, usually at the zenith. The vacuum is normally kept on to within 30 degrees of inversion of the individual hopper, where it is automatically cut off and air pressure applied for discharge. This pressure, aided by gravity and the fact that the compartments are narrower at the bottom than at the top, usually insures a clean discharge. The filtrate is drawn through the filter medium and out through the compartments and the filter valve, as in the standard multiple-compartment drum vacuum filter.

Materials Handled. The rotary hopper dewaterer is designed to handle such free-filtering solids as aluminum tri-hydrate; those which settle rapidly and have high specific gravity, such as abrasives or magnetic concentrates; those of such character that they would tend to slough off a filter drum, such as fibers; or those which form a cake with difficulty, such as large crystals.

Advantages. The fact that the slurry to be dewatered is confined in a hopper and that no vat or agitator is used means that settling or stratifying problems are eliminated, gravity is used to advantage, and efficient flood washing can be employed. These advantages are combined with continuous, automatic operation.

There can be individual filter cloth changes in the fixed fin design, and in either design the narrower hopper bottom has a tendency to prevent the cake from cracking when it shrinks on air-drying. Variation in feed concentration and quantity can be taken care of by the hopper depth, usually varying from 8 to 12 inches above the filter medium. From the point of dischargeable thickness the cake can be varied six inches or more. A vari-speed drive permits faster or slower speeds for vari-load depths and for varying drying or washing periods.

Disadvantages. The rotary hopper dewaterer has the disadvantage that its use is confined to free-filtering materials which form an appreciable cake fairly rapidly. The discharged cake is not as dry as it is from a drum filter, and the "dead" section from discharge to reloading is a larger portion of the cycle. Hence this equipment is usually used for free filtering materials which are not readily handled by drum-type filters.

Continuous Vertical Leaf or Tube Filters. The use of square or irregularly shaped filter leaves, cylinders, or tubes for continuous operation under vacuum is not general. Some such filters have been used for ore slimes or chemicals sludges and others in the thickening operations in the carbonation of sugar juices. In these cases, construction of the leaves or cylinders and their basket assembly is the same as that used for the better known intermittent vertical leaf filters.

In the type used for continuous filtering, whether leaf or cylinder, the operation is one of basket-shifting, made automatic and continuous with a drum vacuum type vacuum-blow-off valve. The filter tanks, in this design, are segments of a circle arranged about a central point which supports the basket-shifting mechanism as well as the vacuum and the pressure lines. The basket, of leaves or tubes, is built to fit the tanks; shifting may be by hoists, or by means of a track and trolley hoist.

In the wet discharge type of vertical leaf filter, which is similar to a thickener, the filter basket is not moved, but the same vacuum-blow-off valve is used. A two-compartment V-bottom tank, or a circular segment tank is used, with each section fitted with a repulper. The filter leaves, tubes or plates are suspended vertically in the tank, one basket to each section, all baskets being connected to one vacuum-blow-off valve.

Advantages. The continuous vertical leaf or tube filters are automatic, relatively cheap per square foot of filter area, and quite flexible in control.

Disadvantages. The dry-discharge filter has the disadvantages of cumbersomeness, tediousness of filter cloth changes, difficulty in cake drying, and necessity for a heavy cake for adequate discharge. The wet-discharge filter is not so cumbersome and is free from trouble with cake drying, but filter cloth changing and clogging difficulties are present.

Intermittent Leaf or Cylinder Vacuum Filters. The intermittent vertical leaf or tube vacuum filter, like the continuous one, consists of a unit, or basket, composed of a number of plates, fingers, leaves or cylinders assembled and connected to a common header (Fig. 64). In the

FIGURE 64. Intermittent verticle leaf vacuum filter. (*Courtesy Conkey Filter Co.*)

plate or leaf design each of the plates or leaves is constructed of a pipe or angle frame with interior separation and drainage pieces. The leaf is usually in the form of a rectangle over which a fabric filter medium is drawn, having been previously sewed in the shape of a bag. The open or loose ends of the bag are held tightly together at the top by means of clamps, usually of wood (Fig. 65). If the medium is of metal, it is soldered or cemented to the frame.

The two sides of the filter cloth are held apart by parallel wooden strips set upright and the filter medium is stretched in such a manner as to hold the strips in position. Solid metallic or wooden separators may be used with outside U-shaped rods to give cloth support in blow back. Where blow back does not unduly stretch the medium, the rods are omitted.

Single perforations along the lower horizontal tube or a double set of such pipes for internal drainage causes uniform vacuum application at all points behind the filter medium. In the case of fingers, or tubes, the medium support may be fluted; perforated; or a screen, straight or tapered; usually with the filtrate removal connection at the bottom, and the removal pipe extending to the top for common header attachment.

The filter medium, if fabric, is in the form of a seamless stocking, which is drawn over the frame and wire-wound or clamped at top and bottom; if metallic, it is soldered or welded with a single vertical seam.

FIGURE 65. Leaf construction. (*Courtesy Conkey Filter Co.*)

Operation. In operation the basket of leaves, or tubes, is submerged in a tank containing the slurry to be filtered and suction applied behind the filtering medium. The filtrate is drawn through the filter medium, pipes and header to the vacuum receiver, while the solids are left deposited upon the surface of the filter medium in the form of a cake. After a cake about ½ inch to 3 inches thick has been built up, which may take from ½ an hour to 24 hours or more, the basket of leaves with the adhering cake is raised from the loading tank, suction being kept on, and shifted by hoist and trolley to a wash tank, if washing is desired, and submerged in the tank of wash liquor. In the stationary type, the feed liquor is pumped out of the feed tank and is replaced by wash liquor without shifting the basket.

During washing, the wash liquor may be switched to a second receiver for separate collection from the filtrate. After washing, the basket is shifted to the discharge platform, or the wash liquor is withdrawn from the tank, and the cake is dried by drawing air through it. Discharge is accomplished by shutting off the vacuum and applying air, water or steam pressure through the wash or filtrate lines.

Flexible hose connections are used between the filter basket header and the vacuum line, to allow basket shifting. Often a larger pump is switched on for cake drying and shifting than is used for filtering, since in filtering the basket is entirely submerged, requiring only liquor removal, while in shifting and drying a larger volume of air must be handled. In the stationary type a screw conveyor is used in the bottom of the tank for cake removal.

Materials Handled. The open tank filter is designed for materials which, though slow-filtering, are of a crystalline or amorphous nature, such as ferric hydrate, ore slimes, caliche, etc. The slow filtering rate may be due to fineness of the solids, their weak structure, their dilution, or the impurities present. Many solids that break down in pressure filtration can be handled upon a vacuum filter of this type with its limited pressure differential. For the same reason, the use of a filter aid with semi-colloidal materials may make them more readily filtrable upon vertical leaf vacuum filters than upon pressure filters.

Advantages. Vertical leaf vacuum filters have the advantage of suction behind the filtering medium for the formation of a porous, uniform cake, and the submerged washing gives the highest degree of efficiency. Any period of cake building, washing, or drying can be decided upon by the operator at any time, without changing the operating mechanism. In addition, the entire equipment is open to inspection and control at all times.

These filters are inexpensive to build, allow large areas to be confined in a small space, and require only the partial time of one man, even for many thousands of square feet of filter area, as basket shifting, discharge and cleaning of the filter medium are mechanical operations.

Disadvantages. While only a moderate amount of labor is required, this type of filter cannot be classed as continuous and automatic, which is a decided disadvantage, limiting its use to slow cake-forming solids. Filter cloth changes are not as readily made as in a drum filter or plate-and-frame press, and where sewing is necessary it is considerable trouble.

A good deal of head room is required for the basket-shifting mechanism and for the flexible connections. While this is not true of the stationary type, the liquor must be shifted; and as vacuum is kept on during this period, there is danger that a pear-shaped cake will be formed and that the cake will crack or fall off before the tank can be emptied and refilled with wash liquor.

In lifting the baskets from the filter tank to the various wash tanks or discharge tank, care must be taken to prevent the cake from falling or being knocked off, or cracking, as this would interfere with washing, drying and clean discharge of the cake.

Materials of Construction. Acid- and alkali-resistant construction is rather easy to use in the intermittent vertical leaf type of vacuum filter, since there are no complicated or moving parts. Iron, copper, Monel, stainless steel, nickel or plastic for pipe line frames; cotton, wool, Monel, stainless steel, glass or synthetics for filter media; and wood, metals or plastics for clamps and spacers afford a wide variety of construction materials from which to select. The filter vat also may be of wood or steel, or may be clad with steel, rubber, lead, copper, stainless steel, etc.

False-Bottomed Vacuum Tanks. False-bottomed vacuum tanks are the same in design and construction as the gravity filters of this type (Chapter 6). They are, however, less widely used, being confined for the most part to small units. Greater strength and more careful construction are necessary to withstand the higher pressure differential.

Construction. Construction is simple, since only the filter medium-covered, perforated false bottom separates the lower vacuum chamber from the upper, unfiltered liquor section (Fig. 66). Quantities to be

FIGURE 66. False bottom vacuum tank.
(*Courtesy Maurice Knight*)

handled dictate the size of both upper and lower chambers, and whether the complete batch is to be contained at once in the upper and lower sections of the filter; that is, whether the unfiltered liquor chamber and the filtrate chamber together are to be of sufficient capacity to handle the complete batch, or whether the feed will be in itself a batch lot. For continuous filtrate removal, there is a vacuum connection at the bottom of the vacuum chamber, while for batch removal it is located at a point which will leave the desired accumulation capacity in the vacuum chamber.

Operation. The unfiltered liquor or slurry may be fed either directly to the filter tank, or after a filter aid precoat has been formed on the filter medium, or after a filter aid has been mixed with the unfiltered material.

Vacuum causes the filtrate to be drawn to the lower chamber, whence it may pass to a vacuum receiver for removal after the cycle, by gravity, pumping or air pressure; or the filtrate may be left to accumulate in the vacuum chamber of the filter.

The filter cake may be washed after filtration by flooding with wash water. A most excellent wash can be obtained, if the filter cake does not crack. Cracking sometimes may be avoided by applying wash before the cake has a chance to dry out, by ironing out the cracks with a paddle, or by mixing washed cake with the wash to give a cloudy wash for crack filling.

False-bottomed suction tanks are usually the next step beyond gravity filters, where greater filtration capacity or speed is required, and the extra expense for vacuum is warranted.

Materials Handled. Fine chemicals or pharmaceuticals, which are usually produced in batch lots in relatively small quantities; corrosive liquor where ceramic filters are desired; evaporator salt boxes where the quantity is not sufficient for continuous filtration; small clarification jobs for water or fruit juices; and oil reclamation, where gravity is too slow, are applications of this type of filter.

Advantages. Filtration in false-bottomed vacuum tanks is rapid for the area and cake thickness involved; washing is effective, as the filter is small and all parts are accessible; filter-medium cleaning and changing are readily accomplished, except for rigid media cemented in place; and practically any corrosion-resistant construction can be resorted to.

Disadvantages. The limitations are those of small lot, batch handling, and hand operation.

Materials of Construction. False-bottomed vacuum tanks are readily constructed of ceramic materials, steel, cast iron, wood, etc., as their design is simple and they are stationary. Likewise, flexible or rigid filter media may be used.

Precoat Drum Filters. The precoat drum vacuum filter is an intermittently operating multiple-compartment drum vacuum filter with a special cake discharge scraper device.

Construction. Construction is the same as for the multiple-compartment drum vacuum filter, except that the scraper consists of a knife edge with a micrometer feed. The forward travel of the scraper may be varied from 0.0005 to 0.002 inch per revolution of the filter drum. Sometimes two scrapers are used, one leading the other, to take two cuts from the filter cake.

Operation. In operation the filter vat is filled with liquor containing a predetermined amount of filter aid; as the filter drum revolves through this slurry, a filter cake precoat is formed, generally from 1 to 2 inches thick. When the desired thickness of precoat is obtained, the filter vat is drained of the precoat slurry and the material to be clarified is fed in, vacuum being maintained during this period to keep the precoat on the filter drum.

The knife edge scraper is now set to shave off a thin film of filtered solids with just a trace of precoat material, to present a fresh surface of precoat for the next filtering cycle. If the solids must be absolutely free from precoat two knives are used, one to shave off the solid uncontaminated with precoat and the other to take off the remaining solids with some precoat.

Materials Handled. The precoat filter is a clarifying filter designed for dilute slurries, which filter freely at the start, but which quickly slime over when any appreciable deposit of solids is formed.

Materials of Construction. The materials of construction of precoat drum filters are the same as those which may be used for a standard multiple-compartment drum vacuum filter.

Advantages. The precoat filter has the advantage of continuous automatic operation between precoating periods, which may be lengthened normally to 6 or 8 hours, and sometimes even longer. By removing the deposited solids at every revolution of the filter drum, sliming is prevented and a fresh precoat surface is presented continuously to maintain the rate of flow.

Disadvantages. Precoat drum filters are expensive as compared with filter presses, and precoating makes the operation intermittent, requiring labor for this step in the filtering. There is the danger of fine particles of solids working below the precoat surface; this means retarded filtration or taking such a deep cut as to make re-precoating necessary within a short period.

Sand Filters. Various types of sand dewatering filters of the combined vacuum and drainage design have been used from time to time for handling heavy, free-filtering solids. One type consisted of a wheel carrying a number of buckets which scooped up the sand and water from a trough as the wheel revolved. The solids were dewatered as the wheel turned, and were finally discharged by an automatic bucket tilting at the top position.

Another type consisted of a revolving table containing porous outer sections over vacuum compartments, each of which was connected to a common standard multiple-valve hub. The table was supported by a central trunnion and kept in a horizontal position by a set of rollers. The material to be dewatered was spread over the sections as they revolved. A plow scraper removed the dewatered solids, which were picked up by a conveyor for final removal. With these designs, there are often inefficiencies in operation and difficulties in coordination; in the last type, the plow must be carefully adjusted to remove the solids without tearing the medium.

Chapter 9
Hydraulic Presses and Squeeze Presses

General. In hydraulic press work, very high pressures are employed to separate liquids from solids. Cake building is usually carried on at normal pump pressures, after which the hydraulic pressure is applied to obtain the final dry cake. Especially strong, substantial construction is therefore required, particularly in the pressure-creating mechanism.

Usually the press feed and discharge are in batch lots, by hand. This increases the cost of operation considerably; on the other hand, very high percentages of extraction are obtained, and the materials handled are usually those which could not be treated in any other way.

As regards separation of liquids from solids, hydraulic presses may be classified as follows: plate presses, box presses, cage presses, pot presses, and curb presses.

Plate Presses. In the plate press class, there are three main types: the screw type, the knuckle-joint type, and the hydraulic press proper, including the hydraulic filter press. The use of these types depends upon the material to be treated and the amount of output desired.

The screw type with steel beam and combination platform is shown in Fig. 67; it is designed for heavy work and is operated by the mechanism on the top, with the pressure downward.

The knuckle-joint type is a very powerful machine. The right- and left-hand screw produces tremendous force when the levers are near the perpendicular. The motion of the follower, rapid at first when the material is soft, decreases in speed and increases the force as the levers straighten out, and the material becomes dense. The machine is especially adapted for making cider and other beverages. The knuckle-joint press has a reversible platform so that one pile of cakes (called "cheese") can be pressing while another is being prepared for the press. Hand-operated presses of this type are made for use in small plants.

The regular hydraulic type plate press is generally designed for heavy work and constructed with a view to giving great pressures. There are two designs of this press, the upward and the downward pressure types. In both of these, the cylinder is made of steel; the ram is of cast iron, turned and polished; the platen is a heavy iron casting extending to and babbitted around the rods; the racks and material to be filtered are between the head and the platform. Both types of presses have transfer car systems.

Racks are made square, of wooden strips about ½ inch thick by 1⅜ inch wide, placed about ¼ inch apart, with strips 2 inches apart and ⅜ inch thick nailed across them. Double racks are also sometimes used with the same number of slats both ways. Although they are more difficult to clean and somewhat heavier, they are very strong and durable.

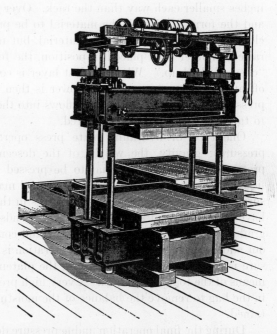

FIGURE 67. Screw type hydraulic press.

The regular hydraulic press for dehydrating obtains its high preliminary pressing speed by the combination of pump plunger sizes, or by the action of a hydraulic steam pump. The steam pump has the advantage of rapid preliminary ram travel. The pressure and steam governor with which the steam pump is equipped automatically reduces the volume of discharge, regulating the pressing speed in accordance with the resistance encountered.

The press is usually built of an all-steel frame, consisting of head, base and uprights, with a hydraulic power cylinder mounted on the base.

Hydraulic cider presses often are equipped for both grinding and pressing. A power-driven inclined elevator delivers the fruit to the grinders, which have a high-speed, steel-knifed grater for apples and a double-roll crusher for grapes. The ground pumice is deposited on and wrapped in press cloths, with the aid of a "cheese" form and guides.

The form used to build up the cake in plate presses is square inside and about 3½ inches deep. It is made of boards, usually 1 inch thick and 3½ inches wide. A board is nailed across each end and a casting bolted in each corner to stiffen the form. When it is desired to "lay up a cheese," so called, that is, to build up the layers of materials to be filtered, the operation is commenced on the platform of the press, a rack being laid down and the form placed on the rack. The form is 5 or 6 inches smaller each way than the rack. Over this form a cloth is spread, and the form filled with the material to be pressed. The corners of the cloth are then folded over the material, but not too tightly; the form is raised, another rack placed in position, the form lowered, etc., until the "cheese is laid up." When the last layer is completed, the form is taken off and a rack put on. The follower is then placed in position and the pressing commenced. The liquid flows into the platform and is conveyed to tanks or other points, as desired.

One type of hydraulic plate press operates under three different pressures: gravity, the weight of the descending head, and hydraulic pressure. When the material to be pressed is first admitted, the free liquids flow off by gravity; or the material may be admitted under pressure, forcing the liquids through the bags in this manner. After the bags have become full of solids, the head descends slowly of its own weight, gradually forcing the platens together and compressing the bags, forcing out additional liquors. When this operation is completed, hydraulic pressure is applied to the cylinders and the platens are forced still closer by means of the toggle joint arm. A very high pressure is applied to the cake in the bag to remove the balance of the moisture. A dry cake is thus obtained.

During the final operation undue pressure does not build up at the ends of the bag, because during the first stage of pressing the material is in a liquid state and the pressure is, therefore, approximately the same in all directions. During the final hydraulic squeezing, however, the material in the bag is in the form of a solid cake; the pressure is therefore normal to the platen faces, and very little pressure is applied to the ends of the bag.

Bags and racks naturally vary for different classes of work. For material containing a very small percentage of solids it is necessary to use filter-cloth bags, but where larger percentages of solids are to be handled, metal bags are used. These are hinged at the sides and perforated with holes of suitable size for the material being handled. Metal bags have been used on blood, and hog and beef tankage.

Corrugated racks as such may be placed between the bags and so constructed that the corrugations run vertically, giving free drainage to the bags. A heavy sheet of steel plate forms the backing for the corrugated metal and prevents buckling or distortion under the high pressure. Where metal bags are used, the corrugations are on either side of the backing plate, and where cloth bags are used the backing plates are on either side of the corrugations. When it becomes necessary to use a large number of bags and racks, the ends of the racks are fitted with rollers to allow them to move freely on the I-beam support bar. Some of the uses of the press are in cane and beet sugar factories, and packing houses, for edible and inedible beef and hog tankage, oleomargarine, blood, etc.

Another plate type press of this design is the common hydraulic olive oil press. Pressing oil from olives requires high pressure and a very strong and rigid press. The crushed olives are placed in layers to form a "cheese" on a steel truck, which is run into the press. Each layer is wrapped in a woven cloth made for the purpose, with steel plates between. This retains the solids and permits the oil to flow out. In the main, construction and operation are the same as previously described.

FIGURE 68. Hydraulic filter press. (*Courtesy Watson-Stillman Co.*)

The hydraulic filter press is a plate-and-frame press designed to operate under pressures up to about 6000 pounds per square inch, for handling oils, waste disposal, etc. Operation during filtration is similar to that of the standard plate-and-frame press. When the cake is built up, however, hydraulic pressure is applied to produce a dry cake and obtain further extraction. The pressure is then released, the pan or deflector raised, and the press opened. The cake drops off automatically and the press is ready for another cycle. These operations are by valve manipulation, and the hand-opening usual with plate-and-frame presses is not required (Fig. 68).

Box Presses. The box press, used to a large extent in cottonseed oil manufacture, is illustrated in Fig. 69. The press is fitted with numerous

FIGURE 69. Hydraulic box press. (*Courtesy The French Oil Mill Machinery Co.*)

(up to sixteen or more) built-up, steel boxes. The platen, or ram block, is of semi-steel, the cylinder of cast steel; the ram, usually 16 inches in diameter, is normally of semi-steel. Presses are tested up to 8000 pounds pressure and equipped with 10,000-pound hydraulic gauge and gauge pipe connections. Drainage is effected by setting the press with a slight backward inclination from the vertical. Heavy floor pans are provided to conduct the drippings from the boxes to the drain trough in the rear of the press.

The side walls of the boxes are of heavy steel and the body plate is commonly of ⅝-inch steel. Drainage angles are placed on the sides so that all the liquid drains out.

The underside of the body plate and the top of the steel mat are corrugated to prevent the cake from slipping and creeping and consequent injury to the press cloth. Often the box press cake is formed in another machine called a "cake former," to produce a uniform cake with square ends, so that the oil yield will be at a maximum in the box press. In the "cake former" a charging box at lower pressure travels endwise forward and backward over the forming box, with a ram stroke of less than an inch, compressing the cake in the forming box.

Cage Presses. The cage press is one in which a very high hydraulic pressure is exerted on the material confined in a cylindrical cage, as shown

FIGURE 70. Hydraulic cage press. (*Courtesy The French Oil Mill Machinery Co.*)

in Fig. 70. The operation is by hand and all the hydraulic parts of the press are self-contained. As the presses are supplied with filter plates, no filter cloth is required.

The method of operation generally is as follows. The sliding base with the cage is moved forward to the filling position; several layers of the meal, or pulp, to be pressed are put into a cage, with the filter plates dropped between. The cage and its base are then slid into the pressing position. By means of the lever the press is pumped up until the plunger, descending into the cage, compresses the material, forcing out some of the oil, and making room for more layers of meal to be added. As the press is pumped up again, against the full compressed charge, the oil in the material is forced through the filter plates and edgewise out through the centers to grooves in the side of the cage, thence out into the catch pan of the press. A lever releases the pressure and lets the press down of its own weight. As it descends, the cage, with the pressed cakes in it, is suspended by a latch and the sliding base drops away from it so that it can be slid over to the ejecting position.

The press is now pumped up so that the plunger pushes the cakes out

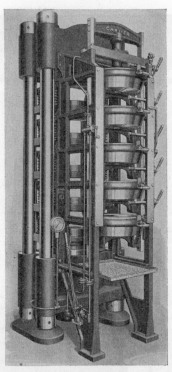

FIGURE 71. Hydraulic pot press. (*Courtesy Fred S. Carver*)

of the cage. As the press is let down, the cage is held by the latch so that the sliding base may be pulled back; the latch is then released, dropping the cage onto the base, which is slid over to filling position again. The press is supplied with either a 7- or a 9-inch diameter cage. The latter gives 1000 cubic inches of space for each filling and 2,400 pounds per square inch pressure on the material. The 7-inch diameter cage gives 600 cubic inches of space for each filling and 4,000 pounds pressure per square inch on the material. The 9-inch gives a larger working capacity but lower pressure on the material and lower yield of oil. The 7-inch cage is better adapted for most oil-bearing seeds, however, as the higher yield of oil is usually desired, rather than handling the larger volume of material.

Pot Presses. The pot-type of oil press is in effect a very high-pressure filter press which will handle semi-liquids or heavy materials at high pressures. In addition to the pressing of oils, this type of machine may be used for various purposes under pressures of 5,000 pounds or more per square inch.

The presses are generally made with two sets of pots for receiving the

FIGURE 72. Hydraulic curb press. (*Courtesy The French Oil Mill Machinery Co.*)

material to be pressed or filtered, arranged so that one set is over the hydraulic ram being pressed, while the other set is in the clear, having the pressed cakes removed from it or being refilled. By alternating in this manner, substantially continuous pressing is obtained.

In operation, the material to be pressed is confined in a series of cylindrical pot units as shown (Fig. 71). The pots have movable bottoms with holes or perforations and outlet channels for the oil or liquid filtrate. Above the pressing position of each pot is another drilled plate similar to that in the bottom of the pot. With the filter pads or plates below and above, material to be pressed is put into the pots. After the filled pots are brought into place, the press in closing seals the top filter pads so that only the liquid matter can escape through the filter pads. As the pressure is increased, a cake of material forms, and very high pressure can be put upon it to force out the liquor.

Higher pressures can be exerted on material than in the oil presses generally used, because the cakes are confined at the edges and receive the pressure uniformly. This type of press is designed to handle material from a semi-liquid to practically a liquid mass.

FIGURE 73. Screw type squeeze press. (*Courtesy General American Process Equipment Co.*)

Fig. 71 is a side view of a pot press showing five pots filling and five pressing. The heavy construction used to withstand the high pressure is illustrated.

Curb Presses. Curb presses are used for pressing lard, grease and tallow from scrap and cracklings, oils from fish, tinctures, whitings and such materials. For making wine a wooden curb, made with staves and bands, is used in some sections of Europe, instead of the more customary method of racks and cloths.

The curb is a round receptacle for holding the material being pressed. It is made either of perforated steel boiler plate, of beveled steel slats encircled with steel bands, or of wood staves re-enforced with bands. The fluid extracted by pressing escapes through the perforations in the curb or between the slats, and flows to a saucer or a truck on which the curb rests. The curb is usually made with an opening at one side; this is closed with a cam lock or a rod locking device, which allows the curb to spring open when released thus freeing the pressed "cheese."

There is made a small curb press with a steel perforated curb. The handles on the side of the curb are used for lifting it off the "cheese." In larger presses a geared attachment is used for lifting, the chains forming the attachment, hooking onto the handles. A larger curb press is shown in Fig. 72. Here the curb is made of heavy steel plate.

Should there not be enough material to complete the filling, wood blocking may be used which may be fitted into the top of the curb to save time in the rise of the ram. After the pump has been put in motion the ram is forced to rise by merely closing the operating valve, which closes the short-circuit escape of the oil or water, used in operating the press, back to the box. The pressure continues until the maximum has been reached, notice of which is given by the safety valve.

The pressure can be continued until it is desired to release it; this may be accomplished by opening the operating valve, when the press will re-

FIGURE 74. Roller squeeze press. (*Courtesy General American Process Equipment Co.*)

turn to its original position without further attention. The curb is then unlocked and lifted from the "cheese."

Squeeze Presses. The screw type squeeze press is a mechanical pressure machine wherein a screw or worm revolves within a shell lined with perforated plate. The taper of the screw or pitch decreases from the feed end toward discharge, thus exerting a powerful squeezing action upon the material being handled (Fig. 73).

In operation, the feed is delivered to the annular space between the screw and the liner, and as it progressively moves toward the discharge end, the liquor is squeezed through the perforated plates and out, while the solids are delivered at the discharge end with the desired liquor content. The consistency of the cake is of particular importance in paper pulp where a definite moisture, from 10 to 44 per cent, is desired for the next step in the process. In other extractions the high pressures insure more complete liquor removal.

Means are provided for flushing out the shell and also for preventing the material fed into the hopper from bridging over.

The liner perforations can be varied, as can the end discharge. At times water cooling is resorted to for lowering the foots, or where frictional heat is detrimental to the quality of oil or meal handled.

The screw press is used for small operations and has the disadvantage, for some processes, of discharging a quantity of fines with the filtrate.

The roller squeeze press consists of an endless, horizontal, hinged, perforated belt passing between rolls. The belt is carried over hexagon pulleys at the head and rear ends of the machine. The top rolls are provided with moveable bearings and tension springs to give regulated pressure (Fig. 74).

In operation the liquor squeezed from the wet material, as it is carried forward between the rolls, passes through the belt to be caught in a pan beneath the lower rolls and above the returning belt, while the dewatered solids pass over the rear pulley for discharge.

The machines are used principally in spent grain dewatering preceding rotary shell dryers, reducing the moisture of the spent grain on the average from 85 per cent to 65 per cent.

Chapter 10
Laboratory Filters

Laboratory filters are either standard analytical equipment for routine and research, or miniature plant units for operation checks, plant expansion, or new development work.

Ceramic Funnels. In the first category come glass funnel filters, most common of all (Fig. 75). Here paper is customarily the filter me-

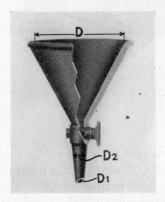

FIGURE 75. Ceramic laboratory funnel. (*Courtesy
General Ceramics and Ste-
atite Corp., N. J.*)

dium and gravity the filtration force. A gradation of filter papers, from coarse to extremely fine, is standard, regularly in circular form, with sizes ranging to fit the funnels. By proper folding, if folded paper is not obtainable, the efficiency of the filter can be increased. If the top corner is torn off diagonally across the entire quadrant, a very tight joint will be made between the top of the paper and the glass. This prevents leakage, when the funnel is filled above the top of the paper, and there is no difficulty in the final washing down of particles of precipitate from the glass onto the filter.

Flat perforated discs are made to fit glass funnels, particularly to provide a firm support so that vacuum may be used by inserting the funnel stem through a stopper in a vacuum flask. There are also porcelain funnels with fixed or movable flat discs, for gravity or vacuum filtration.

Straight-Sided Funnels. Straight-sided funnels rank next to glass funnels as common laboratory equipment, but are usually vacuum-operated. These funnels are of glazed porcelain construction, shaped like a false-bottomed round tank, with an insert consisting of an integral or removable perforated flat or arched plate. The chamber below the insert terminates in a funnel (Fig. 76), for placement through a stopper of a size to fit the vacuum flask to be used.

Filter paper is the common filter medium, although fabric, carbon, asbestos, filter aids, etc., are used.

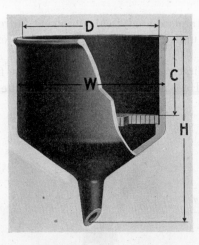

FIGURE 76.   Straight sided funnel.   (*Courtesy   General Ceramics   and   Steatite Corp., N. J.*)

The danger from leakage in filter funnels is usually from oversized filter media. Special care is required in using these filters in this respect, since the filter medium is a flat, loose insert, rather deeply covered with material to be filtered, and is subjected to vacuum pull.

Filter Crucibles. The common filter crucible is a cup with a perforated bottom, inserted through a rubber stopper into the top of a vacuum flask for suction filtration. It is made of porcelain, silver or platinum, as in quantitative analysis the residue, with the filter medium, often must be ignited without being removed from the filter.

Other Filters. There are many less common filters which are extensively used for particular applications, *i.e.*, bacteriological filters or microfilters consisting of a tube, finger or candle element constructed of porcelain or infusorial earths (Fig. 77). Metal caps of nickel, silver or other easily sterilized corrosion-resistant materials form the connection to the vacuum system.

The elements usually range from ⅝ to 4 inches in diameter and from ¾ to 8 inches in length. In sterilizing, care must be taken not to use agents which will attack the cement in infusorial earth filters, such as hydrochloric acid or potassium permanganate; and sudden changes in temperature and high blow-back pressure of air or water (15 pounds is usually the safety limit) should be avoided.

Some micro-filters have filter tubes or sticks with a flared portion to take an asbestos pad, as in the filtering of silver haloids, or a platinum sponge for filtering barium sulfate.

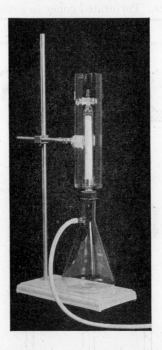

FIGURE 77. Bacteriological candle filter. (*Courtesy Selas Co.*)

Another design of laboratory filter is the beaker-filter combination for precipitates, where there is to be a series of reactions and separations. A fritted glass disc is fused into one side of a beaker, with the outlet of the filter so arranged that the contents of one beaker may be filtered into another. The porosity is of a fineness to retain barium sulfate.

Bacteriological filters may consist of a soft filtering disc (usually 3 inches thick) supported by a silver gauge on a silver-plated cylinder usually locked by a large nut. Particles of sub-micron size, of colloidal nature, are caught in the interstices of the medium for ultra-filtration. Again, blocks of porcelain are used in a layer 10 to 15 mm in diameter by 12 mm high, fitted to a metal mantle with a soft rubber sleeve, made water-tight by screwing together the two metal (nickel-plated) parts.

It is claimed that the porosity and electric charge is such that a 24-hour broth culture of *B. Prodigiosus, B. Typhosus, B. Coli,* and *Staphylococcus aureus* can be filtered to yield a sterile filtrate at a hospital laboratory, a 10-mm filter block retaining only 0.4 cc of fluid.

There are laboratory mercury filters for purifying and filtering mercury, for use in calibrating glassware; these may consist of a rigidly supported chamois medium or a special muslin-packed reservoir, through which a fine stream of mercury is passed.

Cones. Perforated cones to act as filter medium supports, or cones of Alundum construction are common laboratory equipment. The latter

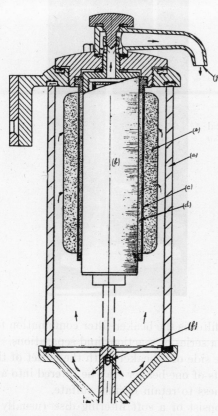

FIGURE 78.   Wire element filter.
(*Courtesy Infilco, Inc.*)

may be fitted with a rubber gasket over a funnel so that the entire surface of the cone is filter area, which can be ignited. Such cones are used for slow-filtering gelatins, and similar materials. Where oils, fats, waxes, agar agar, syrups, glues, etc., must be handled hot, specially shaped electrical heaters or water baths to fit the filter are obtainable.

Water Filter. A special filter for the microscopic analysis of water is equipped with by-passes for keeping the medium wet; inoculated water is used for washing, since the pellets of such filters as used in Pasteur filters operate too slowly for practical purposes in this work. Other special laboratory filters are tincture filters, blood filters, infra-red filters for photomicrography, gas filters, etc.

Tray Filter. One horizontal laboratory filter for gravity filtration is tray-shaped with sheets of filter paper used as the filter medium. It was designed to replace glass funnel filters, where speed and considerable capacity were desirable.

Metal Medium Filters. Another laboratory-type filter is a filter-aid filter consisting of an element with tightly wound wires as the filter me-

FIGURE 79. Laboratory plate and frame filter press. (*Courtesy T. Shriver and Co.*)

dium (Fig. 78). The element consists of an extruded metal or plastic tube having a number of threaded projections along its length to take helically wound wire, which forms the filter medium (⅛th of a square foot), the space between the wires being used for drainage. The filter element may be enclosed by a perforated metal or plastic sleeve to retain the precoat, with a glass or plastic cylinder over both, making it possible to see the cake building.

One particular feature of this filter is that the cake may be dropped and built up on the filter element a number of times. If the outer sleeve is used on the element, the filter cake may be dropped numerous times without disturbing the precoat between the outer sleeve and the element.

Centrifuges. Many types of laboratory separation are handled by centrifuges of the whiz, supercentrifuge or conical-head type.

In industrial laboratories high-speed centrifuges (40,000 rpm), either hand, water or electrically driven, are used both for actual separation purposes and for estimating the settling rate of slurries. The latter is accomplished by the so-called laboratory whizzers consisting of two graduated tube receptacles. In one tube is placed a given quantity of slurry of known settling rate and in the other the same quantity of an unknown slurry; results are obtained by comparison after whizzing. The settling rate, if good, indicates that the filtering rate will be satisfactory; thus the whizzer may be used as a first step in filtration tests of unknown materials.

Miniature Plant Units. The second group of laboratory filters consists of small-sized pressure filters, small vacuum filters of various kinds,

FIGURE 80.   Laboratory verticle leaf vacuum filter unit. (*Courtesy Conkey Filter Co.*)

centrifuges, and special false-bottomed tanks. Whenever a new product, or variation in the present product, or a change of the conditions of filtration occurs, laboratory filtration tests should be made to determine the type of filter best suited to the new setup and the capacities to be anticipated. Laboratory tests also are made as a check of plant results, if the material is in process, and as a means of catching variations in feed or filter operation. Such laboratory filters are used by large industrial laboratories, manufacturing plant laboratories, technical schools and filter manufacturers.

The machines are as nearly as possible of the same design and construction as commercial-sized units, so that the results obtained can be used as indications of what may be anticipated in commercial operation; some filters, however, are built only in the small sizes, *e.g.*, wire or disc medium filters.

If new products are being handled it is often wise to go from laboratory to pilot plant size equipment, before installing commercial units. This is because there is not only difficulty in employing proper factors of safety in the interpretation of laboratory results, but also the difference between careful handling of a laboratory filter by skilled technicians and the necessarily rough handling in plant operations.

Fig. 79 illustrates a laboratory plate-and-frame press, Fig. 80 a vacuum leaf filter unit, and funnels as false-bottomed tank, all almost exact duplicates of large machines. On the other hand, the drum vacuum filter

FIGURE 81. Laboratory hydraulic press. (*Courtesy Fred Carver*)

always has fewer and smaller compartments in the laboratory size; the rotating leaf filter usually has only one disc of a small size with no spacing problem. Hence other factors than actual size difference must be taken into consideration.

Many of the laboratory filters are made in self-contained units; that is, the filter with its auxiliaries, such as pumps, tanks and blowers, is mounted on a common base with interconnections made up. Often the units are portable and are equipped with electrical heating elements for hot filtration.

Corrosion resistant construction is relatively simple in these small sizes; they may be of Monel metal, rubber, lead, bronze, aluminum, stainless steel, or plastic, as desired.

Hydraulic Presses. Laboratory hydraulic presses are used for pressing oils and liquids from oil seeds, waxes, etc. The equipment consists of cages usually 3 ½ inches in diameter by 7 ½ inches deep (70 cubic inches capacity). Plates and cloths usually are composed of six rolled-wire drainage plates 6 inches square, 12 square filter cloths, and a form for

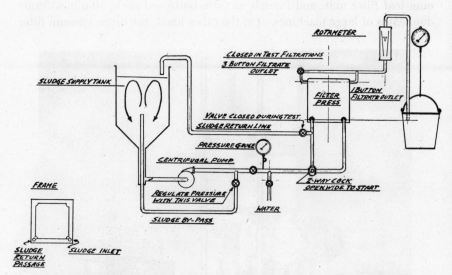

FIGURE 82. Rotameter layout. (*Courtesy Prof. E. L. McMillen*)

laying up 3-inch square cakes of the softer materials to be wrapped in the filter cloths (Fig. 81). The platens have grooves for liquor drainage.

The press is hand-operated, often good for loads up to 10 tons and very high hydraulic pressure. Construction is of nickel-plated bronze, for standard units.

Rotameter with Filter Press. In Fig. 82, a pump is used to keep the sludge thoroughly mixed and supply the filtering pressure, which is regulated by throttling on the sludge by-pass line and may be adjusted to any predetermined valve advance at the start of the test. To measure filtrate flow rates, it is necessary to fill the press and outlet piping completely with water, before the test starts. A stopper is then inserted in the outlet above the tared bucket, while the water within the frame is displaced by sludge. The mixture of water displaced and sludge is returned in a small sludge return line to the conical tank, until its specific gravity is the same as that of the sludge in the tank. This requires a special frame having openings at both bottom corners. The test is started with sludge against the cloth and all outlet piping filled with water. Thus the zero of filtrate weight and time coincide with the start of the test and full filtration pressure is almost immediately applied. In making constant rate tests it is only necessary to hold the rotameter float at some predetermined level, by continually adjusting the valve on the sludge by-pass line, so as to increase pressure as needed.

Testing Leaves. Another useful testing unit is the filter leaf, usually not over 3 inches square that is if rectangular, or 4 inches in diameter if circular. By connecting the filter leaf to a vacuum or pressure system, filtering rates at various temperatures, concentrations, pressure differentials, etc., can be quickly obtained. Likewise, the straight-sided funnel can be used for determination of anticipated results from false-bottomed tanks or hopper top feed filters.

Horizontal-plate pressure filters in the laboratory may have 15-inch discs with upward flow filtration, or up to three $8\frac{1}{4}$-inch diameter discs with a 1-inch spring, or 1 square foot filter area and downward filtration.

For testing, see Chapter 18.

References

1. McMillen, E. L., Prof. Lafayette College, Easton, Pa. Private correspondence.

Chapter 11

Oil Filters, Oil Expellers and Oil Separators

General. Oil separators used in petroleum refineries are of the gravity, pressure, vacuum, or centrifuge type. They are used in the mechanical extraction of oil from seeds, grain or nuts, where high pressures are exerted, and also in the separation for clarification or recovery of used oil from water or impurities.

Petroleum Refinery Filters. By far the largest and most important oil filters are in petroleum refineries, where filtration is employed in decolorizing lubricating-oil stocks, in the dewaxing of chilled oils, and in various clarifications, such as cracking still residues, secondary clarifications, etc.

Kalichevsky[1] states, "Old method oil refining consisted in agitating raw stock with H_2SO_4, settling out the sludge, usually by air blowing, and neutralizing with caustic solution or clay, with the neutralized caustic sometimes finished with clay. Difficulties, however, were encountered in obtaining complete settling.

"Clay treatment is helpful in eliminating possibilities of forming emulsions and improving color. Percolation through clay may be applied to certain raw stocks; Pennsylvania oils are practically never treated with H_2SO_4, but are finished directly with clay, sometimes with upward flow, through the clay.

"Oils may be treated with clay directly in the crude oil still. The clay is mixed with the raw oil charge and the residuum containing spent clay is continually withdrawn from the bottom of the still and passed to filters."

According to Nelson,[2] "with few exceptions all petroleum products must be chemically treated in some manner in producing finished market products. The impurities that must be removed are usually present in the crude oil, but some are also produced during the refining operation of distillation, cracking, etc. Some of the purposes of chemical treatment are as follows:

(1) To improve color
(2) To remove sulfur
(3) To improve odor
(4) To remove gumlike, resinous and asphaltic substances
(5) To improve stability on exposure to air or light

(6) To eliminate corrosive materials

(7) To change properties of the oil, such as viscosity index, carbon residue, etc.

(8) To produce a more salable and desirable market product."

Many of these processes involving chemical treatment include filtration in one or more steps of their operation. Decolorizing clays are widely used for decolorizing lubricating oils. They may be applied either by mixing with the oil and filtering, or by percolating the oil through a column of clay. In the first instance, the clay is usually in a finely divided state, 200 to 300 mesh, while in the second instance, coarse clays are used, about 30 to 60 mesh. The clays used vary from coarse fullers' earth or bauxites, which are simply dried and crushed, to chemically treated bentonites and synthetic materials.

Coarse clays, while less expensive than the finer ones, are also less adsorbent and are normally used in deep, loosely packed beds, through which the oil slowly percolates; with lighter distillates clay contacting may be conducted in the vapor stage. The finer clays with their better adsorbent qualities, are used with direct mixing, followed by settling or filtration. The reaction takes place at elevated temperatures. Normal temperatures are used with light distillates. The use of clay on light distillates was relatively common some years ago when the color problem was important, but it is rare now, except for vapor-phase refining.

With the exception of some Pennsylvania stocks, most oils are given an acid treatment, followed by neutralization before decolorizing. The acid is frequently applied in several portions and often centrifuges are used later for separation.

The properties of lubricating-oil sludge vary so widely that the success of a continuous treatment may depend upon the method of sludge removal.

Percolation. "Percolation was the original method of decolorizing lubricating oils."[1] Gurwitsch[7] says, "The advantage of filtration consists in the better utilization and smaller expenditure of the adsorbent to produce a given degree of decolorization. The oil comes successively into contact with a great number of very thin layers of the adsorbent. The filtration is equivalent to an extremely fractionated mixing, and so its effect on the reversibly adsorbed substance must be greater than that of mixing, even when carried out in several operations with equal quantities of adsorbent."

Nelson[2] states that "in general for gravity flow the longer the packed column the greater the bleaching action, the coarser the earth the less the bleaching, and the higher the temperature the less the bleaching (other conditions being comparable).'' Bauxite and fullers' earth are principally used, and the efficiency as a function of the particles is somewhat as follows:

Mesh	Efficiency (%)
60 to 90	100
30 to 60	87
16 to 30	72

However, a 30 to 60 mesh material is usually used because it can be more easily handled. Although the temperature should not be so high that oil drains through the clay with only a short time of contact, nevertheless viscous lubricating oil stocks either must be heated, or the rate of percolation will be hopelessly slow.

OPERATION OF 1,000-CU. FT. FILTER

Stock	Saybolt Viscosity	Temp. of Filtration (°F)	Rate of Filtration (bbls per hr for a 1000 cu ft filter)	Pressure Filtration† (lbs per sq in)
Light spindles	Up to 200 at 100°	80-100	5-25	0-25
Heavy spindles	200-500 at 100°	100-140	5-15	0-25
Overhead or residual cylinder stock	100-160 at 210°	160-200	2-10	15-50
Naphtha solutions of cylinder stock		100-130	30-50	5-15
Petrolatums	100-160MP*	25° above MP*	5-20	0-15
Waxes	100-160MP*	25° above MP*	5-20	0-15

*Melting point.
†Pressures in the higher range are required where 60-90 mesh earths are used.

The stock may be the acid-treated type of filtrate, but it is usually neutralized before it enters the filters.

The clay is washed with 56 A. P. I. or lighter naphtha to remove the oil from the clay. The filter is then steamed and the clay can be discharged by allowing it to flow from the bottom of the percolator.

The throughput of percolators cannot be definitly stated because of the difference in stocks, difference in clays, and the degree of decolorization that is practiced. In general, 8 to 21 bbls of finished-color motor oil can be filtered per ton of clay. For lighter-finished colors, the capacity ranges from 4 to 8 bbls per ton, and for darker-finished oils, such as dark red oils and cylinder stocks, as much as 25 bbls per ton may be filtered.

Clay Filtering. Direct mixing is now generally used for decolorizing, the time allowance varying from several minutes to a few seconds, depending upon the particular system used, with clay of 200 to 300 mesh or finer.

As it is in a finely divided condition, the spent clay is removed by pressure filters rather than by gravity. Normally these are vertical leaf type filters employing batch operations. Filtration takes place at about 300°F and a cake approximately ¾ inch thick is formed on the filter leaves, and dried by forcing air or an inert gas through it prior to its discharge, in a total cycle of about one-half hour. With 200-mesh clay a capacity of from 1 to 5 pounds dry weight is obtained per square foot per hour.

The oil from the filter is usually sent through blotter presses; these are plate-and-frame filter presses equipped with paper filter media for the removal of the very fine clay particles which pass the leaf filters. The clay is caught within the medium in the blotter press; when the medium becomes clogged, it is thrown away and the decolorized, clarified oil sent to finished oil storage.

The filter cake from the leaf filter, which drops freely from the filter leaf on discharge, is about 45 per cent clay. The spent clay may be blown as free of oil as possible before being dumped; or washed with naphtha, steamed and dumped; or recovered by some reactivation means. The coarse clays are naphtha-washed, steamed free of naphtha and, with two or three per cent of oil, taken to the kiln or furnace for burning, as all coarse clays are reactivated by burning. The fine clays, where used for decolorizing lubricating oils, are expensive but are not generally reactivated, because of the difficulty of recovering fine clays of fair decolorizing activity.

Although some clays in more or less powder form are burned for reactivation, bringing them back, as with coarse clays, to about 60 per cent of their original efficiency with 1 to 6 burnings, the required burning temperature (1100 to 1200°F) often injures them.

Solvent Reactivation. As described by Chenault and Miller,[3] "the introduction of relatively high priced acid improved clays and synthetic clays gave an added incentive for reactivation of spent clays in order to restore them to a high percentage of their original effectiveness. As most of these clays are in powder form and have delicate structure, which might be injured by burning or the usual heat treatment, solvent extraction for reactivation is best employed." As an example, an Eastern refinery is operating with a synthetic magnesium silicate as the decolorizing agent. This clay has the advantage of decolorizing at moderate temperature, allowing easy solvent extraction.

When such a clay is discharged from the filter it is mixed with naphtha and passed to a hooded rotary drum vacuum filter operating in an atmosphere of flue gas (as an explosion preventive). The filters are of the standard drum vacuum filter construction with the addition of a vapor-tight hood covering the drum and the discharge repulper, and the necessary changes for this and washing arrangements.

In operation the warm slurry (170 to 175°F) is fed to the filter carrying 15 to 18 per cent (by weight) clay, building up a filter cake ³⁄₁₆ to ¼ inch thick under 10 to 20 inches of vacuum (mercury). The clay cake is naphtha-washed before drying in flue gas and is discharged over the scraper of the filter by flue gas blow back. A slight water pressure (5 inches) is maintained in the filter hood for positive flue gas pressure, and the gas operates through a closed circuit.

The clay cake is about half clay and half solvent, with a small amount of oil. After discharge from the repulper (aided by some oil filtrate) the cake is sent to a mixing tank where naphtha is added for reslurrying, and the resulting slurry is fed to a hooded drum vacuum filter. The oil filtrate is returned to the heater tanks as pumped from the vacuum receivers.

The filter cake from the second filter, which operates under a moderate vacuum (10 to 15 inches of mercury) and low flue gas pressure, contains about 0.35 per cent by weight of oil and a small amount of solvent. The reactivated clay has an average efficiency of about 85 per cent. The filtrate, composed principally of naphtha and 12 to 15 per cent of acetone together with the coloring matter removed from the clay, is sent to the solvent recovery system.

Various grades of oil, varying from 150 neutral with a Saybolt Universal viscosity of about 145 seconds at 110°F to heavy raffinate having a viscosity of about 240 seconds at 210°F, are regularly treated with this process. It is claimed that this process gives a continuous contacting and clay reactivation in simple operation at low cost, favorable working conditions, complete color removal and small space requirements.

Gravity Sludge Filtration. In some refineries the sludge from acid treatment and neutralization of the oils is filtered by gravity on sand beds. Revolving arms continuously scrape the sticky sludge (with some sand) from the top of the bed. The sand is finally removed to such an extent that it must be renewed, making the operation one of long cycles with renewal of filter medium at the end of the cycle.

Dewaxing. Lubricating oils contain waxes which raise the pour test; they are removed to improve the oil, but are valuable as by-products. There are in general two kinds of wax in lubricating oils, *i.e.*, crystalline wax and amorphous wax. This is in addition to the paraffin wax obtained from low viscosity distillates.

"Crystalline wax is found in wax distillate (paraffin oil) and amorphous wax or petrolatum is found in cylinder stock. The crystalline wax that is found in wax distillates can be filtered from the oil; but amorphous wax is sticky and quickly plugs the filter cloth. In reality both materials are crystalline but the crystals in petrolatum stock tend to be small, so that the petrolatum behaves physically as a colloidal or jellylike material. The crystalline nature of all waxes is evident in the several newly developed solvent dewaxing processes. In these, the so-called amorphous wax can be successfully collected on filters."[2]

Wax particles have been separated by electrical precipitation using high-voltage alternating current, but centrifuging or filtering is the common method of handling.

"Some factors which affect the pressibility of a wax oil are (1) viscosity, (2) fractionation, (3) distillation range, (4) wax content, (5) crystal structure, and (6) extent of cracking."[2]

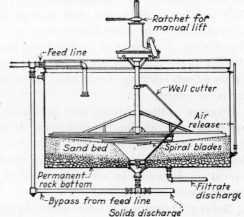

FIGURE 83. Gravity sand filter.
(*Courtesy Hardinge Co.*)

Buchler and Graves[4] conducted experiments which seemed to indicate that wax pressibility was controlled by the amount of soft wax present. Ferris, Cowles and Henderson[5] likewise carried out a series of experiments on wax stocks, but these indicated that no soft wax was present. Thus there is a variance of opinion as to the soft wax factor.

In wax pressing for separating chilled wax from oil, plate-and-frame or recessed-plate filter presses are often used. Pressures up to 300-500 pounds are usual, requiring heavy, closely woven cotton filter cloth to obtain clarity. The cycles are long, as a rule, which reduces the handling charges.

"The press capacity depends upon the property of the wax, etc."[2] For normal stock that contains 5 to 8 per cent wax and for single-pressing operations, one or two 48-inch plates are required for each barrel of Pennsylvania oil pressed per day, and 2 or 3 plates for Mid-continent oil. Even lower capacities are common with double-pressing if the stock contains a large amount of wax. The amount of slack wax obtained from the presses is far greater than 5 to 8 per cent finished wax and may in some cases amount to 30 per cent of the wax distillate.

According to Kalichevsky,[1] "when wax is removed by filtration the oil is chilled first either with or without naphtha dilution, depending upon its viscosity. Dilution is considered undesirable, both because it requires additional distillation for removing the naphtha from the dewaxed oil and from the wax; and because the differential between chilling and pour test of the product must be higher, as some wax is soluble in the naphtha used for dilution.

Centrifuging. In centrifuging cylinder stock from percolations the oil is usually diluted with 60 to 65 per cent naphtha, as the residual stocks are too viscous at low temperatures for centrifuging without dilution. They are then chilled in the same way as distillate stocks and charged to the centrifuge. The centrifuges operate at about 1800 rpm, the oil passing from the top and center of the bowl and the wax from a point lower (see Chapter 14). Water at about 160°F is sprayed on at times to prevent the wax from sticking; centrifuges often average 25 and 45 barrels per day per machine.

Presses. Filter aids are used at times to make the wax more filtrable and reduce the dilution requirements. In such cases leaf pressure filters are often employed rather than plate-and-frame presses. A variety of chemicals, used clays, etc., have been tried for wax oil separation, but solvent oil dewaxing by either the methyl ethyl ketone or the propane process is now common practice.

Solvent Dewaxing. "In the methyl ethyl ketone ("MEK") processes, vacuum will give sufficient differential for filtration, but with propane higher differentials are usually required, necessitating pressure filtration. The "MEK" process is "a development of the benzene acetone process by the use of various mixed solvents consisting of benzene, toluene, methyl-ethyl ketone, methyl-n-propyl ketone, methyl-n-butyl ketone or mixtures of these ketones. The advantages of the lower molecular weight ketones are higher filter rates and low solubility of wax, but they have higher vapor pressure and are somewhat soluble in water."[2]

The filters in the original solvent dewaxing process installation, made at a large midwestern refinery in 1928, consisted of a battery of rotating-leaf pressure filters. Later rotary drum vacuum filters were introduced to provide continuous filtration. With final chilled oil temperatures of about −40°F, filtration rates are about 2 gallons of solution per square foot per hour for a solution containing 17 per cent of oil and 0.3 gallon per square foot per hour for a 35 per cent solution. Heavy stocks seemed to filter at about the same rate as light stocks.

The continuous drum filter used is of fusion-welded steel construction with numerous individual drain pipes manifolded into double drains for each compartment. The filter drum, half submerged, is covered with a vapor-tight hood and provided with insulation, as operation takes place at sub-zero temperature. Observation light ports with glasses and wiper are necessary for a clear view of the washing and discharge. A separately driven scroll conveyor integral with the vat is used to remove the discharged wax continuously and convey it to a discharger, sealed to prevent loss of pressure under the hood.

FIGURE 84. Rotary drum vacuum filter with vapor tight hood. *(Courtesy Conkey Filter Co.)*

The wax at these low temperatures is relatively coarse and free-filtering, a $\frac{1}{8}$ to $\frac{3}{16}$ inch cake being readily built up; this cake is solvent-washed and discharged in the same flue gas atmosphere and closed circuit as used with solvent reactivated clay filters. The flue gas (CO_2) is continuously circulated throughout the system.

As described by David Young[6] the process consists "primarily of refrigeration equipment, wax filters, solvent reclamation units and necessary exchangers and control instruments to correlate the economic operation of the unit." The wax distillate is mixed with about 50 per cent of solvent at approximately 100°F for neutral distillate, and at 160°F for heavy distillate or long residuums; it is then cooled, additional solvent and some dewaxed oil added for the wax crystal formations, and fed to the filters at about −15°F. The filter cake is washed with cold solvent and back-pressure discharged (3 to 5 pounds CO_2) onto a screw conveyor.

From the filter the wax-free oil goes to make neutrals and the wax to make crude scale or a fully refined product. In each the first step is the recovery of the solvent from the oil and wax. Recovery from the oil is made by flash and stripping towers and from the wax by distillation followed by filtration.

The slack wax from the stripping operation proceeds through a rotary vacuum filter for the second deoiling in an operation similar to the first, in place of sweating. Here, however, a greater ratio of solvent to wax is used. The resulting wax is finished except for the final chemical decolorizing. For this it is agitated at 160°F with 66° Bé sulfuric acid (10 pounds to the bbl), neutralized with caustic soda (5° Bé), washed free of caustic, deodorized and sent to fullers' earth percolating filters. If a higher melting point or lower oil content wax is desired, it is sent back for a third solvent processing, including the acid wash and fullers' earth filtration.

Propane Process. In solvent dewaxing by the propane process continuous filtration is carried on by rotary drum filters, as described for the "MEK" process, operating under moderate pressure (20 to 30 pounds). The general construction of the filter is similar to that already described, except that often instead of a hood the filter drum is placed in a heavy cylinder with a removable head similar to a stationary pressure vertical leaf filter. Operation is carried on under flue gas pressure and is, of course, continuous and automatic.

The wax-forming presses in the final stage of preparation for shipment do not function as filter presses, although they are similar in construction to plate-and-frame presses, as they consist of concave plates held together by a hydraulic ram and equipped for cooling-water circulation.

Distillate Filters. Cracking still residues from which carbonate of lime and other solids are to be removed are handled by pressure leaf filters. In quick contact and settling processes for cracked distillates the acid stage oil is delivered to caustic breakers or mixed with 200 to 300 mesh clay for a few minutes and filtered upon a pressure leaf filter. "The short time aids in avoiding polymerization of the valuable olefin hydrocarbons and thus allows the use of acid for desulfuring high sulfur-cracked distillates without destroying the anti-knock properties of the gasoline."[9]

In the clay process for cracked distillates the vapor from the cracking tower is taken through towers that are packed with clay, 30 to 60 mesh being commonly used, although 60 to 90 mesh is used by some refineries.

The throughput per ton of clay is often 3000 to 5000 bbls, the yield being greatly increased by elevating entrainment in the gasoline vapor line. The clay chambers range in size from 6 to 16 feet diameter and 25 to 40 feet high. The clay is sometimes used as a neutralizer for acid-treated pressure distillates, as in the clay-contact process for lubricants. The clay is removed by pressure leaf type filters. From 1 to 5 pounds of 200 mesh clay per barrel is required to neutralize the acid.

Mechanical Oil Expeller. Oil is removed from seeds (principally cotton seed), grains or nuts by positive mechanical pressure, *i.e.*, the screw press or the hydraulic press. These have been described in Chapter 9. In operation with screw presses the coarse-ground, warmed seed is fed into the feed hopper, where the screws break the shells for oil extraction. Pressures up to 450 pounds are used for such materials as peanuts and up to 800 pounds for items like copra. The operation is continuous, the oil being constantly expelled through the perforations in the cylinder, dropping into the oil strainer, and thence into an oil pan. The "foots" accumulating in the drainer are fed automatically into the elevator, which returns them to the feed hopper. The pressed cake is discharged at the opposite end of the cylinder and carried away.

The oil as extracted from the screw press is not clear, because of the high pressure used, and must be polish-filtered, usually by "blotter" presses which remove the fine suspensions which cause cloudiness. With the screw press, cold-pressing is possible and the power requirements are moderate; the very high pressures possible with hydraulic presses are not obtainable, but of course they are not always needed.

While cottonseed oil extraction is the largest individual product handled, a rather large variety of seeds is screw-pressed, *i.e.*, almonds, apricot kernels, castor beans, coconut skins, copra, corn germs, flax seed, mustard seed, palm kernels, peanuts, poppy seed, rape seed, sesame seed, soya beans, sunflower seed, tung nuts, etc.

Oil and Water Separators. As a rule, oil is separated from water so that the water may be used as better feed water or for industrial applications. The presence of oils or grease, whether from exhaust steam or other sources, causes scale formation in a boiler, with subsequent decrease of heat transfer. Such scale is difficult to remove and will eventually necessitate tube replacement. As the oil or grease in these cases is in the form of small globules dispersed throughout the body of water, single-flotation separation is satisfactory.

The re-use of exhaust steam is a means of heat conservation, but for such re-use the steam must be oil-free, clean, and free of condensed volatiles. The same is true of boiler feed water. The separation is often accomplished by fabric filters inserted in the return line between the feed pump and the boiler.

Such fabric filters are quite similar to the feed water filters described in Chapter 12. They usually consist of vertical perforated plate tubes, horizontal cages, or horizontal circular sections, covered with linen terry. In the vertical type, double filtration may be accomplished by having one cylinder within the other (Fig. 85) and in the horizontal design, a number of discs are attached to a common bolt. The rate of flow here is reduced to obtain a clear effluent by providing a large filtering surface, 150 to 1000 times the area of the feed pipe. The water passes slowly to the

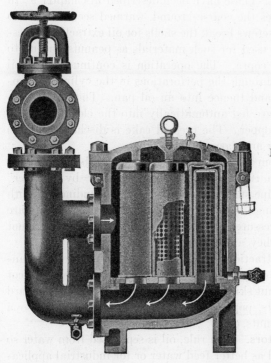

FIGURE 85. Verticle double cylinder pressure filter. (*Courtesy Blackburn Smith Co.*)

interior of the filter units and out to the boiler. The oil, grease or other matter separated from the water accumulates on the outside of the filter medium. When the accumulation results in a sufficient pressure differential (2 to 3 pounds) the filter must be cleaned. If possible, this is done by reverse blow, otherwise by changing the filter cloth. By-pass valves are provided so that during filter-cloth changes the feed water by-passes the filter either to go through a spare unit or to go temporarily without filtering to the boiler. Although differentials are usually low, the filters are made to withstand up to 500 pounds pressure for the feed line work.

Where quantities of oil are present, rather than scattered globules, separation can be made by taking advantage of the difference in specific gravity between the oil and water. Continuous operation is obtainable by overflow connection, and a clean separation is possible.

Another design depends upon capillary action. In operation it is said that "the current of steam entering the separator flows downward through a comparatively narrow annular passage formed between concentric perforated sheet metal cylinders. The downward flowing current of steam is faster at the center or mean diameter of the annular passage and slower next to the perforated walls. Water, oil or dirt contained in the steam will move into the slower current and to the perforated sur-

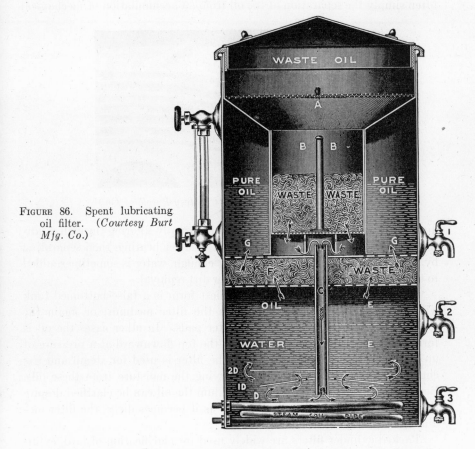

FIGURE 86. Spent lubricating oil filter. (*Courtesy Burt Mfg. Co.*)

face, where capillary action and gravity will cause them to pass through the perforations and over the metal lips out of the current. After passing downward through the annular passage the flow is reversed upward through a central cylinder for separation."

Where the oil separation is used in the exhaust line, it should be placed as near the engine as possible in order to avoid reduction in velocity of the steam between the engine and the separator. The apparatus is used for removing oil, water and gasoline from natural gas mains and for removing water and oil from compressed air lines.

Water may be removed from fuel oil by centrifuges, and these are also used for clarification of lubricating oils and cutting and heat-treating oils (Chapter 14). Oil-water emulsions may be broken by chemical agents, electric dehydration or surface separation.

Spent Oil Clarification. The reclaiming of used oils by filtration is often simply the separation of the oil from an accumulation of mechanical

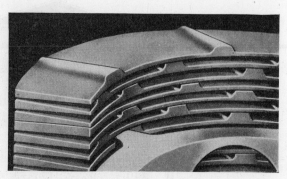

FIGURE 87. Edge oil filter. (*Courtesy Purolator Co.*)

dirt. There is a variety of these oil filters, usually filtering through a fabric, edge discs or other medium directly or after heating, then separating by flotation or centrifuging. Strangely enough, water is sometimes added to the oil for temperature, or washing for dirt removal.

The oil-clarifying filter in its simplest form is a false-bottomed tank with heavy cloth and filter paper as the filter medium; or again the medium may consist of a series of filter pads. In other cases the oil is forced through the filter medium from the top downward at a pressure of up to 100 pounds per square inch. The filter is used for steam and gas engine lubricating oil, etc., and for drying the moisture from these oils. Because of the heavy double filter medium the oil can be clarified despite the high pressures employed. As soon as it becomes dirty, the filter medium must be replaced.

Packed cylinder filters are widely used for clarification of lard, cylinder, gas engine, and heavy oils. The filters consist of a cylinder in a round or in a square chamber with heated or hot water compartments, at the top, which surround the unfiltered oil. The hot-water chamber raises the oil temperature, reducing its viscosity for rapid filtration through the cylinder-packed filter medium. The oil filters horizontally and the heavier dirt and grit particles settle in the sedimentation pan for sewer or other discharge. The oil passes from the chamber to the filter cylinder through the medium to the filter plate where the pressure of the oil above overcomes the resistance offered by the weight of the water. The oil here spreads out in a thin film, becoming thinner as it travels from the center to the outer edge of the plate; this is repeated against the other plates for dirt washing, giving final clarification.

Gasoline is filtered with or without water as it is of low viscosity. Direct gasoline filtration by suction through stationary sand beds gives high flow rates, clarity and long life before sand cleaning is necessary. Bone black, raw wool, white waste, excelsior, sponges, filter cloth, etc., are used as the filter medium. At times high pressures are used to force the oil through the water bath and out through fabric-supported diatomaceous earth.

References

1. Kalichevsky, V. A., "Modern Methods of Refining Lubricating Oils," Reinhold Publishing Corporation, 1938.
2. Nelson, W. L., "Petroleum Refining Engineering," 2nd Ed., McGraw-Hill Book Co., 1941.
3. W. B. Chenault and Miller, A. E., "New Lubricating Oil Decolorizing and Clay Reactivating Process," *Refiner and Natural Gasoline Manufacturer* (November, 1941).
4. Buchler and Graves, "The Petroleum Waxes," *Ind. Eng. Chem.*, **19**, 718 (1927).
5. Ferris, Cowles and Henderson, "The Composition of Paraffin Wax," *Ind. Eng. Chem.*, **21**, 1090 (1929).
6. Young, David, *Refiner and Natural Gasoline Manufacturer* (1939).
7. Gurwitsch, "Scientific Principles of Petroleum Technology," 2nd Ed., D. Van Nostrand, Inc. N. Y. (1924).
8. Kalichevsky, V. A., and Stagner, B. A., "Chemical Refining of Petroleum," 2nd Ed., Reinhold Publishing Corp., 1942.
9. Kalichevsky, V. A., "The Amazing Petroleum Industry," Reinhold Publishing Corp., 1943.

Chapter 12

Water Filtration

General. The object of filtering water is to remove suspended, colloidal and dissolved solids, whether from ground, surface or used water. The filtration may be merely a straining process to remove suspended solids directly; or a coagulant may be required to collect and hold finely divided particles and some of the coloring matter and bacteria. Coagulation may be used, with a sufficient period of time for complete chemical reactions, to allow for precipitation of some of the dissolved solids.

In many cases the pH of water must be corrected after filtration before it can be used for drinking or industrial purposes. This may be effected by passing the water through a zeolite softener, or by other means, followed in some cases by chlorination or ozonization.

The water from highly polluted streams, along which most industries are located, must be chemically treated prior to filtration in order to be usable. These waters have already been contaminated with chemicals, which are largely held in the water as dissolved solids. Precipitants must be applied, therefore, to throw out the soluble chemicals so they will be filtrable.

In municipal water treatment, the first step is the straining or settling out of the larger or heavier solids. This is usually followed by coagulation with alum, sodium aluminate, ferrous sulfate, or similar material, as dictated by the water analysis. The coagulant precipitates dissolved coloring matter, turbidity, bacteria, industrial wastes and other forms of contamination and, by gathering the minute particles together into comparatively large insoluble masses, causes them to settle rapidly. At the same time, the large-sized floc formed will mechanically entangle the lighter suspensions to carry them down with the settling floc.

Every water supply and coagulating chemical has an optimum pH value and range; coagulation should take place within that range, if maximum precipitation and complete removal of the impurities and the proper coagulation is to be obtained.

Sedimentation following coagulation is effected in a basin or tank holding from one to five hours' supply of water, to allow ample time for settling. It is equally important to allow sufficient time for complete chemical reactions between the suspended and soluble solids and the coagulant. The settling basin retains the major portion of the coagulated impurities,

although some of the light, insoluble gelatinous precipitates do not settle
and are carried over to the sand filters, which are used as the next step in
the process. Here they tend to adhere to the sand grains in the upper
portion of the sand beds and prevent the passage of the balance of the
impurities through the comparatively large interstices between the sand

FIGURE 88. Toledo, Ohio, water plant. (*Courtesy City Mgr., Toledo, Ohio*)

grains. The function of the filters is to remove traces of suspended matter from the water, such as the original non-settleables, silt and other impurities that existed in the water, and the by-products of coagulation,
such as aluminum hydrate, precipitated color and solidified colloids which
failed to settle.

Alkali and Chlorine. After filtration it may be necessary to correct
the acidity of the water by treating the filter effluent with a pH-correct-
ing alkali like lime, soda, or sodium silicate. By raising the pH of the
filtered water to 7.0 the acidity is neutralized, the activity of the dissolved
oxygen diminished, and the water made non-corrosive and more effective
for softening and general plant use.

Chlorine, in one form or another, is a very important adjunct to filtration for water sterilization and is usually applied after filtration. In industrial water purification, chlorine is sometimes used before filtration to
prevent fermentation in sedimentation basins, excessive growths in the
sand filter beds, and fungus and bacterial growths in the filter and filtered
water distribution lines. The quantity of chlorine used need only be just
enough to produce a slight residue at the filter plant outlet.

Bacteria. A porous filter medium that is cleaned merely by washing, scraping or scrubbing may become an incubator for bacteria, unless there is prechlorination. The bacteria enter the pores of the finest stone, or other permanent, rigid, porous filter media, and multiply there; no amount of washing, scraping or scrubbing will remove them. Filters having a paper, or a compressed cotton medium, which can be discarded, or a wire-wound filter using a precoat of filter aid, such as diatomaceous earth as a medium, which can be washed completely from the filter, have advantages from the bacterial standpoint in industrial water filtration, where post-chlorination is used.

Besides potable water, where filtration is nearly always required before industrial use, filtration is normally required by textile mills, which demand pure water, as do manufacturers of white papers. Filtration is often economical for low-grade paper, because of the increased life of felts and screens. Boiler feed water in power plants usually should be filtered to free the water from trade wastes, vegetable matter, oil, etc., as these impurities cause foaming, priming, and scaling. Filters are normally used for swimming pools to clear the water for re-circulating and thus eliminate the excessive use of water and/or heat. Laundries use large quantities of water and require a bright, clear water, free from color, turbidity and iron. Because of the large amount of soap used, softening must be used here along with filtration. In many other cases, such as private and public institutions, filtration plants are used both to clarify the water and to effect an economy in system maintenance.

Beverages. The presence of dirt, suspended matter, or any foreign material, in water for use in bottling, is highly objectionable. Clarification is usually obtained by filtering after coagulation, while objectionable taste and odor may be directly removed from clear, clean water with an activated carbon by adsorption, followed by filtration. When water is super-chlorinated to destroy objectionable micro-organisms or organic matter, it may be dechlorinated with activated carbon purifiers to make it palatable.

As beverages generally contain acid in the flavor, it is desirable to use water with low alkalinity, in order that the desirable acidity may not be lost. Alkalinity in water is usually present as calcium or magnesium carbonate, and in such cases is always associated with hardness. Lime treatment will reduce calcium or magnesium carbonate to an unobjectionable amount by precipitation and filtration. This treatment results in an improved flavor in the beverage due to lower alkalinity in the water, as well as better taste due to lower total solids. Moreover, the treated water is softened.

When a water causes spoilage or sedimentation in the finished beverage, it may be assumed that the organic matter is at fault, as a general rule. There are two ways of removing organic matter from water, one by oxidation, accomplished by a water-soluble oxidizing agent such as chlorine, and the other by coagulation and filtration. Excessive foaming, or poor carbonation, may also be due to the presence of objectionable organic matter in the water, and the same treatment can be applied as in spoilage or sedimentation.

Iron in the water for bottling is objectionable because it may contribute off-taste, or form a sediment in the beverage. It is usually possible to remove dissolved iron by aeration and filtration. Aeration precipitates the iron as ferric hydroxide, and this precipitate is removed by filtration. Iron also may be removed by superchlorination, lime treatment or by specially processed zeolites.

Coagulation. As in the case of the slow sand filter, in order to make the rapid sand filter more than a strainer, it is necessary to provide an efficient mat on the surface of the filter bed; this is accomplished by the use of a coagulant. If the water is very turbid, the coagulant must be added and sedimentation provided before the water passes to the filter, so as to remove the bulk of the suspended matter before filtration; otherwise too frequent washing will be necessary. The common coagulant is alum. Lump ammonium or potash alum is used in pressure coagulant feeders, and aluminum sulfate (sometimes termed "filter alum") when the coagulant is made up and fed as a solution.

Practically all waters are alkaline because of the presence of calcium carbonate and magnesium carbonate; this natural alkalinity decomposes the alum, with a resultant heavy white flocculent precipitate of aluminum hydrate. If the water is not naturally alkaline (or its natural alkalinity has been exhausted by continuous circulation and refiltration, as in swimming-pool filter systems) artificial alkalinity is established by adding soda ash or lime, or sal-soda if a pressure alkalinity feeder is used.

The action of the insoluble, gelatinous aluminum hydrate is to entangle the suspended matter, absorb the color, and gather the finer particles into flocs that will readily settle, or which can be caught on filter sand, if they are too large to pass through the spaces between the grains. The coagulum forms a gelatinous mat on the surface and in the upper part of the filter sand; this constitutes the real filtering medium.

During coagulation, the originally turbid or cloudy water undergoes a complete change in appearance, for in place of the murkiness the impurities become coarse-grained and flocculent, the surrounding water itself being fairly clear. Filtration is then a comparatively simple matter.

Underdrain Systems. The underdrain system for slow or rapid sand filters serves a two-fold purpose: to distribute the water uniformly during washing, and to collect the filtered water without loss of sand. The underdrain itself consists of the graded gravel layers and the distributing manifold system. Aside from supporting the sand bed, the gravel is the principal means of distributing the wash water; and many cases of faulty filter operation can be traced to improperly graded, poor quality or insuffi-

FIGURE 89. Underdrain system. (*Courtesy Infilco*)

cient filter gravel. To collect the filtered water uniformly, and more important, to supply the wash water uniformly to the underside of the gravel is the purpose of the distributing manifold.

The systems in common use are: A pipe manifold with bronze "strainers" or orifice nozzles screwed into the tops of the header pipe and laterals; a pipe manifold with the pipes perforated on the underside in either single or double rows, and distributing pipes with large perforations interspaced by slotted pre-cast concrete blocks.

A typical filter underdrain system as shown in Fig. 89 provides a primary distributing system consisting of a manifold with laterals on wide centers, the laterals having distributing orifices along their undersides, distributor nozzles on the manifold, and a secondary system consisting of pre-cast blocks between the laterals. The blocks do not change the function of the primary system, as the orifice areas in the laterals provide for the essential primary distribution. Jet action is dissipated by the concrete floor. A freeway is provided over the entire filter floor, and any slight differences in pressure are averaged. The blocks then complete the distribution of both the filtered water and the wash water and tend to assure uniform downward flow of the filtered water and upward flow of wash water throughout the filter bed. The top of the blocks and laterals form a practically flat grid upon which the gravel or other supporting material is spread, permitting its easy replacement or removal.

Many distributing systems depend upon the considerable depth of large gravel, which surrounds and covers the nozzles, acts as a sec-

FIGURE 90. Cut-away view of expansible strainer with arrows to show flow during backwash. (*Courtesy Permutit Co.*)

ondary distribution system to aid flow uniformity during backwashing. The nozzles are usually spaced on not over 6-inch centers, and must be supplemented with special nozzles at the wall of the filter shell for proper washing at this point.

Another design has a special movable top strainer which provides a small opening during filtration; but when backwashing occurs, at a much higher rate of flow than during filtration, the top or "flapper" is lifted and the openings widen. This avoids excessively high pressures, yet allows a high rate of flow.

Porous Plate Underdrain Systems. The greatest source of trouble in water filters employing loose, rigid media is in the backwashing. There must be uniformity in backwashing if there is to be efficient operation; otherwise mud balls will form, sand will be lost, and the gradation of sand and gravel or other media cannot be maintained. In many ways porous plates, such as bonded alumina grains, are adapted to this work. There can be no sand loss with them; the use of graded gravel is eliminated; and a uniform backwash is assured at all points (Fig. 91).

There are, however, two possibilities of trouble: one from bacterial growth within the plates and the other from clogging with slimy suspension which may occur at times and which cannot be completely cleaned from the plates.

Gravel Layers. The filter gravel must be small enough at the top layer, and yet be fairly large at the lowest layer around or on top of the distributing manifold to diffuse the wash water. Each grading must be of fairly uniform size, practically free from flat pieces, and must be so arranged as to prevent small pebbles from falling through the lower layers.

Present practice usually calls for as many as five and a minimum of three gradations, ranging in size from 2½ inches diameter at the bottom to ⅛ inch diameter at the top.

FIGURE 91. Porous plate underdrain. (*Courtesy Carborundum Co.*)

Filter Sand. Silica sand, which was the first material used, is still the most commonly accepted filtering medium. Crushed quartz, crushed marble, magnetite sand, charcoal, coke and screened anthracite have also been used, but usually to take care of some special conditions. Porous filter materials present difficulties in washing and are danger points for bacterial breeding.

Whereas little attention was formerly paid to the quality and uniformity of filter sand, now definite standards must be met. Sand performs its function as a filtering medium through its ability to hold back the coagulum or floc containing the suspended and colloidal impurities in the water. Theoretically, the top surface of the sand performs this duty, and it is assumed in practice that none of the coagulum penetrates beyond a depth of 6 inches into the sand. It is customary to provide a depth of sand of from 18 to 24 inches in industrial filters, and as much as 30 inches in municipal filters, this extreme depth being required by some boards of health or the individual practices of some engineers. The sand bed should not be so shallow as to be easily channelled or broken through during filtering, and yet not so deep as to offer unneeded resistance to the flow of water.

Suitability of a sand as a filtering medium depends upon its chemical character, freedom from clay, dirt, organic matter and other impurities, and its uniformity. Unless it is of uniform size the smaller grains will pack in the voids between the coarser grains, causing undue resistance to flow.

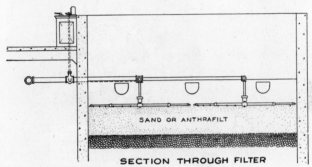

SAND OR ANTHRAFILT

SECTION THROUGH FILTER

Figure 92. Sand or anthrafilt filter medium. (*Courtesy Stuart-Brumley Corp.*)

Two measurements are used to draw a fairly accurate picture of the size and grading of filter sand: the "effective size" and the "uniformity coefficient." By "effective size" is meant the size of the sand grains— usually expressed in decimal fractions of a millimeter—than which 10 per cent by weight of the sand is finer and 90 per cent coarser. Thus the "effective size" is the minimum size of the great bulk of the sand particles, but it does not indicate either the limits of coarseness, or the degree of variation in the size of the particles included in the 90 per cent. Therefore, to assure that the variation is not too great, a second measurement of the sand is made. This is the size of sand grains than which 60 per cent by weight of the sand is finer and 40 per cent coarser. This size, divided bv the "effective size" is called the "uniformity coefficient."

For example, if a screen analysis showed than 10 per cent of a sand were finer than 0.40 millimeter, and 60 per cent were finer than 0.64 milli- meter, the "effective size" would be .40 mm and the "uniformity coeffi- cient" would be 0.64 divided by 0.40, or 1.6. Obviously, the more uniform the sand, the more nearly alike will be the sizes of grains than which 10 per cent is finer and than which 60 per cent is finer; in other words, the closer will the "uniformity coefficient" approach 1.0

The most desirable "effective size" and "uniformity coefficient" depend upon the conditions of filter operation and the quality of filtered water desired. Modern practice calls for at least two gradings of filter sand; gravity filters are usually provided with silica sand of "effective size" of from 0.35 to 0.50 mm, as conditions warrant, and a "uniformity coefficient" of not over 1.75. Pressure filters are usually provided with

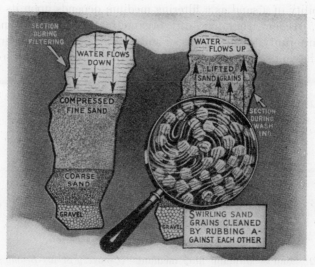

FIGURE 93. Filter bed during filtering and lifting of bed during washing. (*Courtesy Permutit Co.*)

filter sand of "effective size" of 0.50 to 0.60 and a "uniformity coefficient" not over 1.7.

When a filter is washed, the entire sand bed rises and grades itself— the finest particles on top, grading down to the coarsest at the bottom; such a sand automatically produces the size distribution that is most desired (Fig. 93).

Chemical Requirements. The filter bed must be insoluble in water. The usual specification for filter sand and gravel is that it shall not lose more than 5 per cent in weight when treated with concentrated hydrochloric acid for 24 hours. This is principally to insure the absence of limestone, which, because of its relative softness and appreciable solubility would not stand up under agitation during washing.

Types of Filters. Sand filters for the filtration of water may be classified as slow and rapid, and the latter may be open and the pressure enclosed type.

Slow Sand Filters. The practical application of filtration to entire water supplies probably dates from about 1800. Since the installation of the slow sand filter in England and Scotland in the early part of 1800, the filtration of water by slow sand filters has been known as the English system (Chapter 1).

Slow sand filters are still used to a considerable extent in Europe and in a number of localities in America. These filters consist of a number of beds of sand, usually rectangular in shape, varying in area from one-quarter to one acre. The beds are covered, if the winter temperature is lower than 32°F. The filter medium is fine filter sand superimposed on three or more layers of graded gravel, beneath which is some form of underdrain. Each bed is provided with suitable piping to control the influent and the effluent. Some waters may be sent to slow sand filters without any prior treatment, but in the great majority of cases preliminary sedimentation and sometimes both sedimentation and coagulation are used to prepare them for filtration.

With slow sand filters, large surface-filtering areas are necessary. In order to obtain the desired clarification, the rate of filtration should be low. The rate is usually maintained at about 3,000,000 gallons per acre per day, although in some plants it is but half and in others twice this figure. As the sand used is of rather small grain size and the rate of flow very low, the filter in itself acts as a strainer, taking out considerable suspended matter. However, with the slow sand filter the surface of the sand bed provides a place for great numbers of organisms to grow and develop. These form an adherent mass that holds back and collects the bacteria and organisms in the water. This mat or film is the active part of the bed, and until it has been formed the efficiency of the filter is low. To "ripen" the filter bed, the slow sand filter is started at about one-third of its normal rate and the rate is then increased gradually, so that not until three or four days later is the filter operated at its regular capacity.

Depending upon the character of the raw water, whether or not it has been given preliminary treatment, the rate of filtration, the maximum loss of head allowable, etc., the slow sand filter will deliver anywhere from 50,000,000 to 400,000,000 gallons per acre of filter area before cleaning is necessary.

The slow sand filter is cleaned by scraping and removing from the filter an inch or two of sand from the surface of the bed, the sand being washed and either placed back on the bed immediately or put in the storage bins and replaced after several scrapings and cleanings.

Slow sand filters are limited in use to handling waters of low turbidity and color and where sufficient ground area is available to provide for the large filter beds and settling basins required.

Rapid Sand Filters. The first rapid sand or "mechanical" filters were built in the United States during the early 80's. They were installed by

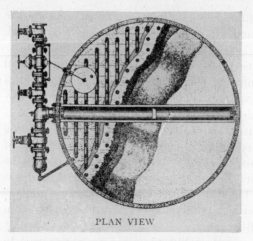

PLAN VIEW

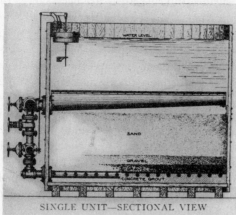

SINGLE UNIT—SECTIONAL VIEW

FIGURE 94. Gravity rapid sand filter. (*Courtesy Infilco Inc.*)

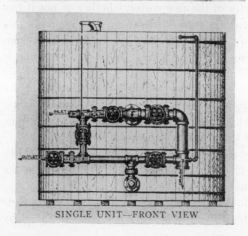

SINGLE UNIT—FRONT VIEW

the paper industry to solve the problem of handling large volumes of water and removing the coarser particles of suspended matter that were detrimental to the paper products. These early filters consisted of cylindrical tanks provided with a simple strainer underdrain system, a bed of gravel and sand, wash water troughs and operating piping. They were not capable of removing the finer or colloidal suspended matter and had but little effect on removal of bacteria. However, they served their purpose and represented a step forward in water filtration because of savings in first cost and space requirements.

Rapid sand filters differ from slow ones not only in the rate of flow of water through the sand bed, but also in design, construction, and operation. The smaller area of the filter unit, and consequently its more rapid clogging, requires means for rapid and automatic cleaning. The methods used to wash the sand quickly gave rise to the early term "mechanical filter." The high rate of filtration (125,000,000 gallons per acre per day, or even more) necessitates the use of a coarser and more uniform filter sand—as well as the formation of an "artificial mat" on top the sand bed, by chemical coagulants.

Gravity Rapid Sand Filters. Gravity rapid sand filters for municipal water works and for industrial plants generally are made in cylindrical or rectangular form. Cylindrical tanks may be made of wood, steel or concrete. Rectangular basins usually are made of concrete. Where conditions require frequent inspection of the sand bed a gravity filter as shown in views of Fig. 94 is frequently used. In the bottom of the filter, as shown in the section view (Fig. 94) and in the plan view (Fig. 94), is placed the water-collecting system, consisting of a central header with lateral pipes spaced about every 6 inches. The laterals are provided with bronze strainers (distributor nozzles) 6 inches apart. Being evenly distributed under the entire bed, the strainers assure an even draft on all parts of the filter bed, during the process of filtration, and an even distribution of wash water, when backwashing the filter.

Conditions often exist that make the use of distributor nozzles in the laterals inadvisable; in such cases the laterals are provided with perforations or orifices on the underside. The type of manifold system used depends upon the character of the water, the construction of the underdrain, and the various conditions under which the filter has to operate.

The incoming raw water is distributed over the top of the filter bed by means of one or more troughs, so that the surface of the bed is not disturbed. The water passes down through the sand and gravel, being collected underneath by the manifold pipe system, discharging from the filter, either into a clear water basin, located below the filter, or into a sump supplying the service pump.

A gravity filter made in rectangular form is illustrated in Fig. 95. The basin is made of cement. The vertical section shows the underdrain system, the filter bed and the troughs. The horizontal section shows the manifold, the laterals, how the blocks are placed between them, and the

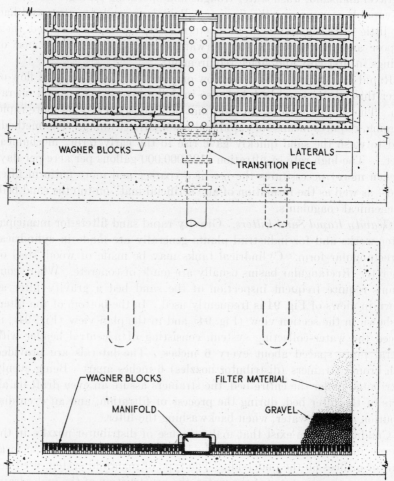

FIGURE 95. Rectangular gravity filter. (*Courtesy Infilco Inc.*)

transition pipe from the round inlet pipe to the rectangular manifold. Referring to Fig. 89, in the upper right-hand circle will be seen the bronze distributing nozzles on top of the manifold and in the upper left-hand circle the orifices in the bottom of the laterals. As stated, these nozzles and orifices are used for collecting the filtered water, and for distributing the wash water in backwashing.

Pressure Filters. The use of pressure filters is as old as the practice of rapid sand filtration. The term "pressure" is used to designate that type of rapid sand filter wherein the filter bed is placed in a closed container, through which the water passes under pressure. This does not mean that high pressure is required to pass the water through the filter. To operate

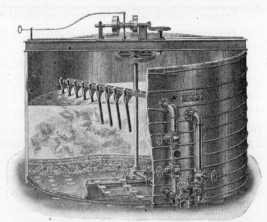

FIGURE 96. Wash rake filter for high percentages of suspended solids. (*Courtesy Hungerford & Terry*)

economically, the pressure consumed is not more than 5 pounds at its maximum, with a minimum of about one pound directly after the filter is washed.

In comparison with gravity or open-type rapid sand filters, the pressure filters have certain apparent advantages. Connection may be made in any pressure line without loss of pressure for water distribution except that consumed in the filter, as mentioned above. Repumping of the water after being filtered is not required. The filters may be quickly installed on simple foundations and usually fit into some available space. Settling basins and clear water storage can frequently be eliminated. Less precision in operation is demanded and the first cost is low.

Rates of Filtration in Rapid Sand Filters. The maximum rate of filtration depends upon the required quality of the filtered water, the character and condition of the filter sand and the character of the water to be filtered. Water can be forced through a pressure filter at very high rates if sufficient pressure is applied, but it will not be filtered—in fact, at excessive rates it will hardly be "strained," the coagulum will be driven deep into the sand, and the filter bed ultimately ruined.

For efficient operation and proper quality of effluent, the rate of filtration should be carefully controlled and rapid fluctuations avoided. Standard practice has set from 2 to 3 gallons per minute per square foot of filter area as being a conservative rating. Lower or higher rates may be required or allowable under special conditions.

The standard specifications for pressure water filters, as approved by the American Waterworks Association and the American Society of Mechanical Engineers give the following rates of filtration as standard:

"Whenever the water is to be used for domestic purposes or to secure full bacterial purification, the capacity shall be based on a rate of filtration not to exceed 2 gallons per minute per sq ft of filtering area and a coagulant must be used.

"Rates of filtration for various uses should conform to the following schedule: 2 gals per sq ft per minute for all supplies used for drinking or for the preparation of food products, 2 to 4 gals per sq ft per minute when filtering a treated municipal supply of approved bacterial purity, 2 to 4 gals per sq ft per minute for swimming pools, and for all industrial uses, 2 to 5 gals per sq ft per minute as conditions may warrant for double filtration, using sand followed by charcoal, where reduction of color, odor, taste or certain forms of iron is desired. This method of filtration is not to be applied for bacterial purification."

Washing. Provision for proper washing of the sand bed is as important as the area of the filter. The filter retains what is removed from the water and will continue to function satisfactorily only so long as it is properly washed. A filter is usually run until the maximum allowable loss of head is reached, or until the desired rate can no longer be maintained. Therefore, at regular intervals the filter is cut out of service, the waste valve opened and water—preferably filtered water—admitted to the underdrain system at a rate sufficient to expand or float the sand bed, to scrub or scour the sand and to flush out the accumulated impurities.

From 3 to 8 minutes' washing is required to clean the sand bed, 6 minutes being the average figure. From 1 to 5 per cent of the total water filtered is the customary amount of wash water used, with 3 per cent the average.

The rate of flow of wash water required for efficient cleaning depends upon the size of sand, the system of washing, and the efficiency of the wash water distributing system. The simplest method of filter washing is the "high velocity" wash where the velocity of the water alone thoroughly scours and cleans the sand.

High-velocity wash needs careful gravel grading to prevent disturbance of the gravel layers and to provide uniform distribution of wash water. The rate of flow of wash water required is usually 15 gallons per minute per sq ft of filter area (24 inches vertical rise per minute), although under certain conditions flow rates as low as 12 gallons per minute (19 inches vertical rise) have been found satisfactory.

Where insufficient water is available for high velocity wash, steam, air, or mechanical agitation may be used to loosen the filter bed. With such preliminary agitation effective washing requires water at a velocity of 12 to 15 inches vertical rise per minute (8 to 10 gals per sq ft). Mechanical agitators are sometimes used, particularly for top cleaning, and where heavy media such as magnetite sand are encountered.

The proper rate of flow of wash water is most important; washing at low rates of flow for even long periods of time usually wastes water and does not clean the filter effectively.

FIGURE 97. Flow comparison, filtering and washing. (*Courtesy Infilco Inc.*)

Backwash. Efficient and successful washing of a filter bed normally requires:

(1) Uniform and adequate expansion of the filter bed.

(2) Sustained suspension of the grains of filter material while the bed is expanded.

(3) Agitation of the grains while they are in suspension.

The rate of wash water application necessary for these requirements is a function of the temperature of the wash water, its specific gravity, and the shape and size of the grains of the filtering medium. While the degree of expansion for a perfect wash is irrespective of the type of underdrain used, the uniform application of whatever quantity of wash water is re-

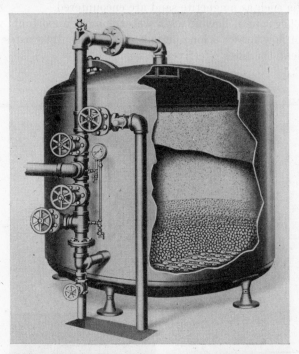

FIGURE 98. Verticle pressure sand filter. (*Courtesy Infilco Inc.*)

quired for proper expansion is of utmost importance, for without uniform wash-water distribution proper backwash cannot be obtained.

Freeboard. To prevent sand from being washed out with the impurities during backwashing, the waste outlet, trough or pipe should be a definite distance above the surface of the sand bed. This distance is designated as the "freeboard" and depends upon the depth and size of sand (which determines the bed expansion) and the rate of washing. The general rule is that the freeboard in inches approximates the wash rate in inches of vertical rise per minute. Fig. 97 shows the desirability of the proper freeboard, as sand will be lost during washing if it is not high enough, and the impurities will not wash out if it is too high.

Pressure Sand Filters. A pressure sand filter for the filtration of water is a closed cylindrical steel shell of either vertical or horizontal construction, containing a bed of granular filter medium. This medium consists of graded gravel, with fine filter sand on top, placed carefully upon a built-in collector and distributing water system. The unfiltered water enters at the top of the shell, percolates downward through the filter bed and is drawn off through the collector system at the bottom of the filter. As stated, under gravity filters the collector system is also used to distribute the wash water during backwashing.

Pressure sand filters can be built in any convenient size. Usually, for required areas up to 80 sq ft, they are built in the vertical type, and for greater areas in the horizontal type. In determining pressure filter sizes, the rate of filtration and volume of water to be filtered decides the total filter area of the plant. The available water for backwashing purposes decides the maximum size of the individual unit. If the filter is backwashed with unfiltered water, the filtered water should be drained to waste for a few minutes directly after backwashing, but if filtered water is used for backwashing this filtering to waste is not necessary.

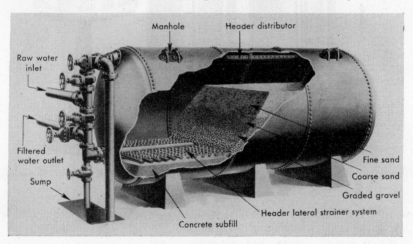

FIGURE 99. Horizontal pressure filter—multiple valve control. (*Courtesy Permutit Co.*)

A sectional view of a horizontal pressure filter showing the distributing manifold system, gravel beds, filter sand bed, necessary piping, and valves, is shown in Fig. 99. A smaller type of filter is generally employed in large hotels, office buildings and institutions. It is also used for filtering the water supply of industrial plants and in small municipalities. It is built of steel, suitable for any working pressure up to 67 pounds per square inch. A sight glass on the wash outlet shows the condition of the wash water and re-wash after backwashing with unfiltered water, so that the operator can see when the filter is clean (Fig. 100).

A battery of three or more of these units is installed where it is desired to wash with filtered water. The connections can be arranged so that any-

FIGURE 100. Verticle pressure sand filter with final horizontal disc filter. (*Courtesy Infilco*)

one of the filters may be washed with filtered water from either one or both of the other filters.

Small Office and Household Filters. There is a great variety of small office, household and laboratory water filters. The majority of these attachments consist of a rigid filter medium in rigid contact, in thimble or cylinder design for direct faucet attachment. Other designs consist of paper sheets or fiber, packed or supported by perforated rigid backings. Sometimes fabric media are used, as described in Chapters 7 and 11.

While such filters are widely used and are of importance in their particular fields, they are not generally considered under the heading of water filtration. This does not refer to apartment house or home water-softening installations, as these are actually small commercial plants.

Chapter 13

Sewage Clarification and Sewage Sludge Dewatering

General. Sewage filtration is a clarifying problem, while sludge handling is a dewatering of solids. As large volumes of water containing small percentages of solids must be handled at low costs in sewage clarification and as the solids to a considerable extent are of a colloidal nature, direct mechanical filtration is difficult. The removal of the larger par-

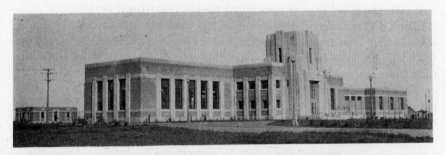

FIGURE 101. Mechanized sewage disposal plant, Winnepeg, Manitoba. (*Courtesy Director Sanitary Eng. Dept. Health, Toronto*)

ticles in sewage by grit-chamber settling (by decreasing velocities) and coarse bar screens, often followed by finer bar screens or perforated plate discs or cylinders, is a relatively simple operation.

Bar Screens. Both coarse and fine bar screens or racks consist of a number of flat parallel bars set on edge at an angle (30 to 60°) in the direction of flow, and on close enough centers to hold back the coarser particles. This may be from ¾ to 2½ inch centers, on the coarse screens, to ⅟₃₂-inch on the fine screens. The screens are simply interposed in the sewage stream and as the solids are screened out the bars are manually or mechanically combed to remove the accumulations at estimated or definite intervals. The open area at the vertical projection of the open spaces across the discharge flow normally should be twice the area at the discharging sewer. In some states, the area required for fine screens is 2 sq ft per million gallons daily, for separate sewage and drainage systems, and 3 sq ft for combined systems.

Coarse bar screens generally remove the relatively large solids, over ⅟₁₆ inch in the narrowest dimension, such as pieces of wood, cans, bundles

221

of rags and other debris. Fine bar screens collect the smaller items of sticks, rags, and such industrial wastes as hat fur or wool fiber. The fine bar screens reduce scum accumulation in digestion tanks and all removals aid subsequent operations.

The coarse screenings are usually easily drained off and buried or burned. The solids which can be squeezed may be dewatered by wringers, by perforated belts and rollers, or by centrifuges. In the first case, a rubber conveyor belt carries the screenings between rubber-covered rolls, which squeeze out the water, as in a clothes wringer. The water runs off the sides and the solids remain on the belt. In the second case, a dewatering machine is used of the same sectionalized, perforated, hinged belt construction as used in paper mills. The belt passes between upper and lower rollers which reduce the moisture content of the solids to about 65 per cent. In the third case, a perforated basket centrifugal is used.

Disc or Cylindrical Plates. For the removal of some of the finer solids, which pass the bar screens, flat slotted metal discs with slots $\frac{1}{32}$ to $\frac{1}{16}$ x 2 inches long are sometimes used. These discs are set at an angle, so that they are half submerged in the sewage stream. A central collar carries the disc or plate and the revolving mechanism, as well as supporting the cleaning brushes. In operation, the disc slowly revolves through the sewage stream, catching such solids as will not pass the slots, and carrying them into the air to be removed by brushes. These brushes turn against the disc, and roll the solids up and off, for bucket or other collection.

The cylinder types, wing types or shovel types are of the same general design as the disc in that they are inserted in the sewage stream, carry the solids into the air as they revolve, and the solids are brushed off for discharge.

A number of installations of fine screens have been made, and it has proved to be of considerable advantage in later treatment to have the medium-sized solids removed. This is particularly true of such solids as rags and sticks, which clog valves, pipe lines and revolving distributor arms. However, considerable replacement expense for brushes is required with turning screens; as an alternate, there are types of knife screens that cut coarse sewage matter into small pieces.

Settling usually follows screening, with or without activation or coagulation, for further solids removal before actual sludge dewatering. This leaves only the finer, lighter particles to be handled, where secondary treatment for high suspended solids removal is necessary.

Sand Filters. Sand filters of the intermittent slow sand type, have long been used for final effluent polishing. A high degree of clarity can be obtained while the beds are clean; but cleaning and replacements are a burden, large areas are required, as capacities are low (100,000 gallons per day per acre), and winter weather may be troublesome.

The sand bed is composed of washed uniform sand placed over a drainage system. For a high degree of clarity, an effective size of 0.3 to 0.5 mm is usually taken. Coarse sand will give a higher rate of flow, but at the sacrifice of clarity, while a finer size may retard the flow to the point of clogging. In operation, the sewage, whether raw, activated, contact bed, trickling filter, or otherwise, is fed over the bed to a depth of several inches and allowed to percolate through by gravity. After an application or dosing, a considerable time lapse is allowed, from hours to days, to provide for aerobic bacterial activity. This is because the clarification is due both to physical straining and to bacterial decomposition. The bacteria are active near the top of the sand, where the first and bulk of the organic solids are strained out; here they form a gelatin-like film around the sand grains.

Some recommend applying sewage at the rate of 1 gallon per second for each 5000 square feet. This takes 21 minutes to reach a 3-inch depth and over an acre 27,150 gallons are held in the 3-inch penetration.

Numerous attempts have been made to devise mechanical filters (not sprinkling filters or biological filters) for this fine solids removal. Two general designs, which have been installed in several plants, are sand filters, modified for automatic cleaning. One of these takes advantage of the magnetic qualities of magnetite sand to employ an electromagnet for sand cleaning.

Hydraulic Sand Filters. The other type of automatically cleaned sand filter is hydraulically operated. Some filters are circular, others rectangular, with up- or down-flow filtration. Operation is more or less similar in both types, except that fine jets of water are used to raise silica sand for water-wash cleaning in the hydraulic type, whereas an electromagnet raises the magnetite sand. In either case the wash water is segregated for separate removal. The cleaning units are mounted upon movable carriages covering a small strip of sand at a time. These cleaning carriages are automatically thrown into operation, as the solids filtered out begin to clog the sand bed, and thus increase the head. Washing continues until the cleaning of the sand causes a drop in head, which automatically stops the cleaners.

In one design (Fig. 102) the sand is confined in a series of cells, each of which, on the width of the tank, is connected with a corresponding outlet port for individual washing, using about 25 gpm per square foot of sand. Filtration is downward; and it is claimed that as the separation of solids from liquids takes place principally in the top half inch of sand, top cleaning by back washing through small screen caps is very effective.

Drum Filters. One or two drum filter installations have been made for sewage clarification, wherein paper pulp was used as a precoat, but clarity in handling fine suspensions was not very satisfactory. At Rockville Center and at Great Neck, Long Island, such drum filters are used

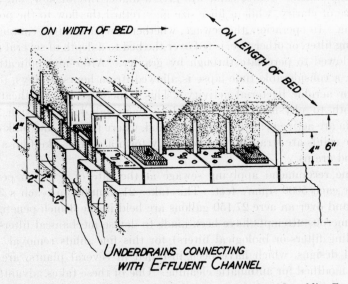

FIGURE 102. Filter bed of hydraulic sand filter. (*Courtesy Laughlin Equipment Corp.*)

for the clarifying of activated effluent, which contains some floc that is rather easy to strain out.

Sludge Handling. In the settling of sewage for safe discharge into streams and bodies of water, a volume of sludge is created which must be disposed of. The sludge may be barged to sea (New York), lagooned (Bridgeport, Conn.), dewatered and the solids incinerated (Chicago), used as fill or buried (Perth Amboy), or used as fertilizer (Milwaukee). Occasionally liquid sludge is used as a direct fertilizer (Battle Creek, Michigan).

The dewatering of sewage sludges depends upon the way the varying factors in the solids make up its concentration, etc., and these factors should be taken into account in considering such dewatering.

Physical Properties. According to A. L. Genter,[1] "Sewage sludges are characterized by their high moisture content, which is dependent on the amount of organic matter present in the sludge solids. The moisture content ranges from about 80 per cent, in some digested sludges, to about 99 per cent in some activated sludges. Normally, sewage contains solids of low mineral and high organic content. The organic matter present is usually measured in terms of volatile matter, *i.e.*, all the solid combustible matter left in a sludge after removal of the water moisture by evaporation.

In America, the solids in fresh domestic sewage sludge average about 72 per cent organic and 28 per cent mineral matter. Sludge collected from combined sewage, namely, diluted by storm drainage, contains more mineral and less volatile matter than the foregoing average indicates. For example, the solids collected in the primary sedimentation of domestic sewage at Baltimore, Md., average about 80 per cent volatile and 20 per cent mineral matter, whereas those collected in the primary sludge from the combined sewage at Minneapolis-St. Paul, Minn., contain approximately 69 per cent volatile and 31 per cent mineral matter.

The net effect of natural mineral matter in any sludge solid is to increase its specific gravity, stable structure and percentage of solids concentrated in the sludge and filter cake. The net effect of organic matter is just the opposite. The specific gravity of the mineral portion varies from 2.5 to 2.65. Therefore, any increase in the organic fraction present in a sludge is practically equivalent to a corresponding increase in sludge moisture. Conversely, decreasing the organic or volatile fraction of the sludge solid increases the mineral fraction and the specific gravity of the solids and sludge. Aside from the fact that this decreases the mathematical equivalent of water present in the sludge, the water-imbibing properties of the sludge solid are also decreased. These properties are largely a function of the organic matter present, and therefore account for the high compressibility or plastic nature of sewage sludges. This is because the organic structure of sewage solids, even with some chemically bound mineral matter, is largely capillary porous or gelatinous. Such solids swell and become plastic by imbibing water. In other words, compressibility in sewage sludges and their filter cakes correlates closely and varies directly with the volatile content of the sludge.

The effects of compressibility during the pressure filtration of such sludges are twofold: namely, solid compacting action in the filter cake, which increases with increasing moisture content, and the contraction of the void spaces between the elastic solid aggregates into narrowed filtrate flow channels. Obviously, the bulkier or more voluminous the sludge is per gram or milliliter of actual sludge solids, the more plastic they will be under compression."

Sludge Coagulation. Sewage sludge cannot be filtered directly by vacuum filtration, but must first be chemically conditioned to coagulate the organic solids and thereby materially reduce their compressibility. This is done by using such coagulating agents as ferric and aluminum chlorides or sulfates. Except in elutriated or activated sludge, lime is used in conjunction with ferric salts to raise the pH and to diminish the amount required of these more costly salts.

"As such coagulants are added in aqueous solution to sludges containing from 80 to 90 per cent sludge moisture, depending on the sludge processing and mineral content of the sludge solids, unavoidable chemical solution reactions take place between the coagulant ions and the biochemical and other natural reagents present in the sludge moisture. These reactions become progressively more pronounced and detrimental to filtration economy, with increasing time allowed for the bacterial decomposition of the organic fraction of the sludge solids, to the point of complete digestion."[1]

Biochemical and Chemical Properties of Sewage Sludges. The bacterial decomposition of sewage sludge, either by storage of freshly collected raw sludge or by purposely controlled sludge digestion, is a mineralization process. The bacterial action destroys the organic fraction of the sludge, thereby increasing the mineral fraction of the remaining solids. This mineralization even takes place during the storage period required to thicken raw sludge prior to vacuum filtration.

However, partial decomposition produces a sludge which is extremely difficult to condition and is almost unfiltrable. It may be said that the fresher, or the more completely digested a sludge is, the more easily it is conditioned and the more readily it filters. The difficult sludges to filter are the stale or partially digested ones, which are highly compressible even after conditioning. Fresh raw, or chemically precipitated sludges floc readily, filter most easily and yield high capacities and low moisture cakes.

Digestion of sludge bacterially decomposes the organic matter in the solids, usually reducing the volatiles 50 to 70 per cent and thereby producing a sludge of high mineral content and low compressibility. Such a sludge is readily thickened.

"The biolytic agents employed to destroy the chief cause of compressibility, *i.e.*, the volatile fraction of the solids, automatically use the large moisture fraction of the sludge as a solute concentration medium for a lot of their biochemical waste products, chief among which is ammonium bicarbonate. The large moisture fraction to be drained from the solids thereby becomes the chief economic enemy. Most of these inimical biochemical reagents result from the decomposition of proteins into their structural linkages, the amino acids, and finally into simpler compounds like ammonia, carbon dioxide, fatty acids, methane, etc. Urea and proteins are the chief source of these agents. Naturally, the decomposing protein matter concentrates to a greater degree in the sludge than in the supernatant sewage."

Generally the desired effects of sludge mineralization are somewhat offset by the contrary chemical influence of these waste products on the added coagulant and resulting filter rates.

In some sludges fatty acids also form gelatinous and smeary precipitates with the solutions of such coagulants. All these precipitates are, therefore, difficult to dewater by filtration when associated with coagulated sludge solids in excessive amounts. This excess, measured in percentage of sludge solids present, depends on the total bicarbonates and other precipitate-forming compounds present in the sludge and sludge moisture. Although sludge digestion materially decreases the compressibility of the sludge solids, it greatly increases the concentration of bicarbonate alkalinity in the sludge moisture. As a result, the compressibility of the hydroxide precipitate formed in eliminating this alkalinity with ferric and aluminum coagulants often counteracts the gain in sludge solid stability through sludge digestion. Consequently, some digested sludges require considerably more coagulant doses for easy draining than do relatively fresh raw sludges.

Although the alkalinity of waste-activated sludges may be relatively low by analysis, the high moisture content associated with the high volatile content of such sludges can mean a higher percentage of alkalinity on sludge solids than one encounters in most fresh raw sludges. These related factors easily result in a relatively high coagulant dose for rapid filtration. The digestion of waste-activated sludge and other sludges containing a high percentage of volatile matter, like those containing ground garbage, results in a sludge having a higher coagulant demand than that of any other type of sewage sludge.

In addition, to the unavoidable solution reactions in the natural sludge moisture as indicated in the foregoing, enough coagulant must be added to act directly as a curdling agent for the gelatinous structure of the sludge solids. This is the direct action primarily intended. However, in using ferric coagulants another reaction is involved. As ferric salt solutions contain the oxidizing ferric ions, part of the ferric chloride or sulfate is used for the oxidization of some organic and perhaps some inorganic matter present in the sludge moisture and solids. In some investigations of digested sludges dosed with ferric chloride, almost half of the iron present in the filtrate has been found in the ferrous state, indicating that a considerable portion of the coagulant solutions added to these sludges serves purposes other than that primarily intended.

Sludge Elutriation. Investigation of sludges relatively free of such sludge moisture reactions led to the development of the sludge elutriation process. The studies revealed the fact that progressively mineralized sludge solids, surrounded by relatively pure water, showed progressively increasing filter rates and yields at low coagulant additions.

In its simplest form elutriation involves (1) dilution of the sludge with comparatively pure water; (2) rapid mixing of this water and sludge to form a weaker solution of the natural sludge moisture; (3) sedimentation of the sludge solids in the diluted mixture to a new sludge; as the solids

Types of Sludge

Basic Analyses	1 Primary Raw	2 Primary Raw Thickened	3 Digested Primary	4 Same Elutriated	5 Waste Activated, Thickened	6 Digested Primary and Activated
1. Alkalinity (ppm)	260	300	3000	160	140	3500
2. Water (%)	92.26	90.88	91.1	88.0	98.0	96.5
3. Solids (%)	7.74	9.12	8.9	12.0	2.0	3.5
4. Volatile (Solids) (%)	64.8	63.6	42.6	39.2	80.0	60.0
5. Mineral (Solids) (%)	35.2	36.4	57.4	60.8	20.0	40.0
6. H_2O/lb Solids (lbs)	11.92	9.965	10.24	7.33	49.0	25.57
7. Alkalinity per lb Solids (lb)	0.0031	0.003	0.0307	0.00117	0.0069	0.0965
8. H_2O/lb Volatile (lbs)	18.394	15.67	24.0	18.71	61.25	45.95
9. H_2O/lb Mineral (lbs)	33.863	27.37	17.83	12.06	245.0	68.93
10. Vol/lb Mineral (lbs)	1.841	1.747	0.742	0.645	4.0	1.5
11. Alkalinity on Solids (%)	0.31	0.3	3.07	0.117	0.7	9.65
12. $FeCl_3$ for Alkalinity (%)	0.33	0.32	3.32	0.126	0.76	10.42
13. $FeCl_3$ for Coag. and Oxidation (%)	2.95	2.80	1.19	1.032	6.40	2.40
14. Total % $FeCl_3$ Calculated	3.28	3.12	4.51	1.16	7.16	12.82
15. Total % $FeCl_3$ used in Practice		3.0	5.0	1.1	7.5	13.0
16. Filter Yield (lbs/sq ft/hourly)		4.0	5.0	9.0	2.5	2.5

settle in the wash water they are washed; (4) removal of the supernatant weaker solution by decantation.

Elutriation may be continuous or in batch lots, countercurrent or direct, its effectiveness varying somewhat with the grade of elutriating water used. The best results are obtained by using river, lake or ground water of low alkalinity. In some cases final plant effluent is the only water available, but even with this, when used on digested sludge, material savings in coagulant may result.

The amount of elutriate returned to the primary sedimentation of the treatment plant is but a small part of the total sewage flow into the plant, *i.e.*, about 0.5 per cent in some instances, and rarely as much as 2 per cent. Consequently there is no closed circuit accumulation of impurities.

Due to elutriation and extra sludge thickening in the elutriation sedimentation system, the alkalinity percentage on solids is reduced in some cases over 96 per cent, and by using only about one-fifth the coagulant dose the filter yield is almost doubled. (Ferric chloride only is used as a coagulant, no lime being required, as shown in the table on page 228.

General. In designing a sewage plant the question often arises as to whether the sludge should be filtered in the raw or activated state, or whether it should be digested before filtration. There are a number of points in favor of digestion, particularly in small installations of less than 1,000,000 gallons per day: (1) sludge storage space is available during shutdowns and whenever desired; (2) there are sludge uniformity, reduced volume and odor, and safer sludge, particularly when the ultimate disposal is as a fertilizer (except activated sludge, which is converted into a safe material); (3) the digestion of sewage sludge seems to reduce the clogging tendencies of filter cloths due to greases and oils, even though they are not all decomposed by the digestion.

On the other hand, digesters occupy a good deal of room and are quite an item of expense to install; moreover, while gas is produced which may be utilized, digesters require considerable control and attention, especially with activated sludge. If raw sludge is fresh, it filters readily with small quantities of conditioning chemicals and can be directly incinerated—a great advantage for quick disposal with minimum space requirements. However, raw sludge often is not fresh, especially in summer, and incineration may not be economical for plants of 5 to 10 million gallons daily.

In general, when stale sludge is encountered, when sludge storage space is a great advantage, when large capacities are encountered (20 million gallons daily, or over) or when the filter cake is to be utilized as a fertilizer (except activated), digestion should be given careful consideration.

Sludge Filtering. Sewage sludge is dewatered in order to facilitate its handling. In view of the high moisture content of such sludge, a reduction to the point where the solids are spadable means a very large reduction in the volume to be ultimately disposed of, as the filtrate can be discharged to the incoming sewage or into the effluent. For the dewatering of the sludge, sand beds were used almost exclusively for many years and they still find wide application in small plants and in sandy, dry localities.

Sludge Beds. Sludge-filtering beds consist of drainage sections commonly laid out from 15 to 25 feet wide by 50 to 150 feet long with partition walls of wood, galvanized steel and concrete separating one bed from the next. These walls should be low enough to allow free air circulation over the beds.

At the bottom of the beds are drainage channels for removing the separated water. The bottom of the bed is covered with a layer of gravel about 8 inches deep, over which is usually placed 12 inches of clean graded sand which should be finished level (or slightly graded for sludge flow) and smooth (Fig. 103). In some sandy areas underdrainage may be dis-

FIGURE 103. Open sludge drying bed with dried sludge removal car. (*Courtesy LeRoy Van Kleeck*)

pensed with. The sludge from Imhoff tanks and separate digestion will dry readily in such beds, but activated and chemical sludges dry very slowly, unless conditioned with such chemicals as alum or ferric chloride.

In operation, the sludge is brought to the bed or beds (which should be wet) by pumps or gravity, entering either at the corners or the center of the bed and covering the bed to a depth of from 6 to 12 inches. The thinner the layer the quicker the sludge dries, but the smaller the quantity dewatered and the more often the bed has to be cleaned; therefore a balance for the particular sludge has to be selected.

The drying time is likewise affected by the percentage of solids in the sludge. For example, a 7 per cent sludge may dry in 10 days, while a 10 per cent sludge at the same plant may take 26 days to dry.

Not only do sludge-drying beds allow free gravity dewatering but, because of the time the sludge remains upon the bed with the large surface exposure, there is considerable loss of moisture by evaporation. One of the greatest uncertainties about the time of open sludge-bed drying is the weather. There is the danger of actual addition of water from rainfall and the retardation of evaporation from high relative humidity, as well as of winter freezing.

Glass Housing. For this reason many sludge beds are covered with a glass housing, like a greenhouse (Fig. 104). This protects the beds from rainfall, allows artificial heat to be used (often from sludge gas), takes advantage of sunlight for heat direction and retention, and allows natural or forced circulation of air over the beds to prevent high humidity zones.

FIGURE 104. Air dried sludge on bed in greenhouse. (*Courtesy LeRoy Van Kleeck*)

In sections where the air is dry and there is little rainfall, such a high rate of evaporation is obtained that after 24 to 36 hours the open beds may be dry enough to permit removal of the sludge by fork or spade, which greatly reduces the area and expense of filtering the beds. The average area of open beds is from 1 to 5 sq ft per capita; this is reduced to from ½ to 3 sq ft per capita by the use of greenhouses. Where no underdrainage is used, the area per capita is usually doubled.

In dry sandy areas, open sludge beds are common, unless there is winter freezing. Where such conditions exist, the open beds may not be used during the winter, the sludge being held in the Imhoff tanks or digesters until spring. On the other hand, some sludge beds are used in winter and the frozen cake removed with picks, often with less loss of sand than in summer.

Normally, glass covering of the beds reduces the drying time by about one-half, although this is not always true. Cases are on record where open beds dry faster than closed ones, because of greater evaporation. A further reduction in drying time can be made by the use of coagulants.

Dried sludge is removed from the beds by spade or fork, except in a few large installations, where crawler type tractors or horse-drawn scrapers are used. The sludge may be forked or shoveled directly into wheelbarrows in the smaller installations or into overhead carrier buckets or industrial cars.

The cost of operating a sludge bed depends a good deal upon the labor rates in the locality. Sand must be replaced to the amount of about one inch in depth per year and greenhouses must be kept in repair and painted.

FIGURE 105. Sewage sludge drum vacuum filter. (*Courtesy Conkey Filter Co.*)

While sand is the common filter medium used on sludge beds, anthracite crushed to 0.37 mm, slag, and sand top-dressed with ashes, have been used at various times with some local success; but such media have not been generally accepted.

Because of the relatively large areas required, the labor necessary, the sand replacements, weather dependence, etc., mechanical filters are rapidly replacing sand beds, except in the small installations or in sandy areas of dry localities.

Filter Presses. Filter presses of the plate-and-frame type occupy much less room than sand beds, and in many cases are considered more desirable. The filter press is used extensively in Europe and there is at least one large filter-press installation in the United States at Providence, R. I. However, these presses require sludge conditioning, a great deal of labor and have considerable filter-medium expense, to the extent that they cannot compete with continuous drum vacuum filters, now that sludge conditioning with such filters has been made feasible and economical.

Continuous Vacuum Drum Filters. While continuous drum vacuum filters have been used from time to time for many years in various sewage and sludge dewaterings the first successful large installations were in activated sludge plants. Their success here caused them to be tried on other sludges. Equal success was achieved, so that now they are in use with all types of filtrable sludges—Imhoff, digested, raw, elutriated, chemical and special process.

FIGURE 106. Sewage sludge drum vacuum filter with ventilator hood. (*Courtesy Conkey Filter Co.*)

The filter used is the standard multiple-compartment drum vacuum filter of the low container type with 25 to 30 per cent drum submergence, since the cake is readily formed and a long drying arc is desirable. The filter valves have two vacuum outlets, one for cake formation and the other for drying; these are connected to a common vacuum line beyond the flexible and individual valve connections and are of use primarily in the starting operations (Fig. 105). The filters are equipped with filter cloth washers of the jet or spray type located on the side opposite the scraper.

Vari-speed drives are used for turning the filter drum, with ranges usually of 1:6 or 2:12 minutes per revolution. This range takes care of varying filter rates due to sludge inconsistencies, shutdowns, cloth cleaning, rewinding, etc. Rocker-type agitators are used in the filter vats with overlapping coverage (approximately 15 oscillations per minute) and often with surface-breaking fingers or ends to prevent sludge stratification. Care must be taken, on the other hand, to prevent breaking of unstable flocs; at times no agitation is used with elutriated, digested sludges, the agitation from incoming sludge being sufficient to maintain uniformity. To remove odors the filter drums may be hooded and equipped with exhaust air connections (Fig. 106).

The materials of construction of sewage sludge drum filters vary with the sludge to be handled, being dependent to a large extent on the pH. The following table gives the construction materials normally used with the particular sludges indicated:

General Materials of Construction of Sewage Sludge Filters

Sludge	Vat	Drum Deck	Drum Piping	Drum Heads	Backing Screen	Filter Cloth	Wire Winding
Activated	Lead or rubber-protected steel	Wood	Monel, copper or rubber-lined steel	Rubber-covered steel or painted cast iron	Monel bronze or	Wool	Monel
Chemical	Steel	Wood or steel	Wrought iron	Steel or cast iron	Steel	Cotton	Steel
Digested	Steel	Wood or steel	Wrought iron	Steel or cast iron	Bronze or Monel	Cotton synthetic	Stainless or Monel
Elutriated Digested	Lead or rubber-protected steel	Wood	Monel, copper or rubber-lined steel	Rubber-covered steel or painted cast iron	Monel	Wool	Monel or Stainless
Primary	Steel	Wood or steel	Wrought iron	Steel or cast iron	Steel or Monel	Cotton	Monel, steel or Stainless

Auxiliaries. The auxiliaries for the sewage sludge drum vacuum filter are those customarily required for any multiple-compartment drum vacuum filters, *i.e.*, vacuum pump, wet or dry, vacuum receiver, filtrate pump, moisture trap, and blower, plus the sewage sludge-conditioning requirements of feeders and conditioning tanks (Chapter 16).

Where sludges are thin, concentration tanks are used for sludge thickening. These are actually settling tanks, cone-bottomed for sludge removal and equipped with an overflow for removal of supernatant liquor. The presence of agitators is an advantage in discharging these tanks, to prevent water breakthrough and to insure uniform sludge removal.

Sludge thickening by centrifugal machines has been tried; but, while thickening can be readily accomplished, the tendency is to break the solids into such a fine state of subdivision that conditioning and filtering are extremely difficult. The effluent from the centrifuge is cloudy and the suspended solids therein are so finely divided they will not settle; this constitutes a serious problem, which is cumulative.

After cake discharge it is often desirable to convey the cake to a storage bin for later truck or car removal. By using a hopper bottom with a slide gate located at sufficient elevation, the gate can be opened to drop the cake directly to the truck or car. The cake can be fed to the top of the bin from the filter by an inclined, or combined horizontal and inclined conveyor.

Sewage Sludge Conditioning. As has been stated, sewage sludge must be chemically conditioned before it is filtrable. This may be either by one conditioning agent, as ferric chloride in activated or elutriated digested sludge, or by two agents, such as lime and ferric chloride in raw or non-elutriated digested sludge. In any case it means that feeders and conditioning tanks become a part of the filter installation.

Feeders. Chemicals are seldom fed to the sludge in the dry state, as in this condition an intimate mix is difficult. Dry feeders, when used, most frequently act at metering devices, the discharge of which is mixed with water before going to the sludge.

Where lime is required, it is handled either as a hydrate, in which case a metering dry feeder is used; as an oxide with a slaker and wet or metering dry feeder; or as spent lime sludge through a wet feeder. For hydrated lime, or alum, two types of metering dry feeders are commonly used, the positive-displacement type and the vibrating type.

Ferric chloride, or chlorinated copperas, is handled as a solution, fed to the conditioning tank by a positive-displacement pump type of feeder, or by a feeder of gravimetric design. This holds true whether the coagulant is received in the liquid, the anhydrous, or the crystal form. In the last two cases it is dissolved in water before use.

Chemical feeders are often connected one with another as well as with the sludge feed to the conditioning tank, all being operated by the filter float control. This arrangement conserves coagulants and prevents over-conditioning, as the feeders operate only when unconditioned sludge is called for. However, to have sufficient flexibility in operation for varying the coagulant dosage, there should be a hand-off automatic switch for each feeder, pump, or elevator, for optional manual control and operation.

With all conditioning, dilute solutions are easier to mix with sludges than are concentrated ones because of their lower viscosities; likewise, the heavier sludges are more difficult to condition. Consequently, higher agitator speeds and more agitator arms are necessary to prevent stratifying and to obtain an intimate mixing for complete coagulation in thick sludges. Yet from a filtration standpoint these thick sludges are most desirable as long as they can be properly handled.

The conditioning requirements of any particular type of sludge vary considerably, depending on the constituents of the sludge that is, the industrial wastes present, their concentration, pH, age, etc. Digested sludges, especially those that are elutriated, are uniform; but raw sludges are quite certain to be most variable. The following table gives some average figures on the requirements of conditioning agents for various types of sludges.

Average Results Which May Be Anticipated in Sewage Sludge Filtration

Type of Sludge	Conditioning Agents Per cent of Dry Solids in Sludge FeCl₃	CaO	Dry Solids per sq ft per hr (lbs)	Solids Content of Sludge (%)	Moisture Content of Filter Cake (%)
Activated	4-6	—	½-1½	¾-1½	79-83
Activated & Primary	4-5	—	1½-3	1½-3	74-78
Chemical	0-1	3-7	6-8	9-14	58-65
Digested Activated	3-5	8-15	2-5	4-10	70-75
Digested Primary	3-4	5-10	5-13	5-10	58-70
Elutriated Digested	1-3½	—	5-15	5-10	63-70
Guggenheim	2-3½	7-10	2-3½	7-10	72-76
Primary	1½-4	7-12	3-8	6-14	58-70

Of the two most common conditioning agents, ferric chloride and lime, it should be noted that the percentages of lime are measured as CaO and the percentages of ferric chloride as $FeCl_3$, on the dry solids, per square foot per hour basis, as the customary method of calculation. This means that the percentage of CaO in each lot of lime used and the percentage of ferric chloride in each lot of ferric chloride used must be accurately known and interpreted for intelligent conditioning.

The time required for coagulation, after the chemical dosing, differs widely with the type of sludge. Digested sludge is coagulated quickly, often within a minute or two, and thereafter the filtrability of the sludge decreases. Raw sludges, on the other hand, require 7 to 15 or more minutes for the maximum filtering point to be reached. In order to accomplish this, time-control baffles and overflow weirs are used, so adjusted to the requirements as to give the necessary retention period.

Proper mixing of the conditioning agents with the sludge is of great importance, and for this positive mechanical arms or paddles seem to give the best results. Air has too great a tendency to channel, short circuit or by-pass, leaving unconditioned zones. The speed of agitation is also important: too slow mixing is inadequate, particularly with heavy sludges, while too rapid mixing will break the floc formed, especially in elutriated, digested sludges.

Operation. In sewage sludge drum vacuum filter operation the unconditioned sludge is sent directly from an intermediate sludge storage or feed tank to the sludge conditioning tank. This transfer may be accomplished by gravity, by pumping, or by a bucket elevator. In any case, after conditioning, the sludge is usually fed by gravity, to avoid breaking of floc, to the filter vat for dewatering by the filter drum. A float control in the filter vat or intake line regulates the feed to the conditioning tank for weir overflow to the filter, feeding either by a pump or by a bucket elevator. Where gravity feed is used (to the conditioning tank, not the filter vat), valves must be manipulated. Such operation is usually confined to batch lots.

Inasmuch as the feed to the conditioning tanks is intermittent, the pump, or elevator, is subjected to continual starting and stopping, and care must be taken to prevent clogging during the down periods. Rags and sticks are the greatest sources of trouble, particularly with pumps, which are usually of the diaphram type. With the bucket elevator a full bucket load and complete discharge is necessary to get a consistent feed to the conditioning tank and, when calibrated, to show the correct quantity readings.

Filter drum vacuum, in starting the filter operation, is first applied to the lower or cake-forming section; then as the drum revolves and the filter cake emerges into the air, vacuum is gradually increased through the drying section. This initial filtration is controlled by manipulating the vacuum hand valves at the filter valve cap connections, which enables a filter cake to be built up quickly and easily; operation thereafter is automatic.

After dewatering, the semi-dried solids are automatically blow back discharged (except in string filters) over the scraper for ultimate fill, burial, incineration or fertilizer use. The filtrate, normally clear, is drawn to the vacuum receiver by the vacuum, removed by the filtrate pump and delivered to the influent, effluent or other sewage station.

As in standard multiple-compartment vacuum filter operation, a cake of sufficient thickness (⅛ inch or more) must be built up within a reasonable time upon the filter drum and the cake must be cleanly discharged, in a sufficiently dry condition for handling. On the other hand a too free-filtering, coarse floc will produce a cake so heavy that the vacuum will not hold it on the filter drum and it will slough off as it emerges into the air with the drum turning.

After discharge from the filter drum, the filter cake is carried away by a belt or screw conveyor for drying, incineration, immediate use as a fertilizer, fill, etc.; or it is fed directly to a disintegrator for incineration, or into cans or cars, on a small scale, for hand disposal.

Filter Media. Since sewage sludge filtration is simply a dewatering operation, no washing of the filter cake is required and no special rollers, flappers, or cake compressors are used.

Among the several filter media available there are a number of styles from which can be chosen that best suited to the particular sludge to be handled.

(1) Thin cotton, or unbleached muslin, will give a high rate of flow in primary or chemical sludge, but is short-lived.

(2) Cotton duck has a relatively long life, but gives a lower rate of flow and aggravates sloughing off with a coarse floc.

(3) Canton flannel combines open pores with close spacings and its nap retards clogging on digested sludge and those containing fine clays; but it is short lived. It also may reduce flow, if spongy ferric hydrate deposits accumulate in its fabric backing.

(4) Long-nap wool can be used only with a sludge on the acid side (here lime is not used as a conditioning agent). This limits its use usually to elutriated and activated sludges. The life is long, rate of flow is high, and sloughing off is lessened; but its cost is many times that of cotton.

(5) Copper sulfate-treated cotton has been used for heavily limed sludge and has a fair life with not too much tendency to clog.

(6) Synthetic cloth (Vinyl acetate) has given some success on digested sludge (Winston-Salem), but it is expensive.

(7) Glass cloth has a long life, if the pH is kept near 7.0 or below, but it also is expensive. Its smooth surface does not catch fine particles and will not hold very free-filtering solids as a cake.

(8) Stainless steel wire cloth, in the double crimped plain weave, showed excellent results in tests at Baltimore for elutriated sludge, giving a high rate of flow and having a long life; but like glass or synthetic cloth it is very expensive.

General Conditions. In sewage sludge filtration seven general conditions should be guarded against as much as possible.

(1) Presence of oils, greases, rags, or unfiltrable wastes (largely eliminated in digested sludge).

(2) Poorly digested, or stale primary sludges.

(3) Thin sludges.

(4) Inadequate conditioning, or inadequate agitation in the conditioning tank.

(5) Dirty or unsuitable filter media.

(6) Leaks in pipe lines.

(7) Small sludge lines.

In Chapter 19 results of the vacuum filtering of various sludges are reported and suggestions made for operation efficiency.

Reference

1. Genter, A. L., Consulting Engineer, Baltimore, Md., private correspondence.
   Genter, A. L., New Method of calculating coagulant requirements, A.S.C.E. San. Eng. Div. 7-21-43.

Chapter 14

Centrifugals and Centrifuges

General. Centrifugal separation, or extraction, as it is sometimes called, is ordinarily used either for the separation of liquids from solids, or for the separation of two or more immiscible liquids. Centrifugal extraction and centrifugal filtration, which are alike, remove liquid from solids supported on a porous surface by employing centrifugal force. Centrifugal clarification is a process in which centrifugal force is substituted for gravity settling; as it takes place by virtue of the difference in densities of the components, liquids which are mutually miscible or soluble cannot be separated by this means. The centrifugal force developed on materials to be separated may be many thousand times gravity, but it is always perfectly uniform at a constant distance from the center of rotation. Each individual particle of liquid is pulled away from the solids by force, for ready separation.

The degree of centrifugal force may be given as proportional to the square of the revolutions multiplied by the diameter of the revolving basket and is not proportional to the peripheral speed of the basket, as a 10 inch basket having only half the peripheral speed of a 40-inch drum will develop the same force. There is a distinction between equal speed and equal centrifugal force. If D is the diameter of the basket and if N is the revolution per minute for equal peripheral speed, $DN = \text{constant}$. The equation for equal centrifugal force, however, is: $DN^2 = \text{constant}$; accordingly, as the diameter of the basket increases, so also must the peripheral speed, if it is desired to keep the centrifugal force constant. "A convenient means of estimating the effect of centrifugal force is to compare it to gravity, which may be done by the following approximate formula.

$$\frac{(\text{Diameter of basket in feet}) \times (\text{rpm})^2}{6000} = \frac{\text{Number times centrifugal force}}{\text{is greater than gravity.}}$$

The force developed on one pound of material within the basket of a centrifugal may be determined by multiplying its radial distance in feet from the axis of rotation by the square of the revolutions per minute and dividing this product by 2932. The result is the pounds with which this pound of material is urged to move in a radial direction. If the pound of material were resting on the inner surface of a basket 40 inches in diameter revolving at 850 rpm, the force acting on it would be approximately 400 pounds. In other words, its normal weight is multiplied by 400, somewhat as if the force of gravity were increased 400 times. In consequence, the force rating of such a machine is often stated as 400 g.

TABLE A. Centrifugal force in relation to centrifugals. (*Courtesy American Machine and Metals*)

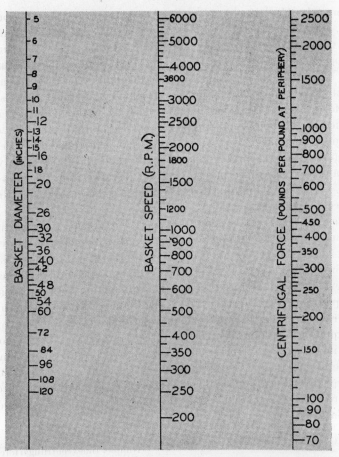

"The trend in centrifugal practice seems to be towards higher speeds which are made possible by alloys of high strength and corrosion resistance. Because the stress in a centrifugal basket increases with the square of the speed and with the weight, not only of the product but of the metal of construction, there is a limiting speed beyond which even an unloaded basket would be over stressed."[1]

The first centrifugals were designed for 1440 rpm, with reference to a 30-inch machine, which for a number of years was the only size built. Later the speed was reduced to 1200 rpm and the centrifugal force corresponding to this diameter and to this speed remains generally as standard. The table below gives the rpm, in other sizes required, to give an equal peripheral speed and an equal centrifugal force.

Equivalent Speeds Referred to 1200 rpm and 30-Inch Machine

Diameter (inches)	Equal Peripheral Speed (rpm)	Equal Centrifugal Force (rpm)
30	1200	1200
36	1000	1095
40	900	1039
42	851	1013
48	750	948
54	667	894

Subsidence, in any system, takes place according to Stokes' Law, which states that the velocity of sedimentation is proportional to the square of the radius of the suspended particle, to their relative density, and to the accelerating force, and inversely proportional to the viscosity of the fluid medium. This may be expressed mathematically $V = \dfrac{2r^2 \times (d - d^1)}{9^n} \times g$. In practice, the results from centrifuging depend on the effective mass of the particles in the dispersed phase, the viscosity of the medium through which these particles must move, and the time they are subjected to centrifugal force and the centrifugal force itself.

In a continuous centrifugal system sedimentation occurs at an angle to the liquid flow that may approach 90°. In order that centrifugal action may be effective, the velocity of sedimentation must be great enough to separate out the dispersed phase, during the time the liquid is being subjected to centrifugal force; and for any given system the rate of throughput of liquid has an important bearing on the degree of separation or clarification.

There are many variations of centrifugal separators but in general they fall into three classifications: (1) Batch type machines, of large diameter and slow speed, generally referred to as "centrifugals" and primarily used for recovering a solid from a liquid; (2) automatic bulk settling centrifugals, likewise used for recovering solids and sometimes called centrifugal filters; (3) small-diameter, higher-speed machines, usually referred to as "centrifuges." These last have low capacity for solids, but are used for clarity, for separating two liquids of different specific gravity, or for clarifying a liquid containing less than 1 per cent of solids.

Batch Centrifugals. Batch centrifugals consist of a curb or casing and a removable or permanent basket suspended therein (Fig. 107), together with the frame, the bearings, brake, unloaders and drive. The

curb is usually a bowl of heavy, welded construction with tangential outlets.   The baskets, for filtrable materials, are perforated and usually
lined with a filter medium.   For those materials which are so fine as to
seal a filter medium, or which cannot be retained by a filter medium, the
baskets are not perforated but solid, and as such act as settlers.

FIGURE 107.   Suspended type batch centrifugal.   (*Courtesy Fletcher Works*)

The centrifugal usually rotates on a vertical axis; in the case of the
solid basket, baffles are provided to prevent short-circuiting of liquor
flow and to promote more efficient clarification.

Proper anti-friction bearings and balance are of great importance, as
are quick-acting brakes.   Centrifugals also are often equipped with automatic motor shutoff timers and signal lights.   Drives are normally by
motor, direct-connected, or clutch-connected for speed changing, or V-
Belt and vari-speed drive.   Centrifugals may be constructed of various alloys or corrosion-resistant materials, as bronze, Monel, stainless
steel, or maybe lined or coated with lead, rubber, tin, etc.

Machines of the batch type are usually of one general design and may be either underdriven with open top (Fig. 108) or overdriven with suspended basket (Fig. 107). The open-top machines are preferred by pharmaceutical houses, where production is likely to be intermittent and absolute cleanliness in the basket is a factor, or for drying in textile plants, laundries, etc. This type also lends itself readily to vapor-tight construction, for the handling of volatile solvents and fumes. Sight glasses often are provided and arrangements made for discharging with-

FIGURE 108. Open top underdriven centrifugal. (*Courtesy Fletcher Works*)

out opening. In addition, this type requires little headroom. For all-around chemical duty, however, the suspended type is generally used. It has the advantages of: highest running speed per diameter of basket, bottom discharge for the solids and greatest stability with unbalanced loads. However, the size range is usually somewhat less than in the under drive type, ranging from 12 to 48 inches as compared with 12 to 72 inches for the underdrive.[3]

Operation. The feed to the above machines is by batch lots, by pipes with spreaders for slurries, or by other means for non-flowing materials. The loading is made to large solid baskets running at full speed but to perforate baskets at low rotational speed and the machine is not brought to full speed until the basket is fully charged. The speed of the centrifugal depends upon the material to be handled, those with perforated baskets being spun at relatively high speeds, in order to obtain a dry cake. When it is necessary to wash the solids in the basket a spray system is used within the basket; the spray is applied at the stage of dryness desired, without speed reduction.

For unloading, the basket may be stopped completely or slowed down to 50 rpm or less. Mechanical unloaders, spacers or paddles are generally needed, as most solids are packed into a relatively hard cake. Comparatively few solids form such a loose cake that the entire load will drop out through the bottom opening when the basket is stopped. For such materials, cone-bottom or self-discharging baskets are often used. Here the bottom opening in the basket must remain uncovered. A distributing plate fastened to the basket spindle distributes the load on the basket wall and prevents it from dropping out during loading. One operator can usually run two or more machines; unloading and loading one while the others are spinning.

FIGURE 109. Continuous centrifugal machine. (*Courtesy Bird Machine Co.*)

The earliest use of the perforated basket machines was for rinsing and drying of sugar. Sugar refineries are still one of the largest users of this type of centrifugal.

Automatic Bulk Centrifugals. Many modifications of the bulk centrifugal have been introduced, in order to reduce operating labor by automatic discharge and improve performance. One of these involves rotation of the bowl or basket on a fixed axis, so that the sludge or cake can be scraped out with a mechanical cutter and dropped into a chute leading away from the rotor.

Another modification involves rotation of a solid bowl, in the shape of a truncated cone revolving on a horizontal axis. A screw conveyor rotates inside the bowl, at slightly lower speed, in the same direction of rotation. The solids are moved forward by the conveyor, as fast as deposited, being carried above the level of the filtrate for an interval before leaving the bowl (Fig. 109). Filtrate discharge parts are so located in the large end of the bowl that the level of liquid is maintained at the desired height. Wash is delivered through a series of nozzles located directly in front of the conveyor blades and passes through the cake and toward the large end of the bowl with the filtrate.

In one design, a 20 inch bowl operating at 1800 rpm will handle an average of 50 pounds for a 45-second cycle of loading, washing, drying, and unloading. The operation is made automatic by an interlocking system of pneumatic and hydraulic valves controlled from an electrically synchronized panel board.

Another type of automatic bulk centrifugal offers continuous operation based on the principle of a rotating outer bowl carrying either a screen for draining crystals or a solid plate for sedimentation, combined with an inner bowl, rotated at a slightly lower or higher speed, which carries plows or a continuous helix for forcing the solids across the face of the outer member.

When the vertical centrifugal is used for sedimentation it is customary to discharge the clarified liquid over the lip ring. In the horizontal-axis type, the liquid is removed through a decanting horn to minimize splashing and avoid liquid leakage down the chute.

Centrifuges. Small-diameter, high-speed centrifuges are used for separating liquids, for example, separating cream from milk. About 99 per cent of the fat content of a given batch of whole milk may be separated as cream of 40 to 50 per cent fat concentration by centrifuging. The milk is fed continuously through the centrifuge and remains in the rotor less than 15 seconds. Only the very small fat globules remain in the skim milk. By careful control of temperature and pH the separated cream thus obtained may be recentrifuged and its butter fat content raised to 80 per cent, with no agglomeration of the fat particles and with negligible loss of fat in the skim.

For the removal and recovery of suspended particles, an example is in the production of photographic films, where there is necessarily a large amount of scrap. The silver bromide may be washed off this scrap with a suitable detergent and the bromide itself recovered from the suspension by passing the washing solution through a centrifuge.

There are two main types of high-speed centrifuge in commercial use. These are the long, tubular bowl type and the disc bowl type. The tubular type is characterized by a rotor relatively long in respect to its diameter. In this type the highest centrifugal force commercially available, 13,200 times gravity is generated by the rotation of a 4-inch diameter bowl at 15,000 rpm. The rotor is suspended from either a turbine wheel, or a pulley which is belt-driven from an electric motor.

The liquid to be processed is fed into the bottom of the rotor and is subjected to centrifugal force during its flow upwards. Any solids present are deposited on the bowl wall out of the path of the liquid and are periodically removed (Fig. 110). For separating immiscible liquids a separator bowl, constructed with a baffle at the upper end, is used. The

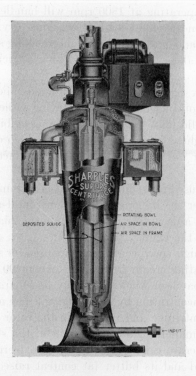

FIGURE 110. Tubular high speed centrifuge. (*Courtesy Sharples Corp.*)

heavier liquid flows out over a weir commonly known as a ring dam, which may be adjusted for different specific gravity ratios in the liquids being centrifuged. In the tubular bowl a simple interior vane or three-wing is provided to keep the liquid rotating at full speed and prevent loss of efficiency due to swirling. This type may be adapted for specific purposes to permit operation under pressure, in vacuum, in contact with an inert gas, and to recirculate volatile solvent in order to prevent deposition of solids on rotating surfaces. The small-diameter tubular bowl can readily be made of corrosion-resistant materials of various kinds.

The disc type of high-speed centrifuge normally has a relatively short bowl with respect to its diameter. It is usually fed at the top and the separated liquids discharge from approximately the same elevation at somewhat greater diameter. The conventional drive is from a motor through a gear and worm located under the rotor. Because of the somewhat lower centrifugal force which can be developed by this type, 7000 times gravity for the 12-inch size running at 6400 rpm, the incorporation of a series of conical discs to stratify the liquid is usually necessary. Rotors also are supplied in this type, which is made in sizes ranging from 41 to 24 inches in diameter.

Self-Cleaning High-Speed Centrifuges. Self-cleaning, high-speed centrifuges are made in a number of types. In one of these there is a peripheral orifice bowl fitted with a series of nozzles, or orifices, at the periphery; through these a portion of the liquid fed to the rotor continuously

FIGURE 111. Self-cleaning high speed centrifuge. (*Courtesy Sharples Corp.*)

leaks out. Since this is the point of greatest pressure in the system, it is necessary that the nozzles be quite small to prevent excessive discharge of liquid at these points. By returning the sludge discharge ports toward the axis of rotation, the pressure on the nozzles can be reduced. This type of centrifuge is used particularly in the concentration of yeast. It is adapted only for the continuous discharge of solids of too small a size to clog the nozzles and which do not tend to pack at relatively low concentrations.

The power requirement is proportional to the volume of liquid discharged through the orifices; any increase in the orifice size due to wear or abrasion will increase the power demand, as well as decrease the concentration of the sludge discharged. Self-cleaning centrifuges reduce operating labor cost at the expense of increased initial investment and higher power demands. In addition, the type of solids which may be continuously discharged is limited to amorphous materials which will not pack or bridge an opening and, in general, to non-abrasive solids.

In another type of peripheral orifice bowl, automatically operated valves are used. These valves, which are normally in the closed position, are actuated by the build-up of solids within the rotor itself. When they open, orifices are uncovered through which the solids are ejected by the centrifugal force. As soon as the sludge level in the bowl has dropped, the valves reseat themselves. With this type, somewhat better control of the concentration of the sludge discharge is obtained and a wider variety of materials may be handled.

One modification of the peripheral orifice bowl, which has been used in handling such substances as starch and oil-well drilling mud, permits recycling a portion of this sludge through the rotor for additional purification. At the same time, a portion of the recycled stream of concentrated sludge is continuously drawn off. This type has this advantage over other nozzle bowls: while wear increases the power demand, it has little effect on the concentration of the sludge.

Flotation may be used in some cases for the removal of solids from the rotor. An instance is the removal of amorphous wax from a chilled solution of lubricating oil stock in naphtha. It is possible to float this wax out of the bowl continuously on a stream of carrier liquid, in this case, brine. A special design of continuous solid discharge bowl has been developed for removing crystalline wax from lubricating-oil stocks. In this case, the oil is dissolved in a chlorinated hydrocarbon selected so that the resulting solution will be heavier than the wax which precipitates from it at low temperature. Under centrifugal force the wax goes to the center of the bowl and is continuously removed by a decanting horn.

Ultracentrifuge. The ultracentrifuge is a device designed to permit optical observation of the progress of sedimentation under theoretically ideal conditions. This instrument is used for the determination of molecular weights and particle sizes by photographically recording changes in concentration over timed intervals. The rotor is operated either *in vacuo* or in an atmosphere of low pressure hydrogen, to avoid the effect of frictional heat on the surface of the rotor, which would set up convection currents in the material being tested and thus interfere with the results. Ultracentrifuges are constructed with both oil and air turbine drives. They operate at speeds up to 100,000 rpm on a 2-inch radius and develop up to 500,000 times gravity.

A modification of the optical system of the ultracentrifuge is a mechanically driven centrifuge used in conjunction with a microscope, permitting observation of plant and animal life under centrifugal force.

A type of bottle centrifuge employing the ultracentrifuge air turbine drive and high rotation speed for the concentration and sedimentation of protein molecules and similar materials is used in the biological field.

The above centrifuges operate only on the batch principle and can process only a small volume in a single run.

Continuous Type. Continuous liquid discharge centrifuges, which rotate at speeds up to 50,000 rpm and develop 62,000 times gravity, permit the clarification or separation of larger quantities of material. These units are equipped with interchangeable clarifiers, separators or batch rotors, or bowls, constructed of a variety of corrosion-resistant metals. The liquid to be processed is fed continuously to the bottom of the rotor, and the purified or separated liquids discharge from the upper end into stationary covers. The sedimented solids are held within the bowl and are periodically removed by hand. By modifications in design and suitable operating technique, this type may be used for classification and determination of particle size of suspended solids, and even for the concentration of proteins and similar molecules existing in true solution.

In centrifuging, as in pressure or vacuum filtration, reduction of viscosity of the fluid medium increases capacity. This may be accomplished by the addition of a low-viscosity solvent, or by heating. With centrifuging, a rise in temperature may also facilitate separation by increasing the difference between densities of materials, as oil and water.

Another method of improving separation is to increase the radius factor r in Stokes' equation. For instance, in centrifuging distillery slop at a pH of 4 to 5, only about half the insoluble solids are removed, while by raising the pH to the eutectic point of the protein, under the same conditions of centrifugal operation, over 90 per cent of the insolubles can be removed. In many cases, however, this is easier to control, under the conditions of quiescent gravity settling, than in the continuous centrifuge, where some degree of turbulence is always present. Suspensions of ferric or aluminum hydrates settle out rapidly under gravity to yield clear solutions, but the removal of these materials from aqueous suspension centrifugally is almost impossible.

In general, separation by centrifugal force is an admirable means of separating immiscible liquids. In the dewatering of crystals a lower moisture in the discharged solids is obtained than in pressure differential filters (at the same temperature). Finely divided solids often can be centrifuged in cases where they could not be separated without difficulty by other means.

The centrifugal machines take up little room and do not require auxiliaries for operation. On the other hand, cloudy effluents are common and, solids of weak structure may be broken to a state of subdivision which is cumulative, and become very difficult to handle. Cake washing is seldom equal to pressure differential filters and horsepower may be comparatively high.   Initial costs also may be high with continuous machines, although with batch operation there is the item of labor to consider.

References

1. Tohlhurst Centrifugal Div., Amer. Mach. and Metals.
2. Amber, C. M., private correspondence, Sharples Corp.
3. Rometch, Jr., W. H., private correspondence, Fletcher Corp.

Chapter 15

Air, Gas and Light Filters

General. The filtration of air and gas is usually a matter of simple purification, either to remove impurities or to conserve valuables, while the filtration of light is selective elimination. In general, gas filtering is a process dust problem, the object of which is usually to recover valuables, while air-cleaning systems include atmospheric as well as process dust, and are of course used to purify air. The suspended solids of atmospheric origin are dust, soot, bacteria, etc.; process dust consists of suspensions which are a result of processing, as in grinding, crushing, drying, and other operations.

The presence of dust is objectionable to many operating units, particularly air compressors, motors and turbo-generators, since its abrasive content, which unduly wears the equipment, usually is from 20 to 40 per cent, as shown in the two following microscopic analyses.

	Pittsburgh District Area	Paper Mill Atmosphere
Smoke carbon (soot)	44-48%	40-44%
Siliceous matter	40-45%	20-23%
Coal dust	2½-3½%	—
Fibrous matter	3-5%	25-27%
Miscellaneous	5-8%	13-17%

Actually, dust consists of microscopic particles of sand, metal, ashes, soot, fiber, chemicals, animal and vegetable matter and other types of disintegrated material, together with bacteria, mold spores, pollens and additional micro-organisms. The size of these varies from that of the head of a pin to submicron. The average is about 0.5 micron (0.0005 mm or 0.00002 inch). Air filtration, based on viscous impingements or the dry mat principle, is effective to 5 microns and electrical precipitation to 0.25 micron.

Process dust, as differentiated from atmospheric dust, is composed of large particles of the same material in considerable concentration. The dust-collecting system usually consists of hoods to confine the dust, piping to carry it away, and exhausters to convey it through ducts to a collector or separator, which actually removes it from the air. There are four common types of dust separators: (1) those which separate by sedimentation, (2) those which separate by filtration, (3) those which separate by sprays, and (4) those which employ an electrical charge for separation.

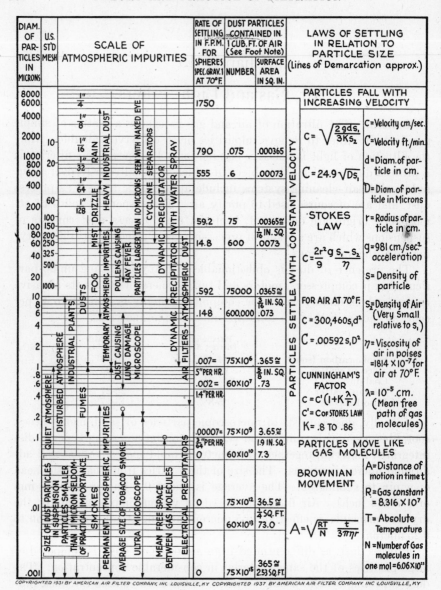

TABLE B.   Size and Characteristics of Air-Borne Solids

It is assumed that the particles are of uniform spherical shape having specific
gravity 1.0 and that the dust concentration is 0.6 gram per 1000 cu. ft. of air,
the average of metropolitan districts.   (*Courtesy American Air Filters Co.*)

Separation by Sedimentation.   The first of these types employs either
open settling chambers or baffles to create "still" pockets through which

the dust particles settle by gravity. This separation is entirely dependent upon the rate of fall of the particle, which, in turn, is dependent upon its size and weight, as given in Stokes' law.

According to Anderson,[1] "the theoretical rate of fall of spherical particles in still air is as follows:

Diameter of Particles (microns)	Nearest Screen Mesh	Rate of Fall (Feet Per Sec)
100	155	3.0
74	200	1.6
44	325	0.6
10	—	.03
1	—	.0003
0.1	—	.000003

"While data on actual dust-fall rates in industrial applications with moving gases and irregularly sized particles are extremely meager, certain experiments indicate that these actual rates of fall may be from 50 to 60 per cent of the theoretical rate. It is evident, therefore, that particles much smaller than 200 mesh, or 74 microns, will have an actual rate of fall less than about 0.8 foot per second and therefore fall too slowly to settle."

The settler should be designed to give the smallest size of particle it is desired to remove sufficient time to settle, and should be made wide and low rather than high and narrow. Chains and wire curtains minimize eddies and tend to collect the fine dust through contact. Fan pressure or natural draft forces the gas through the separator; often centrifugal force is used if there is sufficient difference in specific gravity to make it effective.

In a typical case, the gas stream is reflected 180° by curved plates, until it reverses itself, dropping out impurities into a still box. After flowing a short distance, it is deflected 180° back to its original direction, again dropping out suspensions in the still chamber, and the action is continued for several deflections. Separators of this character are used in cement mills, milk plants, blast furnace installations, grinding mills, etc.

The following table illustrates the centrifugal separating force in a circular gas stream. A 60 foot per second tangential velocity for different radii is used, expressed in terms of gravity, *i.e.*, gravity = 1.

Radius of Curvature of Gas Path	Separating Force
Gravity	1
10'	11 times gravity
5'	22 times gravity
2.5'	45 times gravity
1'	112 times gravity
6"	224 times gravity
4"	336 times gravity
2.5"	538 times gravity
1.5"	896 times gravity

Although Stokes' law is not strictly applicable to moving gases, it can be assumed that even here resistance to the motion of the particles is such that the rate of motion is proportional to the net force and that the resisting or frictional force depends on the same factor.

In the stationary type of mechanical separation, the forces acting

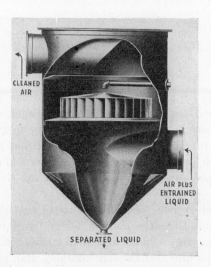

FIGURE 112. Entrainment separator. (*Courtesy Claude B. Schneible Co.*)

upon the dust particles are limited to a relatively small amount of radial acceleration, which is obtained from the circular movement of the air. In the impeller type, however, the forces of radial acceleration are greatly magnified by means of a rotating impeller, which also imparts additional dynamic forces to the dust particles, resulting in higher collection efficiencies even on very small particle sizes. In some designs, a turbine-like impeller with a large number of hyperbolic blades is used, with a housing for primary and secondary air passage. The rotating impeller creates the force necessary to draw in the dust-laden air, separate the dust and discharge the cleaned air. The dust is delivered into the secondary air circuit and passes in a steady stream through a part of the housing to a closed hopper below. The cleaned air becomes the primary circuit and is exhausted through the outlet of the scroll.

The air may be discharged outside, or filtered through a final cleaner for recirculation. At times water sprays are used for handling dusts which are inclined to cake or pack, due to inherent moisture, and for materials which are suspended in wet air. Separation of light and finely divided dust is improved by the wetting of the particles, which increases the mass to the point where they readily respond to dynamic forces.

Separation by Filtration. The most generally used method of dust separation is filtration, with either fabric, wet screens, or liquid sprays acting as the filter medium. In the common form, the gas carrying the suspension is made to pass through fabric bags or tubes, which strain out the suspended solids. The bags must be unaffected by the gas, retain the suspensions and not materially increase the static pressure. Cotton cloth is the ordinary medium, with wool used up to 150°F in slightly acid gases. At times, however, it is necessary to use such resistant materials as Monel, glass, asbestos, vinyl acetate, etc.

After resistance indicates an accumulation of deposits, the system is shut down; or if in duplicate, a switch is made to clean bags and the first lot is cleaned by turning them inside out. In other cases, the air passes from the outside inward, so that cleaning the bags is possible by reversing the flow for blow back and allowing the dust to accumulate in the bottom of the chamber, which is usually equipped with hopper discharge. The bag house collection is a typical example of this type of apparatus. Here tubes from 6 to 30 inches in diameter by 6 to 30 feet long are used.

A porous rigid medium in tubular form may be enclosed in a cylinder (Fig. 48). The inlet, tangential to the shell, is intended to throw the liquid and foreign impurities from the air stream into vertical slots leading to the lower liquid chamber. The air passes through the porous tube, which collects fine particles of oil or other material too light for the first centrifugal separation.

The rapidly expanding use of air conditioning has made increasing demands upon air filtration, for initial as well as recirculated air, as a heat conservation measure. In most cases, the large volume of air to be cleaned makes it desirable to use self-cleaning filters to reduce maintenance and assure a uniform, constant air supply. Should oil vapors or welding furnace gases be present, electrostatic filtration is often used.

Not only is filtration desirable for the purification of the air, but in cases of dehumidification, for prevention of contamination of beds of active material, such as silica gel or activated alumina. The lighter dust particles carry a large number of bacteria with them, necessitating positive filtration for pure air. Powdered coal plants, milk drying plants, spinning mills, air conditioning, etc., use separation by filtration.

For air purification, screen, spray separators and mat filters are the types most employed. In the screen design a series of rotary discs may dip into water and, by being staggered, cause the air to zig-zag in its passage for scrubbing and cleaning. Easily renewable, inexpensive gauze-backed cotton gives excellent filtration, with low resistance to blow. Insertion in metal pockets permits unit handling.

For removing obnoxious odors from stockyards and coal-tar plants or certain types of air conditioning, air is made to pass through sprays, which surround the dust particles and absorb the odor; they fall to a pan below, where they may be drained off or subsequently treated.

Separation by Sprays. In the spray method of separation, it is important that the suspended solids come in direct contact with a wetted

FIGURE 113. Air filter cell with electrostatically charged cellulose fiber collector element. (*Courtesy American Air Filter Co.*)

surface, in order to break through the gas film surrounding the particles. Baffle plates, coated rotating screens, etc., give the desired result and are quite widely used.

The purification of air for engine use is generally accomplished by passing the air through a cylinder packed with steel wool or other material, which will entangle dust particles but will not materially retard the rate of flow. The commonly known automobile air filters are units of this type. In another type of air filter, the following description of operation is given:

"Dirty air, or gas, enters under a rain shield and passes through a removable bug screen, then passes downward through the space between an inner and outer cylinder. It then impinges against oil, depositing the heavier dust particles immediately, picks up oil and then passes upward through vanes, which impart a whirling motion to the air and oil mixture. In a mixing chamber, the whirling air and oil are thoroughly mixed and the centrifugal action developed throws a large portion of the dust against the oil-coated walls of the inner cylinder. The air-oil mixture then passes other vanes, which impart a still faster whirl, throwing the oil with the dust it has collected outward by centrifugal action. At the top of the cylinder is an enlarged chamber into which most of the oil and dirt are thrown from the air stream. The pre-cleaned air then passes upward through an orifice and through double filter cells, leaving the cleaner to pass into the engine or compressor. The air which reaches the filter cells, contains a mist of oil which is collected by the cells and drains out around the outer edges. This continuous flow of oil keeps the filter cells washed so that any dust collected on them is immediately carried away. The oil which drains from the filter cells passes downward through a pipe where it joins the oil thrown out and flows to the oil reservoir. Here the dirt settles out and the oil recirculates.

"Maintenance consists of periodically draining the dirty oil, removing the inspection plate to scrape out accumulated sludge, and refilling with clean oil. If properly maintained, it should never be necessary to remove the filter cells for cleaning; but the top is made removable and the filter cells may be lifted out, inspected, or cleaned in case unusual conditions make this necessary."

Another type of dust collector that is often used is described as consisting of a cylindrical cone bottom tower containing a number of impingement stages. Each stage, shelf-supported, comprises a horizontal disc, from which curved vanes or baffles are suspended. The dust-laden air entering tangentially is given a rotary motion that is further induced by the curved vanes at each stage, causing the air to rise spirally as it is drawn upward. The cone bottom serves as a wet cyclone, collecting the heavier particles as soon as they enter the tower and vortex into which the fine particles are precipitated against the wetted surfaces.

The washing agent, usually water, is introduced at no head pressure above the center of the top impingement plate. The rotary motion of the ascending air sets up a similar motion to the descending water, causing it to cascade over the discs, vanes, shelves and side walls of the collector. The whirling agitation forces the liquid off the edges of the discs and shelves in a curtain of finely divided water through which the air must pass.

Filtered air is a health measure, as illustrated by the improved health among factory workers, when dust-carrying soot, abrasives, bacteria and other impurities are eliminated. It is a property and maintenance advantage by reducing wear on moving machinery. It increases production by reducing shutdowns for repairing and reducing fatigue of workmen, and often improves the product by speck and bacteria elimination, as in synthetic food products, paints, etc.

Where a number of small dust-creating pieces of equipment are used,

FIGURE 114. Sand conditioning exhaust system in a modern steel foundry. (*Courtesy American Air Filter Co.*)

as in spraying or grinding, vacuum hoods are placed over each unit, with a central collection and filtration system.

Electrical Separation. Actually, separation by electrical deposition is filtration only in the sense that the suspended solids are separated from the gas-carrying agent. In this system, the air or gas to be clarified is made to pass through metallic tubes in which charged wires are suspended. A low current with high voltage is used, and the suspended solids, passing between the poles and entering the magnetic field, acquire a strong charge and are repelled by the same charged pole, causing them to fall to a collecting chamber below. Very often the discharge electrode is of small cross-section and curvature, furnishing a high-surface electrical field for gas ionization; the other electrode is larger, with less curvature for collecting. The velocity toward the collecting electrode has been estimated at over 100 feet per second. Since the gas ions are molecular and many hundred times more numerous than dust particles, the effectiveness of the process is not limited to the size, weight or number of suspended solids. The system is continuous and automatic and has found favor in smelters, cement mills, refineries, and acid manufacture for solids recovery and nuisance elimination.

Light Filters. Light, sound, radio and other filters, such as spectroscopes, flame filters, radio band filters, etc., effect separation by selectivity. They are of the utmost importance to their respective industries, but they are not considered here since they do not deal with the separation of solids from liquids or gases.

Reference

1. Anderson, Evald., Chem. Eng. Handbook, McGraw-Hill Book Co., p. 1850, (1943).

Chapter 16
Auxiliary Equipment

The successful operation of any filter is dependent upon the auxiliary equipment used with it, if the filter itself is efficient and is handled intelligently. Such equipment includes that required for actual filter operation, *i.e.*, pumps, compressors and receivers; those items which operate only with the filter, *i.e.*, conditioning feeders, mixing tanks, float controls, conveyors and press closers; and those items which are used in filter maintenance, *i.e.*, cloth washers, pulp washers, wire winders, and lubricators.

Pumps. Filter pumps are the most important of the auxiliary items and are necessary for actual filter operation. They perform four distinct services in conjunction with the various types of filters, although some pumps may be used for two or more services. In this category there are combined filter feed and pressure pumps, feed pumps only, vacuum pumps, air compressors or blowers, and filtrate pumps.

The first type of pump is used in pressure filtrations, serving both as a means of bringing the unfiltered material to the filter and as the force for filtering action. In pressure filtration with pump feeding (gravity head and inert gas pressure are sometimes used), the initial resistance of the filter, with its clean medium, is low. This resistance increases with cake formation so that the initial pump delivery, as well as the mean and final delivery, must be taken into account, when considering pump capacity, whether a constant pressure or constant delivery is desired. The particular type of pressure feed pump used depends upon the design of the filter press, the pressure requirements, and the nature and concentration of the feed liquor.

Rotary Pumps. Rotary pumps are positive-displacement and thus are self-priming. They deliver a constant quantity but can be used only upon thin, light slurries such as soaps, petroleum products, vegetable oils, etc., where no grit or abrasive is present. This is because of their close clearance design, which permits handling materials at high temperatures (800°F) and at viscosities of 500,000 SSU. Pressures may be developed up to 950 pounds per square inch, vacuum up to within 1 inch of barometer and capacities up to 35,000 gpm.

Rotary pumps are built in four general types: (1) a single eccentric with reciprocating blades, which move freely in a sleeve and touch the

260

stationary casing in which the rotor is mounted (Fig. 115); (2) a double rotor design, which may be shaft-mounted as meshed gears, with close clearances between themselves and the casing (Fig. 116). Speed of rotation in either type draws up (by suction) the feed liquor, carries it around the rotor or rotors, and discharges it at the discharge opening, in a positive quantity action. This action is one of the marked advantages of rotary pumps, as a definite quantity of discharge can be maintained under varying head and pressure conditions. These rotary pumps have

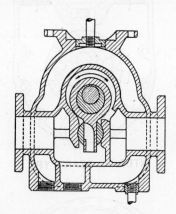

FIGURE 115. Cam and piston type, single eccentric rotary pump. (*Courtesy Hydraulic Institute*)

internal bearings when handling lubricants, and external, when handling other materials. Pressures up to 350 pounds per square inch are obtained and 90 to 95 per cent volumetric efficiency, with the standard direct-connected units. Such rotary pumps are used for greases, soaps, oils, etc. They may be of corrosion-resistant construction, although not readily so made nor are they considered amenable to lining with rubber, lead, or other materials. (3) A third type of rotary pump has two lobe-type rotors. These rotors take the feed by suction and force it between the two rotors (wide edge and narrow edge rotating alternately) and expel it by gearmeshing at the discharge. (4) A fourth type of design is a screw pump, with one or two spirals, which takes the liquid in at one end and forces it along to the other end, where it is discharged. This design is used primarily for very viscous, heavy liquids. It is also used for vacuum service, up to 28 inches of mercury.

Centrifugal Pumps. The open-impeller centrifugal pump is the most used of pressure feed pumps. It is simple in construction, inexpensive, and lends itself to corrosion-resistant construction and lining, *i.e.*, lead, ceramics, glass, rubber, alloys, etc. The pumps will handle a wide range of liquors and slurries, but are limited to about 60 pounds pressure, above which multi-stage construction or a series of impellers is necessary to increase the pressure, which is determined by the diameter of the impeller and the speed. They are adapted to those cases where a low starting pressure is acceptable, with increasing pressure as the cake resistance increases.

The design of the single stage, open-impeller, centrifugal pump is that of a shaft-mounted impeller within a casing with all vanes curved

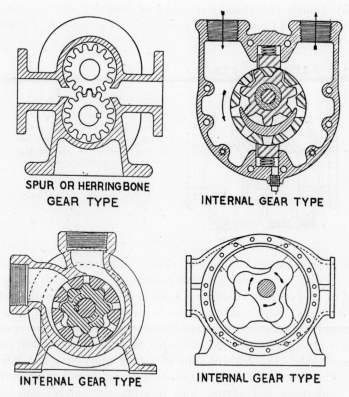

SPUR OR HERRINGBONE
GEAR TYPE

INTERNAL GEAR TYPE

INTERNAL GEAR TYPE

INTERNAL GEAR TYPE

FIGURE 116. Gear rotary pump. (*Courtesy Hydraulic Institute*)

backward (Fig. 119). The impeller may be open or closed, but for slurries the open impeller is necessary to prevent clogging. However, for the very reason of the wide clearance between the suction cover and the face, the open impeller is not very efficient. In new pumps space varies from 0.015 to 0.050 inches, depending on the liquid pumped, such as water, oil, paper stocks, etc.

Normally, centrifugal pumps are not self-priming and, unless construction is modified to take care of this by a discharge air chamber and liquor return, the pump must be primed either by gravity feed, direct pipe-line priming, or a vacuum system.

While centrifugal pumps will handle slurries in which considerable proportions of solids are present, and screening has added to this ability, there is danger of stoppage with heavy, quick-settling materials, particularly as the pump parts begin to wear. The pumps generally are not suited for intermittent operation upon any slurry in which the solids

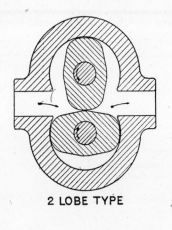

2 LOBE TYPE

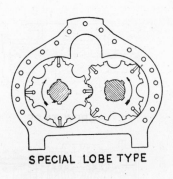

SPECIAL LOBE TYPE

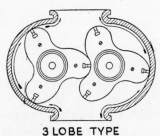

3 LOBE TYPE

FIGURE 117. Lobe type rotary pump. (*Courtesy Hydraulic Institute.*)

will settle out and immobilize the impeller during the idle period, as in the case of lime, starch, sewage sludge, etc.

The capacity of a centrifugal pump is in direct proportion to its speed; with a given material it depends upon the total dynamic head, the head varying as the square of the speed. Pumps with the so-called non-overloading horsepower characteristics prevent injury to the driving motor from any reduction in head, as reduced head increases capacity and horsepower.

There is a turbine type in which interposed vanes practically eliminate the shock and eddying caused by the higher speed discharge of the impeller to a slower casing exit discharge (surge chambers are sometimes used with open impellers). Turbine pumps, on the other hand, become clogged more easily where appreciable solids are present, although they are sometimes used to handle gritty material. One reason for the success of the turbine on gritty materials is the spiral action of the water created by the fins of the impeller, which forces the gritty material from between the impeller and casing; thus grinding out of clearances is prevented. When gritty materials are handled capacities are less than those otherwise obtained.

Diaphragm Pumps. For heavy slurries of solids which would tend to

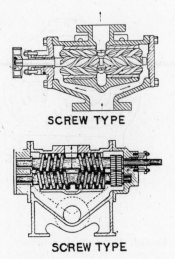

SCREW TYPE

SCREW TYPE

FIGURE 118. Screw type rotary pump. (*Courtesy Hydraulic Institute*)

clog a centrifugal pump, a type called a diaphragm pump, or a pump of the duplex or triplex plunger or piston type, is used (Fig. 120). The diaphragm pump consists essentially of a flexible disc which is fastened to the casing and actuated by a yoke. A cam or plunger on one side of the diaphragm operates in a fluid-filled chamber to flex the diaphragm from a convex to a concave surface and back. This action causes the sludges on the other side of the diaphragm to be drawn to the pump and to be pushed forward. Construction can be such that no metallic part comes in contact with the sludge; action is positive, clearances are wide and pressures up to 100 pounds are obtainable. This makes these pumps suitable for handling heavy corrosive sludge, for intermittent operation and against fairly high heads.

The capacity of a diaphragm pump is controlled by the area of the diaphragm, the length of the stroke and the speed, which sometimes can be varied without stopping the pump. Readily accessible ball valves on the intake and discharge make for quick, easy clearing should a stoppage occur.

Diaphragm pumps will operate normally against heads up to 45 feet;

special filter press pumps go to 100 pounds pressure. Diaphragm pumps
do not have as much tendency to pull a channel or hole in a sludge blanket as do centrifugal pumps, and no water seal is needed. These are particular advantages in handling sewage sludge.

Plunger Pumps. Pumps of the plunger type for sludge handling are
preferably of the triplex construction, as this gives a smoother, more even
flow than the duplex or the single cylinder machine. The action is posi-

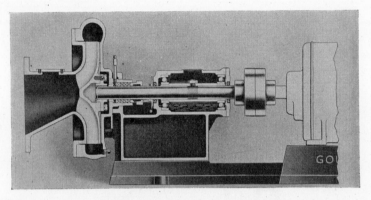

FIGURE 119. Open impeller centrifugal pump. (*Courtesy Goulds Pumps*)

tive, the plungers actually pushing the sludge or liquor ahead with each
pump stroke. The construction consists of three vertical cylinders in
line, fitted with plungers, crank shaft, gear drive, air chamber, inlet and
outlet ball valves and vacuum chamber for the suction side, if necessary.

The materials of construction are ordinarily cast-iron plungers and
cylinders with steel shafts and machine-cut cast-iron gears, bronze valve
seats, and bronze or rubber balls. In special construction, the plungers
are of phosphor bronze, and the cylinders bronze-lined.

The by-pass control is generally used in filter-press service to reduce
the quantity pumped as pressure builds up, and on water supply, as for
boiler feed, where operation is at a fixed speed and enough water is supplied for the maximum demands with variance in the actual demand. The
by-pass consists of a gate-valve discharge check and relief valve, the gate
valve regulating the feed. If slurries are light and in feed pumps only,
by-passes sometimes are an advantage.

Feed Pumps. In vacuum or gravity filtration, the feed pump is not
required to exert any pressure; it simply brings the unfiltered material
to the filter. The type of pump selected is thus entirely dependent on the
material to be handled. Thin and moderately heavy feed liquors are
usually handled by centrifugal pumps (occasionally by rotary pumps),

and more concentrated gritty materials by diaphragm pumps, or plunger pumps of low-pressure design.

It is seldom that sufficient head can be obtained by a gravity feed for pressure filters, except in some clarifying steps, where cake resistance is so small as to require only low pressures for filtration.

For vacuum or gravity filtration, however, a gravity feed may be desired, as it eliminates pumping and gives a positive supply. Here valve

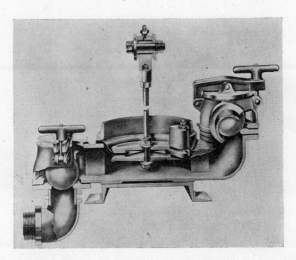

FIGURE 120. Diaphragm pump. (*Courtesy Marlow Pumps*)

regulation of quantity is required, and this presents clogging possibilities unless the pipe lines are sufficiently large. The advantage of overflow is lost, for such would require pumping back up to the feed tank. A float-controlled pump to a gravity feed tank with an overflow weir to the filter makes a very good layout, but this is in reality pump feeding rather than gravity.

Another method of feeding—the use of air pressure upon a closed vessel or Montejus tank—is less frequently used than formerly. Before modern simplified acid-resisting pump construction had been economically developed, the slurry was gravity fed to a closed pressure vessel, sometimes called an acid egg or Montejus tank, to which air pressure was applied. This was a simple, cheap means of force feeding, but on account of its great clogging hazards it is used only in special cases.

Helical Rotor Pumps. One of the newer designs of pumps which has been applied to sludge handling is described as one "consisting of a single-thread helical rotor of double pitch which turns in and meshes with a double-threaded helix of a stator having a single pitch (Fig. 121). Each section of the rotor rolls in the corresponding stator sections with a motion that displaces the open volume of the latter for each revolution and effects an end-wise flow of the contents. Thus feed liquid is continuously fed or drawn into the open helices and forced ahead of the backward progression of the rotor which effects complete endwise displacement, once for each revolution of a double-stage stator."

The pump is self-priming and will handle such sludges as sand and

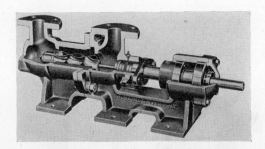

FIGURE 121. Helical Rotary Pump. (*Courtesy Robbins and Myers*)

water in a 1:4 ratio. The maximum size of the solid particles in the feed liquor should not exceed one-half the clearance space of the opening between the stator and the rotor. In the single-stage construction, the range is up to 150 gpm against 75 lbs pressure, and in the double stage 150 gpm against 150 lbs.

Vacuum Pumps. In vacuum filtration piston and rotary pumps as well as ejectors and barometric legs are used to create vacuum. The wet-dry vacuum pump is a relatively high-speed rotary centrifugal displacement or low-speed cycloidal pump, which produces a non-pulsating vacuum and has the advantage of handling both air and water. The rotary pump is used with drum vacuum or disc vacuum filters, particularly in the smaller sizes.

Wet-Dry Pumps. Wet-dry vacuum pumps of the rotary centrifugal displacement type consist of a round, multi-blade rotor revolving freely in an elliptical, liquid-sealed casing. The curved rotor blades project radially from the hub and form with the side shrouds a series of pockets or buckets around the periphery. The speed of the rotor must be sufficient to throw out the liquid by centrifugal force, resulting in a solid ring of liquid which revolves in the casing at the same speed as the rotor, but follows the elliptical shape of the casing.

In operation, the liquid follows the casing due to centrifugal force, withdraws from the rotor, and pulls air in through the inlet port connected with the pump inlet. As the rotation continues, the converging wall of the casing forces the liquid back into the rotor chamber, compressing the air trapped in the chamber and forcing it out through the discharge port connected with the pump discharge. This cycle takes place twice during each revolution. Direct or belt drive can be used and special materials of construction are possible in this design.

While the speed is high (in most cases conforming to standard motor speeds for direct connection) the rotor is the only moving part and it has

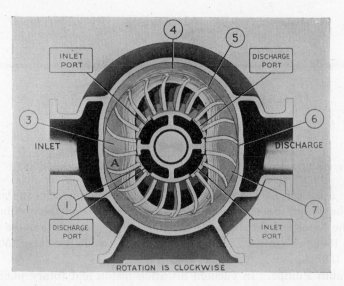

Figure 122. Wet-dry vacuum filter. (*Courtesy Nash Engineering Co.*)

no metallic contact. A vacuum up to 27 inches may be obtained with the single-stage pump, but above this two stages are required, to a maximum of 29 inches.

Another type of rotary wet-dry vacuum pump is one of the cycloidal design, consisting of a cast-iron casing containing a pair of machined impellers, supported on roller bearings and timed by a pair of cut matched gears. The casing is split for accessibility, and the design is similar to that of a blower, except in its heavy construction to take the shock of sealing water for higher differential.

This pump operates with top inlet and bottom discharge, so that water is spilled through the pump; as the points at which the shafts extend through the head plate are not subjected to water pressure, but are under vacuum, stuffing boxes are eliminated. Seals are provided to prevent the passage of water along the shafts when the pump is not running.

The impeller alternately traps and displaces a measured volume of

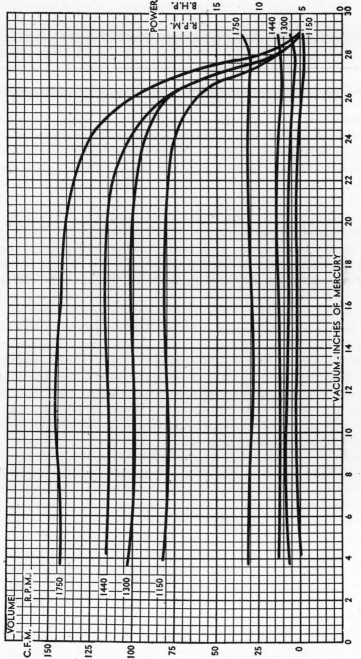

FIGURE 123. Wet-dry vacuum pump horsepower curve. (*Courtesy Nash Engineering Co.*)

liquor. The clearance between the impeller and casing is water-sealed; as in the centrifugal type, the impeller is the only moving part.

The speed of the cycloidal pump (220 to 750 rpm) is lower than the centrifugal type, but its maximum vacuum of 20 inches of Hg is likewise less.

The design of rotary centrifugal or rotary cycloidal pumps permits hot gases and saturated vapor handling because of the condensing action of the liquid seal. The principal disadvantage is the horsepower requirement, as compared with that of piston-type dry vacuum pumps.

Wet-Vacuum Piston Pumps. The piston or plunger wet-vacuum pump is self-priming, creates a high vacuum and gives efficient operation, but no solids or air can be handled. This limits the use of these pumps to a narrow field for, even with the submerged leaf type, there is exposure of leaf to air, either in shifting the leaves or in pumping the slurry and wash back and forth.

If exposure to air occurs when a wet-vacuum piston pump is being used, it is normally advisable to have a standby dry vacuum or rotary wet-dry vacuum pump available to throw on the line. As operating horsepower is low for the piston wet-vacuum pump, there is horsepower saving on this combination. For the liquor to be handled, dry vacuum pumps like the wet type may be either of the rotary or the piston design. A rotary pump of the centrifugal, liquid-sealed variety has the same ability as the wet-dry type to handle warm vapors, due to the condensing action within the casing. This is an advantage over piston dry-vacuum pumps, where carrying over a small amount or "slug" of water may cause breakage of piston, shaft or cylinder head. Rotary pumps have the disadvantage of higher horsepower requirements in the larger sizes, and the nearly flat horsepower curve (Fig. 123).

Exhausters. In the rotary type of cycloidal or blower design, the pump is usually called an exhauster. Its primary use is for handling large quantities of air at a lower vacuum (3 to 6 inches), as in salt filtration, although occasionally, in the smaller sizes, these pumps are designed for vacuum up to 16 inches. Though these pumps will not handle water, its presence is not likely to cause breakage, as with the piston type. In the strictly low vacuum design, a centrifugal turbo-compressor is sometimes used, which consists of a number of fan-type impellers mounted upon a shaft, direct-connected with the motor. Wide clearances are used, and by running up to 3500 rpm as much as 5 inches of vacuum can be induced with moderate horsepower requirements.

Dry-Vacuum Piston Pumps. The majority of vacuum filters are served by dry-vacuum piston pumps of the horizontal, reciprocating, single cylinder, double-acting, water-cooled type, except for small capacities

(180 cfm piston displacement), where either vertical air-cooled pumps or rotary types are normally used, unless corrosive liquids are to be handled. The vertical units are single-cylinder and single-acting in the smaller sizes (up to 34 cfm), and double-cylinder, single-acting in sizes up to 80 cfm.

Both vertical and horizontal dry-vacuum pumps are similar to air compressors in their construction. The latter are usually single-cylinder

FIGURE 124. Reciprocating dry vacuum pump. (*Courtesy Pennsylvania Pump & Compressor Co.*)

up to 2800 cfm and double-cylinder for higher capacities. Single-stage units are commonly used, as it is seldom that vacuum over 28 inches is necessary. The action of the piston is positive; the double-acting valves prevent pulsating and large volumes of air displacement are possible at high vacuum with relatively low horsepower requirement. The volume of air is the piston displacement, and must be modified by the efficiency factor, as contrasted with the rotary pump where the rating is on air actually handled.

Since piston dry-vacuum pumps cannot handle liquids and even a small amount may damage a piston rod or cylinder head, it is necessary to use a filtrate receiver and a moisture trap with this pump for separation of liquids from air, before the air is passed through the pump. In addition, the intake line should be equipped with drains for condensate. As the cylinder is water-cooled, a continuous flow is passed around the cylinder and out to the discharge in an open funnel, where water temperature can be tested to determine whether the quantity of water used is sufficient or an excess. Besides water-cooling, dry vacuum pumps require forced feed lubrication for the cylinder walls and crosshead and for splash-oiling of the crank shaft.

The speed of operation is relatively low (200 to 400 rpm), so that when the pump is given proper care maintenance cost is low.

Barometric Legs. Barometric legs, which are gravity discharge pipes with the tail ends submerged in a liquid seal, find an ideal place in conjunction with moisture traps, if there is head room available. At times, where the filtrate can be discarded or pumped from a wet well, barometric legs can be used with filtrate receivers and filtrate pumps dispensed with.

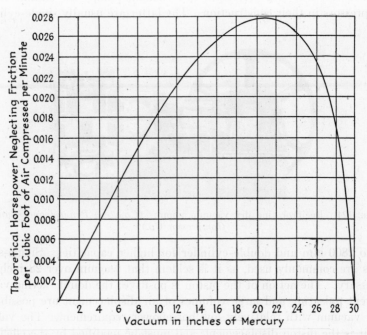

FIGURE 125. Reciprocating dry vacuum pump curve. (*Courtesy Pennsylvania Pump & Compressor Co.*)

Occasionally they can be used directly at the filter to create required vacuum. For such use, the solids to be removed from the feed liquor must be very free-filtering and must be carried in a large volume of liquor, so that there is continuous liquor flow in the barometric leg without break due to slowing down of the filtration rate. The vacuum created depends on the velocity of flow, therefore the rate of flow and size of the discharge line are vitally important. At times the leg takes the place of the filtrate receiver, by having the top connected to a vacuum pump, as in bicarbonate of soda filtration. In any case the barometric leg should be as nearly straight as possible and of sufficient height to obtain the required vacuum gravity head (1.13 feet to the inch).

Ejectors. Steam or water ejectors are extensively used with evaporators but rarely with filters. They have a place, however, where low-cost steam or water is available and the filtrate is to be discarded. In such cases a jet type barometric condenser may be worth considering, particularly with high-temperature filtration. One type, illustrated in Fig. 126 consists of a baffled stream of water with a hollow cone center which carries the filtrate and air by the induced vacuum.

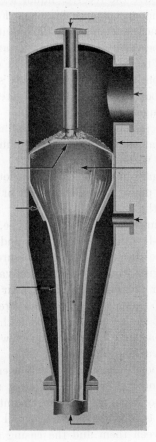

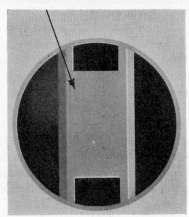

FIGURE 126. Condenser. (*Courtesy Henry E. Byer*)

In steam jet ejectors, where low-priced steam is available, a simple construction is a steam nozzle mixing chamber and diffuser. This ejector is capable of creating a vacuum up to 26 inches in the single-stage design and up to 29 inches in the two-stage design.

The advantage of ejectors is the simplicity and absence of moving parts; the disadvantages are the use of large amounts of steam or water required. Although water may be recirculated, the pumping involved usually counteracts any power saving over a vacuum pump.

Filtrate Pumps. The filtrate pump is a wet-vacuum pump which serves to remove the filtrate accumulating in the filtrate receiver while the latter is under vacuum. Filtrate removal is accomplished by locating the filtrate pump below the receiver (3 feet minimum usually) to give the required head. If the pump is not self-priming, an equalizing line from the pump suction to the filtrate receiver, above the receiver liquor level, effectively removes any air in the line and prevents air binding. For the proper selection of a filtrate pump, it is necessary to know the quantity of filtrate to be removed in a given time, the vacuum in the receiver and the vertical distance from the liquid level in the filtrate receiver to the center line of the pump. In addition, a line from the plant water supply should be run to the sealing ring in the stuffing box to prevent air from entering.

Filtrate pumps are usually of centrifugal design, although some of the helical rotor design are being used; as piston or rotary pumps have a clogging hazard and there is always danger that a filter medium will break and allow sludge to come through with the filtrate.

The self-priming feature of centrifugal pumps consists of various devices for liquor recirculation within the pump, in order that air or gases may be carried off by entrainment with the liquor.

Compressors and Blowers. Except in the string-discharge type, compressors and blowers are generally used with vacuum filters and with continuous-pressure disc filters for cake discharge. Low pressure differentials only are needed, normally ranging from a few ounces in vacuum disc filters to 2 to 15 pounds in drum or pressure disc filters. Air pressures up to 100 pounds for feed and 115 pounds for blow back are used with continuous pressure disc filters, but the actual blow back is the differential of 2 to 15 pounds. A timer may give the pulsating blow back sometime used with interior-drum and vacuum-disc filters.

For low pressures, blowers of the positive rotary type blowers are generally used. Here two impellers, mounted on parallel shafts, rotate in opposite directions, their relation to each other being maintained by a pair of timing gears located at one end of the shaft. A small space is kept between the impellers and between them and the casing at all times, their action on air being the same as that of rotary pumps on liquid. This gives a positive action, which is repeated twice for each revolution of the impeller, or four times for each turn of the drive shaft.

As blowers of this type may be noisy in operation, inlet and relief valve mufflers are desirable. A combination inlet muffler and air filter is also a worthwhile blower attachment. Adjustable weighted air relief valves are supplied to prevent overload, should the discharge line become partially or wholly obstructed.

Another blower used is the fan type, described under vacuum pumps.

In the single-stage construction, pressures up to 16 oz can be obtained, and in the multi-stage, up to 5 pounds. Varying volumes are possible and a uniform pressure is given by the curved blades and discharge channels, which tend to eliminate eddying currents.

Air receivers are usually necessary with compressors to insure a steady pressure and as a means of storing up air capacity for intermittent operation, as in air-pressure feed lines of intermittent filters for cake discharge.

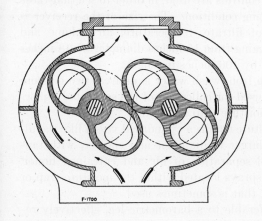

FIGURE 127. Rotary blower. (*Courtesy Roots-Connersville Blower Corp.*)

With continuous filters less horsepower is usually required with a blower than with a compressor.

Vacuum Tanks. Filtrate receiving tanks are used with vacuum filters interposed between the vacuum pump and the filter, to act as surge chambers and separators of the filtrate from the air or gas. With piston dry-vacuum pumps two vacuum tanks are normally needed, the first to separate the air and filtrate, as drawn from the filter, and the second to act as a moisture trap, to separate the entrained moisture carried over with the air from the first filtrate receiver.

The filtrate receiver is normally a cylindrical, cone-bottomed tank connected directly to the vacuum filter with a flexible connection in the line to take up vibration and piping misalignment which would cause valve wear and make vacuum tightness difficult. The intake to the receiver should be somewhat below the filter center line discharge, to take advantage of gravity drainage. The intake to the receiver is customarily at the center line, and it should be internally baffled.

At times, glass gauges are put on the side of the receiver for observation of liquor depth, although surging and staining of the glass make accurate observations difficult. Discharge is from the bottom of the cone of the receiver, which is usually set in a vertical position. Air is removed from the top of the receiver, connecting to the moisture trap or directly to the vacuum pump.

Vacuum receivers are sometimes fitted with vacuum breakers, which are float-operated devices to admit air to the system and "kill" the vacuum should the liquor level in the receiver reach a predetermined point (because of filtrate removal failure) and lift the float.

Manhole openings to the interior of the receiver are always desirable and are a necessity where float controls are used, in order to see that these are kept in satisfactory operating condition. The size of the receiver is determined by the quantity of filtrate, temperature, air volume and foaming properties, usually ranging from 15 inches diameter by 18 inches in length to 60 inches diameter by 106 inches in length.

Where separation of filtrate from wash water is desired, two or more separate vacuum receivers are used for collection of the separated liquors (Chapter 8) with a common moisture trap and pump.

Moisture Traps. The moisture trap is a cylindrical vessel like the filtrate receiver, but is usually larger in diameter and shorter, with tangential inlet and outlet to aid separation of air and entrained liquor. With hot or acid liquors wash sprays located within the moisture trap or in a preceding condensate tank that is sometimes used.

A bottom drain outlet, preferable to a barometric leg, effectively removes the separated liquor. While the outlet drain may be connected to the filtrate pump, with a check valve interposed in the line to prevent short-circuiting, there is always the possibility of filtrate pump failure with subsequent carryover of water to the vacuum pump. This, of course, applies only where a piston-type dry vacuum pump is used. In the case of a rotary type pump the carryover would do no mechanical harm to the pump, although it would reduce its air capacity and thus affect filtration.

Conditioning Chemical Feeders. It is often necessary to add a coagulating chemical or chemicals to feed liquors to make them filtrable, and this is always true with sewage sludges. There are a number of feeders designed to perform this work, particularly for handling dry chemicals.

Vibrating Dry Feeders. The vibrating feeder is used for such substances as hydrated lime or alum. It consists of a hopper equipped with an electromagnetic vibrator, located above a spring-mounted trough also vibrated by a pulsating electromagnet. The hopper vibrator prevents arching or bridging over in the feed to the trough below. A rheostat controls the intensity of vibrations to conform to materials of different characteristics. The rate of feed is controlled by the speed at which the trough vibrations cause the material to flow through the trough, and by the size

of the stream. The speed is adjusted by an electric dial switch for changing the amplitudes of the pulsations, adjustable from a flow of six inches
per second down to almost imperceptible movement. The size of the
stream is proportional to the size of the opening between the hopper and

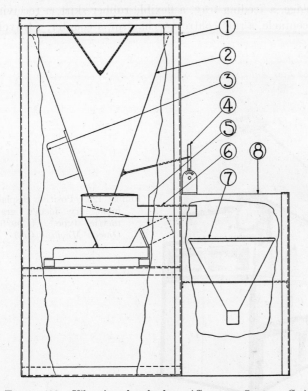

FIGURE 128. Vibrating dry feeder. (*Courtesy Syntron Co.*)

the trough and can be set through calibrated mechanical adjustment on
the machine from a full trough down to a thin layer.

For gravimetric feeding the chute discharges onto a short, constant-
speed, synchronous motor-driven belt suspended from a scale. Electric
controls, actuated by over or under movement of the scale beam, speed
up or slow down the rate of flow of material through the vibrator. Normally the material discharges into a Vortex-type, funnel-shaped solution
pot where a swirling stream of water meets it for a slurry discharge to
the sludge.

The unit requires little electrical power and can be provided with
ample overhead hopper storage for continuous operation. Lumps of
damp material are likely to cause trouble by clogging the hopper feed.

Mechanical Feeders: Gravimetric. There are numerous designs of mechanical feeders; the one most used for filtration conditioning is of the undercutting type. One variation in the gravimetric construction consists of a constricting scale mechanism on which the hopper is mounted, a control wedge, a feeding tray, a flexible rubber skirt, a receiving or dissolving receptacle, a rate control mechanism, a counter, a traveling poise,

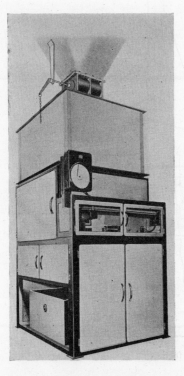

FIGURE 129. Positive displacement dry feeder, gravimetric type. (*Courtesy Omega Machine Co.*)

a micrometer screw, an alarm, a synchronous feed-control and a feeder motor in a steel frame with reversible panels or doors. Glass doors make the control mechanism and scale beam visible and accessible during operation.

When operating, the hopper is filled with material and the scale is balanced by manually adjusting the poise. The rate-control dial on the speed changer is set at the desired rate of feed in pounds per hour and the small synchronous motor, which drives the speed changer, is started, as is the motor operating the feed mechanism. The rate-control motor turns the micrometer screw, thereby moving the poise slowly backward to unbalance the scale at the rate in pounds per hour indicated by the setting of the rate-control dial. This unbalancing results in an upward movement of the outer end of the scale beam, which in turn imparts a downward movement to the control wedge through a lever system.

The control wedge, thus actuated, immediately increases the intensity of the oscillating movement and the feeding tray, thereby rapidly feeding material from the hopper until the scale beam is brought back into balance; at this point the intensity of oscillations of the feeding tray is reduced to the degree required to feed just enough material to keep the scale in balance.

The operation is entirely mechanical, with an alarm system as a check if the hopper becomes empty or the material is not continuously fed at the desired rate. There is a recording by the micrometer screw of the material received from the feeder, which usually does not vary over 0.1 per cent.

Mechanical Feeders: Volumetric. In the volumetric feeder, a motor-driven speed reducer transmits motion by a rod connected to an oscillating hopper, moving it backward and forward, thus pushing a measured portion of material off the receiving tray into a mixing chamber. The length of stroke, or the degree of oscillation of the hopper, is controlled by the micrometer on the connecting rod; the degree of movement is indicated and means are provided for adjusting the height of the tray. A special agitator prevents arching when feeding.

The feed material (*e.g.*, alum) fills the lower part of the main hopper and the oscillating hopper and rests on the tray beneath. As the oscillating hopper moves back and forth the scraper, which rests on the fixed tray below, is moved first to the right and then to the left; as it moves, it pushes a ribbon-like layer of material off the tray. The width of the ribbon is fixed, but the depth may be changed to suit varying conditions by raising or lowering the tray. Ordinary changes in the rate of feed are made by changing the stroke of the oscillating hopper, not by moving the tray.

Liquid Feeders, Pump Type. Liquid feeders are used in handling such materials as ferric chloride solutions. One type of feeder is in reality a small diaphragm pump which gives a positive displacement and therefore meter service. The diaphragm consists of a rubber disc actuated by a piston, and the capacity can be varied by the speed and length of stroke, as with a diaphragm pump. This feeder has the advantage that it can be located above the supply tank and can raise the solution by suction and discharge it at the desired rate against a head, as in the case of a pump; this removes the hazard of having ferric chloride, or other corrosive solutions, above the feeder, should leakage occur.

Customarily, sight glasses are furnished; these are transparent cups, so that the action of the diaphragm and check valve can be seen and checked as to whether both are operating correctly. Check valves usually have a sloping contact to insure dependable feeding on a horizontal pressure line, and do not require spring loading. The action of the check is to keep an even flow.

FIGURE 130. Positive displacement liquid feeder. (*Courtesy Proportioneers Inc.*)

Gravity Discharge. In the gravity discharge feed, a circular calibrated rubber-lined tank is equipped with an outlet hose. This hose may be on the outside or inside, but one end is connected near the bottom of the tank while the other is arranged for vertical movement from the top to the bottom of the tank. In operation, the outlet on the free end of the hose is raised above the liquid level; the tank is filled and the hose end is lowered to the liquor level; at this point an automatic chain or cable lowering device, actuated by a combined speed reducer and speed changer driven by a small synchronous motor, dial adjusted for rate of feed changes the head differential to maintain a constant rate of flow. These feeders are easily made of resistant materials, have few parts and can discharge large capacities.

Another type of liquid feeder is one combining mixing and feeding, particularly for such slurries as milk of lime. It consists essentially of a half-round tank containing a horizontal revolving shaft to which is affixed an agitator with chemical collecting and measuring cups which discharge through orifices into a collector funnel. A manual variator apparatus gives the desired proportional feeding.

Slaker Feeder. When handling quick lime a slaker is used, either following a gravimetric dry feeder or preceding a liquid feeder. The slaker consists of agitator equipped compartments of sufficient capacity to give 15 to 30 minutes retention time at the maximum slaking rate. Agitation is by a hydraulic jet created by a screw-type impeller. A clinker compartment for removal of the clinkers during operation is provided, an average of one-fifth of a cubic foot per ton of lime being removed. The body of the slaker is insulated to retain the heat of reaction developed, which is about 3500 Btu per pound of lime slaked, or sufficient to heat about 3 pounds of water and lime 100°F above the temperature of the incoming water. The temperature is automatically regulated by a valve which admits sufficient water for this purpose. The water is the same as that previously used in the dust and vapor removal system and has already been warmed from 10 to 20°F. The greatest danger is from short circuiting of lime and clogging of the discharge; feeders require careful design of agitators and baffles and correct hydraulic control.

Special Feeders. There are many other special types of feeders, both wet and dry, such as roller, screw, paddle, apron or plunger dry feeders float valve-controlled rotating perforated pipes and disc liquid feeders; but those described seem to be the most representative and the most extensively used.

Filter aids of the diatomaceous earth or the carbon type are usually hand-fed in batch lots. Paper pulp is first disintegrated and then fed in batch lots or continuously as make-up slurry.

Pulp Washer. In sugar clarification there is sometimes an elaborate paper-pulp recovery system. This consists of a pulp-mixing tank and several dewatering drum filters with washing attachments for washing the pulp cake. The dewatered pulp passes to a mixing tank, where water is added, and then to the next drum filter for further washing and dewatering. There is about 5 per cent makeup of new stock in the procedure; for handling this a disintegrator is usually necessary. With diatomaceous earth or carbon, revivifying systems often are used with or without preliminary washing. The revivifying may be by burning, by steam, by distillation, or by washing.

A particular type of paper filter media washer is used in breweries. Here the used paper media is agitated with fresh water for washing. The water is injected through nozzles, and overflow manifolds at the top of the tank remove foam and dirty water.

Sludge Elevators. For thick or granular sludges a bucket elevator is the most positive means of sludge feeding to the filter or the filter-conditioning tank. The type of elevator most commonly used has spaced buckets centrally hung between two strands of chain, with a capacity equal to that of the filters being fed. The elevator may be either encased at the foot, in a liquid-tight elevator boot, or the foot shaft of the elevator may be set on the bottom of the sludge tank, which should slope to this point.

In either case the top of the elevator is enclosed in a liquid-tight housing containing the discharge chute, which feeds to the conditioning tank. The take-up for the elevator chain is provided by a weighted, vertically sliding frame to which the foot-shaft bearings are attached. An alternate arrangement is to have the elevator chain in a path somewhat like the numeral "7", with the conventional type take-up bearing at the end of the inclined limb. Operation is at a slow speed, usually from 3 to 20 rpm, through a variable-speed transmission with a change ratio equal to that of the filter change ratio. Often the change of speed is affected automatically by the filter constant-level float, and this, in turn, may be tied in with the conditioning feeders. In any case, provision should be made for alternate manual operation.

As the elevator turns, the buckets scoop up a full load of sludge and at a slow speed discharge it completely to the discharge chute without spillage, thus enabling the buckets to be calibrated and a revolution counter used to record the quantity of sludge handled. Shear pins are provided to prevent chain breakage should sticks or other objects become wedged against the chain or buckets to cause undue strain. Conveniently located doors should be furnished in the elevator casing and chutes should be enclosed to permit interior hose washing.

Construction is of cast iron and steel, as a rule, but buckets, drip pans, chutes and pipe connections should be hot-dipped galvanized or otherwise constructed to retard corrosion.

Conditioning Tanks. The construction of the conditioning tank is of the utmost importance, particularly in sewage sludge filtration. In general, such tanks are equipped with paddle arms for mechanical mixing, as there is danger of channeling from air agitation. The size of the tank, the baffles, and the operating speed depend upon the sludge and the quantity to be handled. Raw sewage sludge may be agitated, at times quite violently, with high-speed mixers, although customarily the paddle arm type at a slower speed (60-70 rpm) is used to prevent breaking of the floc formed by the conditioning chemicals. In small installations portable mixers have been used and in large plants pairs of vertical fan-type agitators. With these, there should be more than one set of bottom blades if thorough agitation is to be accomplished.

In handling digested or activated sludge, paddle-type mixers are common practice; they are usually horizontally mounted in a half-round rectangular tank, or vertically mounted in a vertical cylindrical tank, with occasional air agitation in some activated installations. It is very desirable that agitators be equipped with variable-speed transmission to meet the feed variations, slowing up for thin, light sludge and speeding up for heavy, thick sludge.

The conditioning tank may be constructed of various materials, such as rubber-covered or painted steel, concrete or wood, the corrosion-resistant construction being necessary because of the pH of the sludge and presence of corrosive conditioning agents.

Feed of the conditioning agents is at the intake end of the tank, and in smaller installations the chemical feeders usually are mounted upon the top of the tank. Generally the tank should be baffled to give the proper retention time and to insure thorough mixing. This is particularly true where the conditioning agents are fed to the top of the sludge, a procedure followed to avoid clogging of the feed lines. By the use of the under and over system of baffles, in conjunction with the agitation, a thorough mixing is assured. An overflow adjustable weir, as the last baffle, enables retention and controlled feed to the filter vat to be readily accomplished.

Belt Conveyors. Belt conveyors are the most common means of removing the discharging cake from continuous drum vacuum filters. The belt is usually three-ply rubber-covered canvas supported by float idlers and equipped with belt cleaners of the weighted scraper type at the head pulley, take-up at the tail pulley, drip pan with drain beneath the return and canvas-edged skirt plates to prevent spillage.

The width of the belt is usually determined by the filter size rather than a consideration of tonnage. It is desirable to have the belt extend three or four inches behind the scraper and a distance beyond it, to take the fall of cake as it breaks off, without depending too much upon the skirt plates. If the cake tends to break off in too large pieces, staggered pins on the filter scraper or apron, or other means, are used for cake breaking.

Belts are usually limited to speeds of 125 fpm and slopes up to 25°. The slope of feed and discharge chutes should not be less than 60°, and valleys should be avoided.

Discharge is normally over the head pulley, but there may be removal at one or more intermediate points, handled by means of rubber-lipped scraper plows set at an angle of 60° with the center line of the belt. Where discharge is made to an incinerator, the entrance to the incinerator is often sealed to prevent loss of heat.

In order to keep a record of quantities of filter cake handled, belt conveyors are frequently equipped with a suspended automatic recording scale over which the belt passes for weighing the cake in transit.

Scraper Conveyors. Scraper conveyors are not ordinarily employed for handling filter cake because of the difficulty of keeping them clean. However, when the slope is too steep for the plain conveyor they are sometimes used. Such conveyors usually have simple bar flights suspended between two strands of conveyor chain operating in light-gauge metal troughs. Wearing bars are provided for the chain, and a drip pan with drain outlet is placed beneath the conveyor. The speed of the scraper conveyor is usually limited to 50 fpm to prevent back-spillage and to get clean discharge and complete pick-up.

Spiral Conveyors. At times spiral conveyors are used in the place of belt conveyors to handle filter cake where no elevation is required. Here the flights should be of the ribbon type with speed usually limited to 50 rpm. The conveyor should be encased in a closed housing with easily removable covers, preferably hinged, and the intermediate hanger bearings should be lubricated with grease.

Instead of attempting to use cake breakers on the filter itself, the spiral conveyor may be used for this. As the conveyor action not only breaks the cake but has a tendency to consolidate it, a narrower belt can be used for the following belt conveyors.

In all conveyors, as in sludge elevators, totally enclosed, or at least splash-proof motors should be used because of the daily hose washdowns.

Controls. The feed to filters is very often float-controlled, particularly in continuous filters, where it is desired to maintain a definite filter slurry level. Floats are used also for liquor level controls in vacuum systems, to prevent filling of the vacuum receiver and to actuate alarms for variations or presence of suspended solids.

The feed float control generally consists of a ball or cylinder float in a separate compartment of the filter vat, feed line or feed tank, with the level set at the correspondingly desired filter level. Its action is two-way, operation of a solenoid valve, through chains or rods, for starting and stopping the feed pump or elevator. Where thick sludges are encountered and a feed line float is desired, a small opening connection may be made to the float receptacle, allowing the water to strain through, but holding back the solids. Accumulations of solids on the float and resultant friction lag are thus avoided.

A novel control is one wherein a rubber diaphragm forms one wall of the filter vat and float compartment. The compartment is filled with water to the desired level and the difference in the pressure between the sludge and water is used to actuate controls for starting and stopping a sludge feed elevator or pump at predetermined sludge levels in the filter vat.

Filtrate Floats. Floats in the filtrate receiver may directly lift a relief valve in the head of the vessel as they rise, or this relief valve may be operated from the side. In either case the float generally actuates an arm, which in turn opens a valve to admit air and thus breaks the vacuum, although in some installations the float operates a solenoid valve for stopping the vacuum pump. Again, a filtrate pump may be thrown on if the level rises in the receiver, in which case the water is ordinarily controlled by a barometric leg. Should the water in the leg back up due to non-removal or stream rise, if the stream forms the seal, the float will throw on the filtrate pump. There are many types of remote-control diaphragm float valves, control pressure diaphragm-actuated valves, etc.

Electric Controls. A simple effective control is an electric circuit, using the liquor in the filtrate receiver or moisture trap or other receptacle to close the circuit. Rods inserted in a head piece are insulated from each other and also from the ground and are connected to the control, which is attached to the tank at the liquor level. In operation, as the liquor level rises, the circuit is closed by the liquor, thus automatically opening the pump or other equipment control circuit for stopping operations. When the level drops to the predetermined point, operation again starts. By using a third rod, variations can be made in the above.

Because of the very small current consumption and low voltage, these controls can be used upon non-conductive and combustible liquors, such as oils, as well as upon water, copper nitrate, etc. A further use for the electric control is in determining cloudy filtrate in boiler feed water clarity. Here photoelectric controls are used, which operate upon small light changes.

Construction can be of corrosion-resistant materials for handling a variety of liquors. However, as any deposit on the rods will impair their effectiveness, liquors with a high percentage of suspended solids cannot be so handled. It is possible to handle sludges by straining them to obtain clear liquor for the control, as described under float controls, in cases where such an arrangement is feasible.

Valves. Where liquid discharge is being handled, special check valves of the butterfly type are sometimes used to keep down the noise usually encountered by the larger-sized check valves. Numerous valves are used with filters from gravity feed line valves to vacuum line valves; these may be divided into those which handle liquids or slurries and those which handle air or vacuum.

Globe and Gate Valves. In the first group, globe valves find wide use for clear liquor lines and wedge-shaped gate valves for thin slurries. Globe valves normally have rising stems, and are of the inside screw and yoke design in small sizes and outside screw and yoke in the larger sizes. Gate valves have less pressure drop than globe valves and therefore are used for complete shutoff, while globe valves are used for regulating flow. The gate valves may have either rising or non-rising stems; the former give an indication of the opening and the latter save head room.

For handling slurries, gate valves or lubricated plug valves are commonly used. The gate valves may be made "quick-opening" to speed operation, particularly in filter-vat dumping or in cake discharge. Special clean-out connections and pockets are often provided. It is the usual recommended practice to install gate valves rather than globe valves on the discharge of centrifugal sewage or filtrate pumps to facilitate cleaning.

Plug Valves. Lubricated plug valves have a revolving slotted plug rather than a rising globe or disc. The seating surface is force-lubricated and the valve lubricant-sealed at top and bottom. The machined surfaces are not exposed when the valve is opened and only a small portion is exposed when it is closed; the openings may be two, three or four way.

The wide cut in the plug allows open passage and minimizes danger of stoppage.

Ball Valves. Ball valves, normally used in conjunction with pump seats, are of bronze or rubber balls. Generally, the diameter of the ball should be greater than that of the outlet by $1\frac{1}{6}$. The top cap of the valve is usually locked down with a swing bolt for ready removal.

Check Valves. Check valves are either swing or lift. The swing type is so placed that gravity will close it, while the lift type is so placed that it lifts vertically. The check valve is used to prevent reversal of flow in pump discharge lines, blow-back lines and vacuum lines. There is danger in using them if too much dependence is placed on their tightness, as dirt or corrosion may cause them to stick.

Globe valves are used for air lines and gate valves for vacuum lines. These valves are of the type which may be operated throttled, wide open or tight shut.

Materials of construction in valves range from bare metal to rubber covering, except in the check and plug valves, which are very difficult to cover effectively.

Dials. A desirable adjunct to large valves is a dial indicator, in clock or other form, which will show the valve position immediately and enable future settings to be gauged easily.

Cloth Washer. A filter cloth and bag washer, similar to a laundry cloth washer, is used to some extent abroad and occasionally in this country for washing filter press cloths and bags used on leaf filters. The drum is divided into four compartments having lateral openings. The filter cloth, or bag, is charged and discharged through these openings; the number washed at one time depends upon their size, as the compartments must be only half full to allow them to be thrown around freely. The water must enter under pressure through the central intake in sufficient quantity to thoroughly wet them. The drum revolves in a tank provided with an overflow for the dirty water. Usually four operations can be completed in an hour.

It is doubtful, however, if the cloth can be very well washed unless the solids separate easily from the cloths; therefore the use of a washer is confined to cloths which have been handling such materials.

Other Items. There are many other items of auxiliary equipment which might be discussed; but since they are all fairly well known or described elsewhere, they will not be described; for example, repulpers, piping and fittings, washing showers, motors, starters, vari-speed transmissions, scales, thermometers, lubricators, revolution counters, etc.

Chapter 17

Typical Filter Applications and Flow Sheets

General. Filters are necessary at some stage of all major wet processes. These processes are commonly divided into the following broad industrial classifications:

Abrasives
Beverages
Clay and Cement
Chemicals
Coal
Food Products
Metallurgical Products

Petroleum and Oils
Paints and Varnishes
Pharmaceutical Products
Pulp and Paper
Rubber
Sewage
Water

Subdivisions might be made, but the above has been generally accepted as covering the filtration grouping.

Abrasives. Abrasives are hard, relatively coarse bodies of a rather high specific gravity, which often require dewatering before drying or final use. For this dewatering a hopper dewaterer normally is used, operating under a low vacuum and requiring a large volume of air.

Beverages. Beverage filtration is usually a clarification problem. For this work pressure filtration with plate-and-frame presses or leaf filters (horizontal or vertical) is the common practice. Precoating is largely resorted to, and often filter aids are used. Cycles are generally long, pressures low and construction is of corrosion-resistant material.

Clays and Cement. Clays may be divided into two classes, depending upon their filtrability: those having good filtering characteristics and usually containing considerable percentage of silica and impurities and those which are poor filtering, but usually purer and more finely divided. The former are generally handled on rotary drum vacuum filters or centrifugals and the latter on plate-and-frame presses.

Cement slurries are relatively free-filtering and are handled on drum vacuum filters or rotary disc vacuum filters.

Chemicals. There is such a great diversity of materials under the chemical classification that it may be said that every type of filter is used at some point in handling chemicals. The carbonates and sulfates of calcium, barium, nickel, etc.; being free-filtering, are most often handled on drum vacuum filters. Crystals as coarse, free-filtering particles, are handled by centrifugal machines, top-feed drum filters, or dewaterers. Acids are often clarified in stoneware filters of the gravity or suction type, because of batch lots and the necessity for corrosion-resistant construction; however, pressure filters also are used.

Dyes, organics, etc., as slow-filtering materials, are usually filtered on plate-and-frame presses, or other pressure filters. Caustic liquors are frequently clarified on rotary leaf pressure filters; often precoating is resorted to in order to use metallic filter cloth. For slow-filtering materials where washing is important and large quantities must be handled, the open tank vacuum filter may be used.

Coal. Since coal is free-filtering and large quantities must be handled, continuous, automatic operation is necessary. For the finer grades, drum vacuum, of external or internal filtering medium construction, or disc vacuum filters are used. For coarse coal, top feed filters or dewaterers are employed. For coal-tar products plate-and-frame filters are used.

Food Products. Food products have three particularly large divisions in salt, starch and sugar. Here again the first two materials, for the most part, are crystalline and free-filtering, with large quantities to be handled. For these, drum vacuum filters or disc vacuum filters are used.

For sugar, drum vacuum filters are used for several filtering stages, *i.e.*, cachaza, carbonates, and saccharates, as these are readily filtrable upon such machines. For juice clarifiers the disc-type pressure filter is often used and the centrifugal for crystals. Other free-filtering food products, such as tartrates, are handled on drum filters, grains on plate dewaterers, and gelatins, honey, etc., on plate-and-frame presses or horizontal disc pressure filters.

Metallurgical. As many of the filters now in use were first introduced in the mining and metallurgical fields, most types of filters are still found here. For slow-filtering, low-grade tailings, where careful washing is required, the open tank vacuum leaf or pressure cylinder filter is often employed. Where ore grinding in the cyanide process averages 200 mesh and up to 325 mesh, the thickened pulp is filtered and washed on rotary vacuum filters.

Flotation concentrates filter freely for dewatering upon rotary vacuum filters, or like magnetic concentrates they may be handled on internal medium vacuum filters or hopper dewaterers.

Petroleum and Oils. Filters in the petroleum field usually must be entirely enclosed because of fire hazard. Therefore, many plate-and-frame presses, disc pressure leaf filters or centrifuges are used. However, in some solvent dewaxing and deoiling, hooded drum vacuum filters are employed. In oil extraction from seeds, hydraulic or screw presses are used, with plate-and-frame or horizontal disc presses for clarification.

Numerous edge filters and tubular filters are used in oil recovery or separation.

Paints and Varnishes. Paints and varnishes present a clarifying problem, very often in batch lots. For this work, in the smaller quantities, open gravity filters are used. For larger quantities disc presses or plate-and-frame presses are employed.

Paper. Filters are used in several stages in paper pulp handling where, because of the free-filtering nature of the material and the volume to be handled, continuous filters are desired. These may be either the gravity or the vacuum type. Filter media are coarse mesh wire screens when washing stock, decking after screening, and thickening, with finer screens for white water.

Pharmaceutical Products. Gravity filters are used for small quantities of pharmaceuticals and plate-and-frame presses for larger quantities. However, the service is not always clarification, as often appreciable amounts of solids are present which must be filtered out and washed; for this, disc or other presses are used.

Rubber. In handling rubber products for simple dewatering, endless perforated belts with squeeze rolls may be used. Filter presses and drum vacuum filters are employed for reclaimed rubber. The presses are used when the product is finely divided, making it difficult to filter; continuous drum vacuum filters are used for quantity production, if the material is sufficiently free-filtering to be so handled.

With synthetic rubber continuous drum vacuum filters are employed, because of the free filtering nature of the material and the quantities involved.

Sewage. The filters used in dewatering sewage sludge are normally of the rotary drum vacuum design, as the sludge after conditioning is relatively free-filtering and considerable quantities are handled. Formerly plate-and-frame presses were employed to some extent. Elutriated sludges are particularly free-filtering and probably hopper dewaterers could be used here, although rotary vacuum filters are customarily employed.

Water. Normally water filtration is a clarification problem and sand filters, often with coagulants, are used, although pressure disc filters have been installed for industrial water clarification. The sand filters are of the gravity type in some cases and of the pressure type in others, depending upon the service required.

Centrifugal Machines and Centrifuges. Materials handled by centrifugal machines and centrifuges fall into a somewhat different category than filters, as commonly understood. These categories have been listed as:

(1) The separation of immiscible liquids.

(2) The removal and recovery of solid particles dispersed in a liquid phase.

(3) The removal of excess liquid from a solid phase.

The first of these may be further classified depending on the presence or absence of a solid phase.

The selection of the proper centrifugal equipment, for the handling of a specific material in these categories, depends on such factors as:

Degree of separation, dehydration, or purification desired and the correlation of processing cost with these factors.

Amount and characteristics of the solid material present, such as specific gravity, particle size, and in some cases particle shape, and whether the solids must be recovered at maximum concentration, or whether dilution with one of the liquid phases is tolerable.

The number of liquid phases present and their characteristics such as viscosity, specific gravity, volatility, corrosive action and effect of temperature.

Quantity of material to be handled.

Over two hundred types of the tubular bowl centrifuge alone have been developed, which illustrates the wide range of possibilities for centrifugal machines and centrifuges.

Flow Sheets. One of the best ways to illustrate the relative positions of steps in a process is by the use of flow sheets. By this means the process as a whole can be readily visualized and the importance and position of filtration in the particular industry easily determined.

For this reason the following flow sheets, regarded as more or less typical, are given:

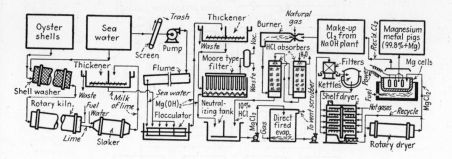

FIGURE 131. Magnesium from seawater. (*Courtesy Chem. & Met. Eng.*)

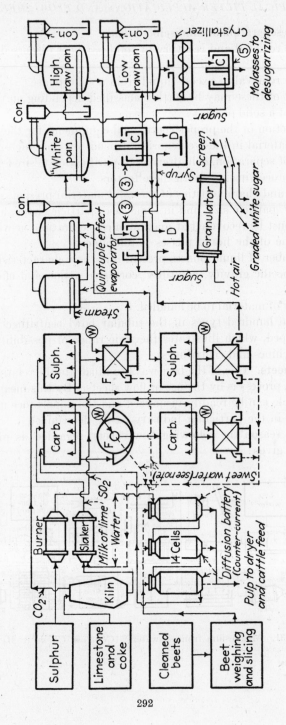

FIGURE 132.   Beet sugar flow sheet.   (*Courtesy Food Industries*)

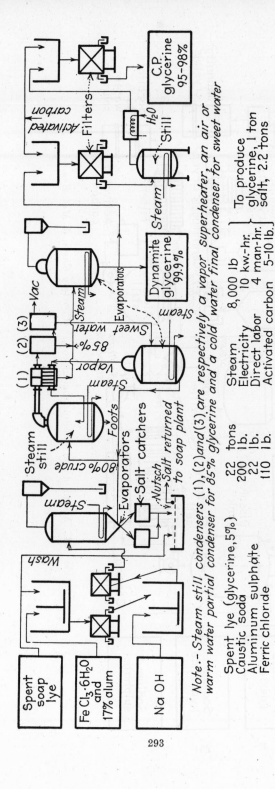

Note.--Steam still condensers (1),(2)and(3) are respectively a vapor superheater, an air or warm water partial condenser for 85% glycerine and a cold water final condenser for sweet water

Spent lye (glycerine, 5%)	22 tons
Caustic Soda	200 lb.
Aluminum sulphate	22 lb.
Ferric chloride	110 lb.

Steam	8,000 lb
Electricity	10 kw.-hr.
Direct labor	4 man-hr.
Activated carbon	5-10 lb.

To produce glycerine, 1 ton salt, 2.2 tons

FIGURE 133. Glycerine. (*Courtesy Chem. & Met. Eng.*)

293

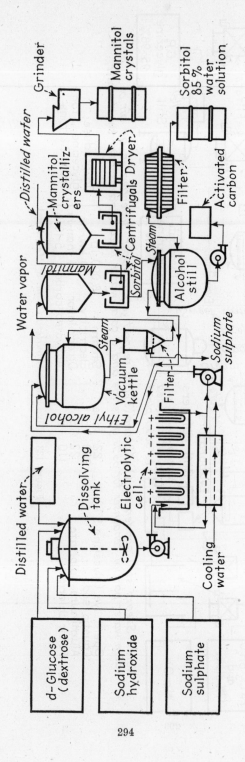

FIGURE 134. Mannitol and sorbitol from glucose. (*Courtesy Chem. & Met. Eng.*)

294

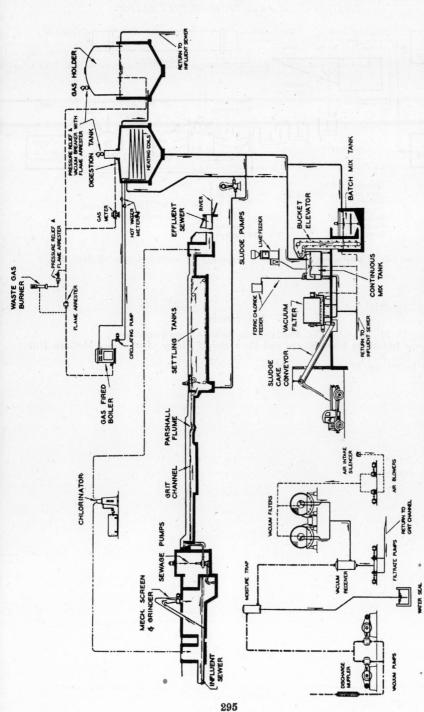

FIGURE 135. Sewage treatment plant, Cortland, New York. (*Courtesy G. D. Holmes, Con. Eng., Sewage Works, Journal 13, 2, Feb. 1942*)

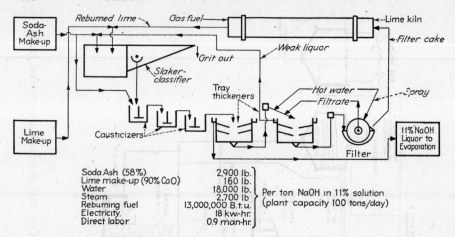

Soda Ash (58%)	2,900 lb.	
Lime make-up (90% CaO)	160 lb.	
Water	18,000 lb.	Per ton NaOH in 11% solution
Steam	2,700 lb	(plant capacity 100 tons/day)
Reburning fuel	13,000,000 B.t.u.	
Electricity	18 kw-hr.	
Direct labor	0.9 man-hr.	

FIGURE 136. Caustic soda (lime soda process). (*Courtesy Chem. & Met. Eng.*)

References

Amber, C. M., Sharples Co., Philadelphia, private correspondence.
"Process Industries Flow Sheets and Data Book," *Chem. Met. Eng.*, McGraw-Hill Pub. Co., N. Y.
Food Industries, Market Research.

Chapter 18

Testing and Selection of Equipment

General. Unless equipment is purchased for increased capacity or replacement, or has a standard rating for a particular purpose, a laboratory check on anticipated results is a desirable safeguard, as there are always variations in individual plant practices that cannot be accurately evaluated without actual tests.

The accuracy by which test data can be translated into plant operation was checked by McMillan and Webber[1] and by Zimmerman and Lavine[2] in the application of the Ruth equation to filtration test data; they found that actual results with commercial filters correspond closely to anticipations so made.

Table C.[1] Summary of Predicted and Actual Filtration Results in a Plate Frame Press

Group No.	Date	Filtration Pressure Lb/sq in	Wt. Fraction of Solids in Sludge	Filtration Time		Washing Rate	
				Predicted	Obsvd.	Predicted	Obsvd.
				Minutes		*Lb/minute*	
I	Nov., 1935	..	....	8.3	10.6	...	...
II	Nov., 1935	..	....	36.5	35.0	5.45	4.82
III	Nov., 1935	..	....	12.1	12.4	4.29	3.62
IV	Nov., 1935	..	....	4.55	6.0	8.73	8.00
V	Dec., 1935	50	0.0217	8.50	10	8.5	6.9
VI	Oct. 15, 1936	20	0.125	5.69	6.16	...	...
VII	Oct. 16, 1936	20	0.125	5.77	7.07	2.06	1.50
VIII	Oct. 27, 1936	40	0.0485	16.38	16.60	2.08	...
	Oct. 27, 1936	20	0.102	10.98	9.3	...	...
IX	Oct. 28, 1936	20	0.120	6.35	6.47	1.84	1.31
X	Nov. 6, 1936	20	0.115	7.95	7.62	1.49	1.33
XI	Nov. 7, 1936	40	0.030	25.41	26.80	2.38	...
XII	Nov. 25, 1936	40	0.044	13.35	13.80	2.91	2.73
XIII[a]	Nov. 28, 1936	50	0.0317	22.0	21.1	...	...
XX	Nov. 1, 1937	25	0.138	13.9	13.4	0.91	0.71
XXI	Nov. 2, 1937	25	0.150	10.62	12.0	...	...
XXII	Nov. 19, 1937	25	0.090	34.8	32.4	...	...

[a]Residue from trisodium phosphate manufacture.

In Table C is given a summary of the predicted and actual results for a plate-and-frame press and in Table D is given the same comparison for rotary drum and rotary disc vacuum filters.

Pressure Filtration. Concerning these tables, McMillan and Webber state that "in pressure filtration the observed filtration time agrees reasonably well with that predicted, under filtration pressures of 20 to 50

Table D.[1] Summary of Predicted and Actual Results in Rotary Vacuum Filter

Group No.	Drum Filter						Disc Filter					
	Thin Sludge			Thick Sludge			Thin Sludge			Thick Sludge		
		Lb dry solid/revolution			Lb dry solid/revolution			Lb dry solid/revolution			Lb dry solid/revolution	
	s	Calcd.	Obsvd.	s	Calcd.	Obsvd.	s	Calcd.	Obsvd.	s	Calcd.	Obsvd.
VI	0.124	1.60	1.57	0.530	11.50	8.60	0.112	13.7	3.7	0.530	90.5	64.2
VII	0.108	1.98	1.50	0.520	11.61	4.50	0.073	17.7	3.8	0.480	74.0	65.0
VIII	0.109	1.68	0.80	0.395	5.95	6.80	0.108	12.3	2.0	0.360	39.2	17.6
IX	0.068	1.21	0.59	0.518	13.6	15.3	0.109	16.1	6.5	0.511	110	54
X	0.089	1.38	0.65	0.360	5.22	4.70	0.117	13.65	9.64	0.366	36.8	38.4
XI	0.125	1.94	1.75	0.503	9.57	13.25	0.117	14.90	9.30	0.512	80	33.8
XII			…	0.481	10.9	12.55	0.112	17.0	10.0	0.480	79.8	41.4
XIII	0.097	1.85	1.35	0.470	9.89	13.12	0.136	19.2	9.92	0.474	76.1	49.7
XIV	0.091	1.40	0.93	0.462	8.09	9.08	0.083	9.34	4.66	0.454	54.4	44.9
XVI	0.146	3.06	2.14	0.506	10.17	9.99	0.156	19.8	12.5	0.318	35.7	33.7
XVII	0.153	2.58	1.34	0.515	10.00	11.25	0.148	15.5	10.25	0.485	62.7	49.0
XVIII	0.134	2.36	0.87	0.542	17.2	15.8	0.126	15.4	7.2	0.473	69.3	53.9
XIX	0.112	2.28	0.70	0.398	8.9	7.74	0.112	14.0	7.0	0.454	52.0	46.0
XX	0.176	2.09	1.90	0.476	6.04	6.95	0.156	16.0	10.87	0.477	42.8	40.0
XXI	0.264	2.88	0.73	0.498	6.68	7.44	0.207	13.5	5.25	0.446	34.1	25.5
XXII	0.150	1.65	1.15	0.532	7.13	9.70	0.206	19.65	6.80	0.450	33.6	33.5
XXIII	0.107	1.51	0.74	0.527	7.97	8.50	0.101	8.68	4.2	0.462	38.6	23.7

298

lbs/sq in and with sludge concentrations from 2 to 15 per cent solids."
Observed filtration time was taken as that time when the expected
amount of filtrate was secured or when the filtrate rate decreased
markedly indicating a full press, whichever occurred first. "Using fairly
non-compressible material having low resistance, it was observed that
actual washing rates were nearly as great as predicted values (81 to 92
per cent), but using a higher-resistant, more compressible calcium carbonate sludge it was found that washing rates were as low as 70 per cent
of the predicted values. Sometimes there was a gradually decreasing
washing rate as washing progressed. Probably this effect is associated
with the compacting of the filter cake at the end of the filtration.

With highly compressible materials of high resistance from trisodium
phosphate manufacture, it will be noted that accurate filtration time was
predicted. Normally compressible materials to do not more than double
their resistance with the doubling of the filtration pressure."

Vacuum Filtration. "With vacuum filtration the predictions were
based upon the cake and cloth resistance observed in test filtrations at
pressures corresponding to the vacuum used. In the test filtration, it was
observed that cloth resistance constant (r_1) varied three-fold, depending
upon the age of the cloth.

"When filtering thick sludge this effect of the uncertainty in filter base
resistance is less, since it comprises only a small portion of the total resistance during the major portion of the filtration cycle. Consequently,
the observed weight of dry solids filtered per revolution checked more
closely with that predicted from the test filtrations when filtering thick
sludge upon the drum filter. One of the chief criticisms of using pressure
filtration tests to predict vacuum filter operation is that in the plate and
frame filter, settling is not particularly objectionable and may even result in faster cake formation, while in the vacuum filters settling is objectionable, resulting in less cake formation. When dealing with sludges
more than 50 per cent solids by weight, the amount of filtrate flow necessary to deposit one pound of solid in the filter cake ($\frac{1-ms}{s}$) varies greatly
with small changes in the m value. For example, a 54 per cent sludge
with an m value of 1.55 would require 0.3 lbs of filtrate flow to deposit
one pound of solid in the cake, while with an m value of 1.65 only 0.2 lb
would be required. Since the predicted amount of cake formed is based
upon calculated filtrate flow, the latter case would represent a 50 per cent
greater predicted capacity than the former. Thus when calculating the
output of a rotary filter using a thick feed, it becomes necessary to have
accurate knowledge of the value of m where (m) is the wet/dry cake
weight and (s) the sludge concentration.

"Taken as a whole, these rotary filter experiments bring out the unsatisfactory operating characteristics of rotary vacuum filters when filtering sludge low in solid content and the fact that almost theoretical capacity is attained when filtering thick sludge. They also serve to emphasize the vastly greater capacity of such equipment when using a thicker sludge. The calculation from test filtration data of the expected capacity of the disc filter soon led to the observation that it was not performing up to its possibilities and suggested improvements in the doctor arrangement and valve adjustment. This is one of the chief justifications for making test filtrations under ideal conditions as a basis for calculation of plant filtration behavior, that it will bring out whether or not the plant equipment is operating at its maximum theoretical capacity."[1]

Constant-Pressure Tests. The following general conclusions were arrived at by McMillan and Webber: "Constant-pressure test filtrations in a small plate-and-frame filter press were found to be a suitable basis for accurate prediction of capacity of larger plant scale filtration equipment, including both the pressure and rotary vacuum types. The new Ruth filtration equations adequately represented the test data and were used in making the calculations of predicted capacities of the larger filters. Test filtrations upon calcium carbonate sludge were made in the concentration range of 10 to 15 per cent solids, at temperatures between 60 and 100°F and at a series of pressures between 5 and 60 lbs/sq in. The larger-scale filtrations were performed at pressures intermediate to those used in the test filtrations, at sludge concentrations ranging from 2 to 54 per cent solids and at temperatures ranging from 60 to 150°F. Not only are the Ruth equations capable of predicting large-scale filter operation when pressure, temperature and concentration of sludge are identical with those used in test filtrations, but when all of these conditions differ from those used in the test filtrations accurate predictions still are possible. Accurate predictions of large-scale operation were secured both with a fairly non-compressible sludge of calcium carbonate and a highly compressible sludge resulting from the neutralization of crude phosphoric acid with soda ash.

"It is shown that only a relatively few constant-pressure filtration equations are necessary in order to calculate plant filtration capacity and that these few equations apply equally well to filter presses and rotary vacuum filters."[1]

However, Spooner and Kriegel[2] state that in most industrial operations filters are fed by pumps the capacities of which fall as the pressure increases, so that for the majority of cases it has been found better to run the filtration test at a constantly increasing pressure, which will approximate the conditions met with in the plant.

Before considering in more detail how the pressure will be increased, it may be well to consider the two common types of solutions that are met with in filtration, those with a high solid content and those with a low solid content, and the usual filter performance specifications. In general, a filter press is required to handle a definite number of gallons of slurry in a given time. If the feed to the filter is sufficiently high in solids content, the problem may resolve itself into one of merely providing sufficient cake-holding capacity in the filter. When several runs a day are being made, as in the case of many pigments, the filter presses are operated in tandem, one filter being filled while the other is being cleaned, so that it is desirable to have the time required to fill the filter equal the cleaning time, so that one filter will always be in operation.

While theoretically the thickness of the frames in a filter can be anything desired, practical considerations limit the minimum thickness to 1 inch on larger-size filters; above this figure, it is customary to increase it in multiples of $\frac{1}{4}$ inch.

Testing. Tests usually may be run at the equipment manufacturer's laboratory. Here there are many advantages in the numerous types of testing apparatus, tabulation of results, experience with similar problems, and translations of results into plant-sized equipment.

However, there are many materials which change in their filtering characteristics within a relatively short period of time, or which require special conditions of treatment during filtration, as refrigeration, special solvent washes, inert gases, coverage, etc.; these can be tested only at the production plant. In such cases it is always desirable to have pilot plant-sized apparatus, rather than the smaller laboratory testing units. Experiments on pilot apparatus can be run over several days or weeks and accurate figures obtained, especially necessary with materials difficult to handle.

Ordinarily, smaller-sized equipment is used in manufacturer's laboratories than at the prospect's plant, since the experienced filtration engineer can more readily interpret results and with all testing facilities at hand, more easily make accurate determinations. A filtration engineer is handicapped in going to a manufacturer's plant with only the rather limited equipment he can bring, and without pilot-sized equipment previously sent and installed, except in general observations, and unless it is a simple project, or the plant is unusually well equipped for such testing.

Where samples are sent to a manufacturer's laboratory, data information sheets giving all pertinent information necessary for making the test should accompany the sample.

Vacuum Tests. For laboratory testing with vacuum apparatus filter leaves or straight-sided funnels are connected to vacuum flasks, to an aspirator or vacuum pump, and to compressed air. The testing filter leaves may be rectangular or round, with filter medium on both sides, or circular, with the filter medium on the bottom only. The former gives more filter area in a unit space, making agitation easier, giving right angle deposits and readily allowing construction in corrosion-resistant materials; the latter enables filter cloth changes to be made more quickly and allows practically all the sample to be filtered. Usually both types are available in the laboratory, the particular sample determining the one to use. Sizes range from 2″ × 2″, or 2″ in diameter to 6″ × 6″, or 6″ in diameter, in a variety of materials of construction.

For heavy solids or small samples porcelain funnels are used, as the material here can be entirely filtered, the size of funnels ranging from 2″ to 6″ inside funnel diameter. Filter paper or any other filter medium may be used.

A series of shutoff cocks (in glass, rubber or brass) in the interconnecting lines permits separation of filtrate and wash water without vacuum loss.

The actual tests may have two or more stages, requiring hand shifting of the filter leaf or funnel (in which latter case the vacuum is broken) between each two stages, *i.e.*, cake formation, washing if need be, or successive washes, air drying, and discharge, the last either by air pressure or scraping with a spatula. Triplicate runs are made for checking average and composite samples.

A careful tabulation must be kept of the various steps; time, quantity, behavior, and method of procedure, so that a reliable translation can be made to cycles of operation upon commercial filters.

Pressure Tests. In pressure filter testing generally small units of commercial construction are used. The sizes range from a fraction of a square foot in the shell type to 4-inch plates in the plate-and-frame design. Tests are run at constant rates or constant pressures.

In shell-type pressure filters, the cake compression, discharge and rates of flow can be directly interpreted into commercial units. For low-pressure filtration runs (up to 60 pounds) the vacuum test leaf is often used, with a factor for conversion into pressure filtration. This is particularly true where preliminary tests are to be made at a manufacturing plant or on a small sample in the laboratory of equipment manufacturer, for observation of the filtration possibilities.

For plate-and-frame tests, if the material to be tested is run through a small suction filter and the volume of solids and liquid determined, it is possible to make a rough estimate of how much filtrate will be passed through the test equipment in order to fill the frames with solids. For most filter press determinations a 7-inch square corner feed washing filter press is used. With one 1-inch frame the holding capacity would be 0.02 ft^3, with a 1½-inch frame 0.03 ft^3, with a 2-inch frame 0.04 ft^3, etc., and in all cases the filter area would be ½ sq ft.

A 1-inch frame is by far the most widely used and would be the first choice for a frame thickness in the absence of any knowledge of the possible use of thicker frames. Knowing the approximate solid content of the feed, the pressure during filtration is increased so that a pressure of 65 to 75 lbs per sq in is obtained when the frame is almost completely filled with solids. The filtrate is collected in measured quantities usually of one pint or one quart, and the time and pressure for each unit are recorded. If the time required to fill the filter is considerably less than that called for, or less than one hour in the case where two filters are to be used, thicker frames should be tried.

If the volume of accumulated filtrate, normally in gallons per square foot, is plotted against the accumulated time, the parabolic type of curve usually obtained will indicate whether or not there is sufficient time left to go to a thicker frame. For a first approximation, the curve is examined; usually a noticeable break in the curve will be seen near the very end of the cycle, which indicates practically complete filling of the frame. From this point the curve may be extrapolated to a filtrate volume 25 per cent more than that obtained in the test representing 1¼-inch cakes, 50 per cent representing 1½-inch cakes, etc. This of course can be facilitated by making the plot on log paper, in which case the curve will approach a straight line. Having decided on a new thickness, a check run with the new frame thickness may be made, but in most cases, this is not necessary. It must be borne in mind, however, that in general the moisture content of the filter press cake tends to increase as the frame thickness increases, and the washing efficiency decreases as the cake thickness increases.

In cases where the solids in the feed are not sufficient to fall into the case above, there is a condition where both holding capacity and filter area must be considered. This type of filtration may be divided into two general cases, *i.e.*, filtrations in which no filter aid is used and those in which a filter aid is used.

Where no filter aid is used the same procedure is followed as in case 1, and if a 1-inch cake were built up in less than the required time the problem would rightly belong to case 1. If the filtrate flow is not too far from the desired value it may be compensated for in some cases by a more rapid increase in the rate of building up pressure; but this must be done with caution, since some materials have a tendency to pack. From the data obtained in the first test, the amount of liquid required to build any given thickness of cake is now definitely known and the pressure may be increased a maximum of about 75 to 100 lbs per sq in, when the frame is about ½ full. Thus the latter half of the cake is made at the full filtration pressure, if the capacity is still short of the desired value, and the size of the filter will not be over the 24 inches square. Frames ¾ inch thick may be used, or, in sizes below 18 inches, frames ½ inch thick; or solid frames may be used, in which case any thickness of cake may be obtained. However, in this case the cakes so obtained cannot be washed in the plate.

When filter aid is used, the problem becomes more or less a case of running several tests of the type already outlined. The filter aid should be the coarsest that will give the desired clarity, and the amount used will, in general, range from 25 to 50 per cent of the amount of suspended solids in the liquid. As a rule, this is in the range of ¹⁄₁₀ of 1 per cent filter aid based on the weight of the liquid. The tests should be carried out as already described, each new percentage of filter aid being treated as a new solution, the size of the filter computed and an economic balance set up. In many cases the largest single item of cost will be the amount of liquid retained by the larger amount of cake that results from the increased filter aid.

Filter Selection. The type of filter medium used likewise will have a considerable bearing on filtration rate. The medium should be sufficiently tight to give the necessary clarity, but no tighter than necessary. A summary of results from testing enables the proper type and size of filter for the particular project to be selected and reported. Recommendations, and the return of samples of such runs, submitted to the prospective purchaser, will avoid later controversies, and if examination proves the samples unsatisfactory, additional tests can be made until the desired results, or the nearest approach to them, are obtained. In selecting any filter initial and operating costs must be taken into account first of all; depreciation, adaptability, control, and conversion must also be considered.

In analyzing a laboratory report sheet upon the separation of solids from liquids by filtration, the first consideration is whether continuous filtration is possible and practicable. While the filtration rate as indicated by the cake formation may be sufficiently rapid to warrant continuous filtration, there are a number of other considerations. Can the temperature be maintained; is there time for the required washing; can a sufficiently dry cake be obtained; is too large filter area required, etc.? Actually these all involve the question of economy in comparison with other methods of handling and the value of the product. Proper insulation with vacuum (limited by the flash point) or pressure filtration, will enable the necessary temperature to be maintained. Washing requirements can be obtained by repulping and refiltering in a series of filters; dryness of cake by a sufficiently slow-speed, rollers, volume of air (hot or cold), etc.; and the necessary filter area can be obtained if sufficient filters are used.

Example Selection, Vacuum Filter. If the filter cake builds up rapidly, discharges freely without clogging the filter cloth, and is as dry as need be upon discharge, a continuous drum vacuum filter should be tentatively selected.

Assuming no complications in a vat type drum filter selection, the size of filter becomes the next consideration. Should it be found, however, that there is danger of the rapidly forming cake sloughing off the filter drum as it emerges from the vat or too rapid settling for proper agitation, a top feed filter or a dewaterer should be considered.

Since a $\frac{3}{8}$-inch cake is formed in 3 minutes and dried in two minutes, the total cycle would be 6 minutes (allowing an additional minute for discharge and resubmergence and a 50 per cent drum submergence). This makes ten cycles or revolutions of the filter drum per hour. If a filter of one square foot is being used and the discharged cake weighs 0.85 pound wet and 0.51 pound dry, there is a moisture content of 40 per cent and a capacity of 5.1 pounds per square foot (0.51×10 cycles) per hour. Allowing 20 per cent margin of safety for laboratory figures over plant operation, a figure of 4 pounds dry weight of solids per square foot per hour can be anticipated.

In order to handle 64,000 pounds in a 20-hour day, 800 square feet of filter area would be required. This could be obtained in one filter; for example, 12'-0" in diameter by 18'-0" long, but as this would make such a large machine, the preference would be for two filters each of 400 sq ft area, in such sizes as 10'-0" diameter by 14'-0" face (439 sq ft).

Example Selection, Pressure Filter. If, for example, the filtration is slow and the temperature is 350°F, too high for a continuous vacuum filtration; and in addition pressures up to 60 lbs are used to obtain the highest rate of flow, then it becomes a pressure-filter proposition. Assuming that only a $1\frac{1}{2}$-inch cake can be built up in 8 hours' time this would eliminate the continuous pressure filter, while the low price of a product, the long cycle and a lack of wash (giving no advantage to a shell type filter in a thin cake) indicate the plate-and-frame press as the most economical selection. The type of filter press now must be given consideration.

Press Types. Filter presses may be divided into three main classes: corner feed, side feed and center feed. The corner feed filter requires cloths with holes punched to match the eyes of the plate. If the solution being filtered is aqueous, the cloths should be pre-shrunk, so that there will be no further shrinkage during operation that might bring the holes in the cloth out of line with the eyes of the plates. No aqueous solutions have a stretching effect on pre-shrunk cloth, causing it to revert to its original length and bring the eyes out of line. In the case of non-aqueous solutions, it is usually advisable to use an unshrunk cloth as a backing and filter paper for the actual filter medium. The paper is thrown away at the end of each run, and the backing cloth, which comes into contact with the filtered liquid only, remains clean. It may be periodically dry-cleaned, which eliminates the possibility of the unshrunk cloth shrinking during the cleaning operation. The corner-feed press has the advantage of having the cloth act as its own gasket, on the one gasket joint of each plate; thus several thicknesses of filter media may be used, as in some special types of filtration, without regard to the possibility that the rubber collars in the channels may not make up properly. The corner-feed press also lends itself more readily to a "leak-proof" type of construction, to steam-jacketing or to rubber covering.

A number of strong salt solutions have a tendency to stretch pre-shrunk cloths, and for this purpose the side-feed press is better suited.

The side-feed filter has the advantage of not requiring a punch cloth and is therefore sometimes considered a safer press to leave in the hands of totally unskilled operators, since there is no need to see that the holes in the cloth line up with those in the plates. Both the side-feed and the corner-feed filters are adaptable to washing, and for most filtration problems may be used interchangeably.

The center-feed type is designed primarily for handling materials likely to contain relatively large pieces of solid matter which might lodge in the parts of a side- or corner-feed filter. The design of a center-feed filter is such that anything small enough to pass through the pipe line will enter the cake recess. As a general rule, it can be cleaned more quickly than either a side- or a corner-feed filter. It is not an efficient filter for washing, although good results are obtained in the vegetable oil industry by blowing steam into the inlet pipe. The cake obtained from a filter of this type is higher in moisture content than from the corner- or side-feed, since the center of the cake never becomes actually solid. The center-feed press is not adaptable to steam-jacketing.

In the case of the corner- or side-feed filter, any general arrangement of the feed and discharge may be used. It is advisable to have the feed at the bottom and the discharge at the top so that the air in the filter at the start is vented. This is the most general arrangement, but in cases where the solids have a tendency to settle and block the inlet eye, a top feed is used. When it is desired to drain off any filtrate that may remain in the plates of the filter at the end of the run, the three-eyed type with bottom feed and bottom discharge and with top air vent is used. In the case of the side-feed presses it is usual to locate the channels just above the side bars, which is suitable for most cake-recovery operations; but for cases where a precoat is to be used, it is desirable to have the channels located in the extreme corners so that excess precoat liquor may be withdrawn.

The type of discharge is largely a matter of plant set-up and operator preference. If the filter is of the closed-delivery type, the filtrate may be piped to some other part of the plant, or elevated by the pressure from the same pump that feeds the filter. If the open-delivery system is used, the operator can immediately detect a defective cloth and close the cock on the defective plate. The filtrate if discharged into a trough may give rise to objectionable fumes; if the filtrate is to be used at a point higher than the filter, an auxiliary pump must be used.

In order to combine the advantages of both open and closed delivery, visible discharge and test and shutoff cocks have been used. In the former the flow from each plate is visible in a glass tube attached to each plate and individual plates may be shut off. In the case of the test cocks, the cock may be opened to withdraw a sample of filtrate, or the flow of the plate shut off completely.

The method of closing filter presses varies somewhat with the size. Small laboratory presses are sometimes provided with wing nut closing, which works on the round side bars, although the most common method for the 7- and 12-inch sizes of filter press is the direct capstan closing. On the 18- and 30-inch sizes it is usual to replace the capstan with a ratchet closing device. On sizes above 30 inches and on many 36-inch filters a gear-and-pinion closing is used in place of the ratchet, as it permits easier tightening of the press. Hydraulic closure is available for the larger sizes.

Careful consideration of the above in light of the laboratory results indicates the selection of a non-washing, open-delivery, side-feed type of plate-and-frame press. As the filter cake is not to be washed, the non-washing press naturally will be chosen. As filtrate is non-volatile and low-priced, the open-delivery type would be selected as an economical machine, and the side-feed type because it requires no cut holes or pre-shrinking. Here the 20 per cent margin of safety is again used, making the filter time 8.6 hours plus 0.4 hour for opening, discharge and closing the press. Therefore, in order to handle 16,000 gallons per day of 24 hours (20 hrs taken) in the two cycles there would be required 100 sq ft of filter area, $\frac{16,000}{80\times2}$, in a press of eight 30-inch frames.

The margin of safety figure is taken to compensate for the less efficient plant handling over laboratory control, while the 20-hour day allows 4 hours for inspection, maintenance and repairs.

Centrifuges. The same degree of purification will be obtained with a high-speed centrifuge at a throughput rate of 200 gallons per hour as on the laboratory machine at a throughput rate of 400 cc/min. This correlation holds for a wide variety of materials with an accuracy estimated at ±10 per cent. It is assumed in making such tests that all such conditions as degree of emulsification, temperature, etc., are constant.

In the field of crystal dehydration a 12-inch perforated basket bulk centrifuge, operated at a speed to give the same centrifugal force as the proposed commercial equipment, may be used for the determination of unit draining rates and final purity. A factor must be applied, however, to compensate for the difference in cake thickness. For bulk centrifuge decantation a 12-inch solid basket operated at the corresponding centrifugal force often is used, and a conversion factor based on the liquid-holding capacity of the test equipment and the full-scale equipment applied.

In selecting the type of machine, laboratory tests on the small units enable a definite decision to be made as to that best suited to the particular project; the size can be directly computed.

References

1. McMillen, E. L., & Webber, H. P., "Plant Operation from Test Data," *Amer. Inst. Chem. Eng.*, Vol. 34, 3, 1938.
2. Spooner and Kriegel, private correspondence.
3. Zimmerman and Lavine, Ind. Research Service, 1943.

Chapter 19

Installation and Operation

General. Before installing equipment a complete layout should be made so that not only the filter may be located for easy, economical handling, but the necessary auxiliaries may be placed to insure most efficient operation of the filter. Instruction pamphlets for the installation and operation of filters and their auxiliaries are published by equipment manufacturers. These instructions should be studied carefully and followed as closely as practicable, since they have been prepared by specialists in each particular piece of equipment.

Installation. A few simple rules should be followed in practically all cases.

(1) See that all equipment and connections are installed as called for by the manufacturer's drawings.

(2) Check to see that all machines and all drives are correctly aligned.

(3) See that all oil and grease fittings are in proper working condition and are filled with the required lubricants.

(4) Turn moving parts by hand to be sure they are free.

(5) Turn on the power to see that all the switches are working and the motors turning in the right direction.

(6) Test the pipe lines for tightness and support.

(7) Check operation with water, where liquor is to be handled.

(8) Check feed to make sure it is the type, concentration, temperature, (pH), etc., for which the set-up was made.

(9) All valves should be readily accessible.

(10) Pipe lines should be equipped with numerous unions for ready dismantling, and tees should be installed for cleaning out at all possible clogging danger points.

(11) The operating room should be well lighted.

(12) Floors should be equipped with drainage connection for washing down equipment and should be pitched to the drain.

(13) The operator should be well instructed in the use of the equipment.

(14) All equipment should be kept as clean as possible.

Operation. Operation of the various equipment has been described under the respective headings, but specific details from plant experience will aid in giving a clearer picture of the functioning of each piece of apparatus.

In order that such operating data may be of practical value, an average of normal operations has been taken. This can be modified where necessary to become applicable to any particular plant practice. Because of newness, limited applications, or inability to obtain reliable operating data, information is not available upon all designs of equipment, and others are only briefly touched upon.

In operating a filter many factors affect a particular material, as to the filtration rate, effectiveness of wash, and the dryness of cake—the three factors in which the filter operator is most interested. Except in special cases, the higher the permissible temperature the better. The feed should be uniform in consistency and nature; the auxiliaries must be functioning properly, etc., for most efficient operation.

Gravity Bag Filters. Gravity bag filters in the separation of solids from liquids are not now of extensive interest, but where they are used, as in the sugar industry, clarity is the important item. Supervision of the intake and outlet, as well as the careful removal and replacement of filter bags, are the chief considerations to secure this clarity.

As the rate of flow decreases markedly the cloths should be removed, washed and carefully replaced, checking for holes and providing for rerunning of first filtrates, which may be cloudy because of new cloths, holes, or improper rinsing of cloths. With the wide variety in textures and weaves to choose from, care must be used in selecting the medium best suited to the conditions at hand.

Gravity Stationary Filters. In gravity stationary filters, ceramic filters and false-bottom tanks, including percolating filters, the selection and installation of the filter medium is the most important factor to be considered. If composed of loose and rigid particles the surface should be smooth and level. Care should be taken to prevent channeling in feeding, and clogged surfaces should be immediately cleaned.

Where rigid media are used in fixed contact, cleaning of the filter medium is the prime consideration in operation. Burning is often resorted to as a means of medium cleaning where scraping, acid washing or brushing is ineffective. Where this is done, absolutely complete burning is necessary in order to avoid blind spots. As filtration is usually by batch lots, reduced flow rates may be readily detected by comparison with previous runs and clogged media corrected.

Water Filters. For efficient operation of gravity water filters, ample-sized sedimentation tanks are important, as are reliable coagulent feeders, properly graded gravel, sand beds, and adequate back-washing and cleaning apparatus. Automatic tabulation of flows enables close checks to be made on operation, and the recording charts should be carefully watched for proper control and regulation.

Table E. Mineral Analysis of Filtered Water. Composite of Daily Samples, Results in Parts Per Million
(Courtesy Baltimore City Water Supply Bureau)

Month	pH	Alkalinity	Loss on Ignition	Total Dissolved Solids	Silica (SiO₂)	Total Iron (Fe)	Aluminum (Al)	Calcium (Ca)	Magnesium (Mg)	Sodium and Potassium (Na and K)	Manganese (Mn)	Nitrates (NO₃)	Bi-carbonates (HCO₃)	Sulfates (SO₄)	Chloride (Cl)	Soap Hardness
January	7.7	37	32.9	84.5	5.3	0.05	0.2	12.9	3.5	2.5	0.00	0.3	45	17.1	5.5	53
February	7.9	37	31.5	79.3	4.9	0.03	0.2	13.9	3.5	2.6	0.04	0.7	45	16.6	4.5	52
March	7.9	35	27.9	80.1	5.2	0.03	0.2	13.7	3.4	2.9	0.04	0.5	43	17.2	5.0	51
April	7.9	34	35.5	83.2	5.9	0.03	0.2	12.7	3.3	2.6	0.00	0.7	41	14.6	5.0	47
May	7.9	36	31.5	79.9	7.0	0.03	0.2	13.3	3.4	2.2	0.00	0.5	44	13.3	5.5	48
June	7.8	39	37.5	84.2	6.3	0.02	0.3	12.2	3.2	2.0	0.00	1.0	47	14.5	5.5	49
July	7.9	39	31.4	80.7	4.7	0.02	0.2	12.9	3.0	2.6	0.01	0.5	47	12.9	5.0	49
August	7.9	41	34.7	80.8	5.4	0.03	0.2	13.9	3.0	2.5	0.00	0.4	50	11.8	5.0	51
September	7.8	42	29.2	82.3	5.5	0.02	0.2	13.3	3.1	2.8	0.00	0.2	51	11.1	6.0	52
October	8.2	46	37.8	84.5	5.0	0.03	0.2	13.7	3.1	2.0	0.04	0.1	56	11.1	6.0	55
November	7.7	40	31.6	78.1	4.8	0.02	0.2	12.9	3.6	2.4	0.00	0.2	49	10.4	5.5	49
December	7.8	38	29.7	72.5	5.2	0.02	0.2	12.1	3.5	2.5	0.00	0.2	46	10.5	5.5	45
Averages	7.9	39	32.6	80.8	5.4	0.03	0.2	13.1	3.3	2.5	0.01	0.4	47	13.4	5.3	50

Pressure Leaf Filters. In installing pressure leaf filters of the vertical leaf or vertical disc type, floor space, headroom and piping connections for accessibility are of particular importance. Where the leaves are withdrawn from the shell, sufficient floor space must be provided for carriage withdrawal; where the bottom of the shell is dropped for cake discharge sufficient space between the floor and the press must be allowed; and where the top of the shell must be removed for filter cloth changes or the top is hinged for both cloth changing and cake removal, sufficient headroom must be provided to accomplish this.

In clarification requiring precoating, additional precoating equipment is required. This may involve considerable equipment if the precoat is paper pulp, which is used at times in clarifying sugar juice or for similar service. In any case it means careful consideration of these factors in the installation for efficient operation.

As one of the largest items of expense with these filters is the filter medium, anything that might prolong the life of the filter cloth should be carefully considered. Often a metallic, synthetic glass or rubber medium can be used, particularly with a precoat; this will outlast a canvas medium many times and may more than pay for its greater cost.

Care should be taken in cleaning filter leaves when the filter is opened for discharge. If the cake does not come off completely and the operator scrapes it off with a metal shovel or sharp tool, it will greatly shorten the life of the medium. Where scraping must be resorted to, wooden, rubber, or snythetic paddles should be used.

Typical Plant Data Pressure Leaf Filters

Material	Filtration Object	Feed Temp. (°F)	Suspended Solids in Feed (%)	Moisture Content Cake. (%)	Cake (lbs per sq ft per hr)	Filtrate (gals per hr)
Aluminum Hydrate 58 Brix	Cake	70	0.20	34	.7	—
Affinated Syrup	Filtrate	180	1.50	60	—	.74
Black Liquor	Filtrate	150	0.30	—	—	70
Cobalt Oxide 58 Brix	Filtrate	65	1.0	—	—	17
Remelt Liquor	Filtrate	175	0.30	60	—	2.96
Kaolin	Cake	65	2.0	54	2	—
Magnesium Hydrate 63 Brix	Cake	65	10.0	59	1½	—
Washed Sugar Liquor	Filtrate	180	0.30	60	—	1.83
61 Brix Low Gran. Syrup	Filtrate	170	0.30	60	—	1.77

Filter Presses

In plate-and-frame presses clean ends on the plates and frames and smooth cloths are essential. The filter press installation is easily made, and usually the feed pump is the only auxiliary piece of equipment needed. Little operating supervision is required, particularly if a by-pass relief valve is used to cut off the flow when the maximum pressure is reached.

On side-feed filter presses rubber collars or cloth pockets require attention for replacements, as do the clip nuts on the center-feed type. Since dumping and cleaning each cycle is by hand, operating carelessness may cause plate and frame breakage due to clogged ports or rough handling. Filter-cloth failure very often is due to gouging, tearing or ripping of the cloth by scrapers, hoes, or other tools in cake discharging.

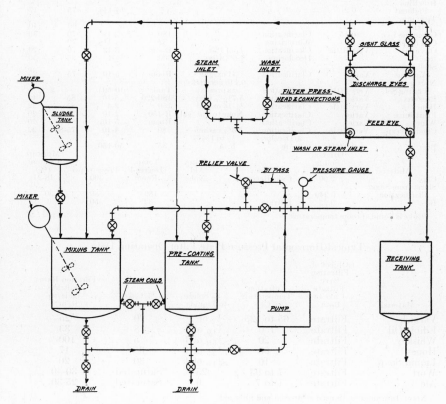

FIGURE 137. Schematic layout for closed delivery washing filter press, when using filter-aid, decolorizing agent or both. (*Courtesy T. Shriver & Co.*)

Unless special, so-called leak-proof designs of plates and frames are used, leakage is likely to occur when very thin, low-viscosity materials, as distilled liquors, alcohol and other solvents are handled, or very high pressures employed; wrinkled cloths, dirty frames, and worn plates and frames must be avoided.

While the filtrate may be cloudy at the beginning of filtration for a minute or two until a deposit has been built up, this cloudiness should not persist. If it does, it may be that pressures are too high or are fluctuating too much, leading to a pulsation which disturbs the cake.

Filter Press (Plate or Plate and Frame) Performance on Various Materials

Material	Original Solids (lbs/gal) Dry Basis	Object	Filter Aid	Filtration Temperature (°F)	Rate Gallons per sq ft per hr	Weight of Cake per cu ft (lbs) Wet	Dry
Aluminum Hydroxide	0.05-0.08	Cake Recovery	None	Room	1-4	75	16
Iron Blue Pigment	0.2	"	"	"	½-1½	75	17
Titanium Oxide	2.6	"	"	"	5	90	40
Glycerine Lye	0.15	Clarification	"	180	2-4	70	30
Cod Liver Oil	*	Winterizing	"	32	½-1½	70	—
Olive Oil	Very little	Clarification	¼ of 1%	Room	8-12	70	20
Rosin	"	Decoloring	4-6% Clay	300	½-1	85	50
Shellac, Aqueous	Varies	Clarification	½-1 oz/gal	Room	5-10	75	25
Ni SO₄ Plating Sol.	Very little	Clarification	0.1 lb per sq ft as precoat	Tank	10-30	—	—
Beeswax	Varies	Clarification	5-7½% Clay	180-220	5-10	85	45
Honey	Very little	Clarification	¼-½ oz/gal	150	2-4	85	22
Fruit Juice	Varies	Clarification	None to 2 oz/gal	R-150	2-10	75	20
Wine	Varies	Clarification		Room	5-10	80	20
Candy Scrap	Very little	Clarification & Decolor.	1-3% carbon ½ to 1½%	180	4-10	75-85	22
Beer	0.025%	Filtrate	F. A.	35	50-150		

Material	Original Solids (lb/gal)	Object	Filter Aid	Temp. (Degree F)	Pressure psi	Moisture Content (%)
Clay	2.90	Cake Recovery	None	Room	300	18-21
Slurry from Sugar Clarification	0.249	"	"	180	80	50
Beer	0.25	Filtrate	"	32	50	

*Cake is liquid at room temperature.

Typical Horizontal Pressure Plate Filter Operating Data

Material	Object of Filtration Save Filtrate Cake or Both	Filtration Temperature (°C)	% Solids to Liquids	% Cake Moisture	Filration Rates Filtrate (gals/sq ft/hr)
Varnish	Filtrate	65 to 125	½ of 1	20	25
Edible Oil	Filtrate	150	¹⁄₁₀ of 1	18	35
Whiskey	Filtrate	20	¹⁄₅₀ of 1	5	100
Honey	Filtrate	60	¹⁄₂₅ of 1	35	17
Liquid Soap	Filtrate	10	¹⁄₁₀ of 1	30	20
Wort	Filtrate	7 to 93	.25	Saturated	30-40
Ale	Filtrate	1 to 7	6	Saturated	25-30

Note: Infusorial earth used as precoat and filter aid.

Vacuum Filters. As vacuum filters require more auxiliary equipment than pressure or gravity filters, particular attention must be given to these items. Starting with the vacuum pump, the proper size for the filter must be selected, ranging from ¾ cfm per sq ft of filter area in some cyanide slimes, to 200 cfm per sq ft in some salts.

With water-cooled pumps water temperature, supply and condition

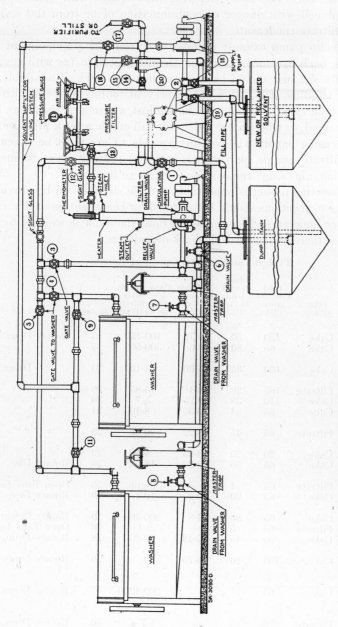

FIGURE 138. Diagrammatic layout of dry cleaning pressure filter plant. (*Courtesy S. F. Bowser Co.*)

must be checked. The same checking takes place with water-sealed pumps, combined with danger of contamination of or from the sealing water and filtrate condensate.

The vacuum pump exhaust is important from the standpoint of exhaust gases, back pressure and noise. In the first case (as with sewage filtration) the exhaust should be to an incinerator stack, if available, or outside the building at a high point to prevent fouling of the air within the plant. The exhaust should not be against a discharge head, as beneath the ground, or where wind resistance will create a back pressure, or where condensing vapors will be objectionable. Care must be taken in installing filtrate pumps, particularly non-self-priming ones, to insure pump flooding, air "slug" removal and discharge head.

Interconnecting piping is important. Ample sizes should be provided for, drainage connections should be installed for condensation at dry vacuum pump or blowers, and blower connections should be downward to the filter valve so there will be no drain-back of moisture.

Typical Vacuum Filter Operating Results

Material	Filter Object	Feed Temperature (°F)	Suspended Solids in Feed (%)	Moisture Content in Cake (%)	Capacity (lbs dry solids or gals filtrate per sq ft/hr)	Vacuum (inches)	Type
Aluminum							
Trihydrate	Cake	130	50	10-12	100-150	5	Rotary Dewaterer
Concentrate	Cake	65	80	3-5	300-500	5	" "
Barium							
Sulfate	Cake	160	35	25-30	8-10	20	" Drum
Calcium							
Carbonate	Filtrate	165	20	43-48	75-85	26	" "
Clay	Cake	110	38	20-25	5-7	26	" "
Tin Oxide	Cake	65	4	30-35	8-10	24	" "
Cyanide							
Slimes	Filtrate	65	45	18-22	20-30	22	" "
Lead							
Arsenate	Cake	20	20	60-65	8-10	22	" "
Cement	Cake	65	55	20-22	18-22	26	Rotary Disc
Zinc							
Cyanide	Filtrate	65	4	—	2 gph	26	Open Tank Leaf
Whiting	Cake	65	20	20-25	10-15	20	Rotary Disc
Barium							
Nitrate	Cake	65	80	6-8	200-300	10	Rotary Dewaterer
Slimes	Filtrate	65	5	—	.9-1½	26	Open Tank Leaf
Starch	Cake	65	45	45-48	20-25	28	Rotary Drum
Ferric							
Hydrate	Cake	165	10	65-70	10	26	Rotary Drum
Washing							
Paper							
Pulp	Cake	65	1½	—	200-1200 gal	5	Rotary Drum
Dewaxing							
Lube Oils	Filtrate	−20	15	—	1.7 g	26	Rotary Drum
Bicarb. Soda	Cake	80	50	11-14	350	14	Rotary Drum
Coal	Cake	65	20	5-7	500	10	Rotary Dewaterer
1st Carb.					100#		
Sugar	Filtrate	80	8	—	Beets	24	Rotary Drum

Within the filter itself the filter medium should be given first consideration in operating attention. With scraper discharge machines the scraper should be carefully adjusted to give a clean discharge, but not excessive wear. The cloths should be backwashed and scrubbed frequently if the slurry tends to clog. Cloths should not be allowed to dry out, as this causes concentration of any soluble salts in their moisture content for attack, crystallization, incrustation, etc. in and upon the medium.

The filter should be easily accessible for inspection, oiling and filter cloth changes. Platforms or other provisions should be made for ease in filter dressing.

Clogging of the filter medium may be indicated by a reduction in cake thickness, rise in vacuum, if it is not operating at the maximum, and slowing up of feed liquor consumption. Holes may be indicated by cloudy filtrate, loss of vacuum, or a whistling sound; these can be patched to some extent with small pieces of medium.

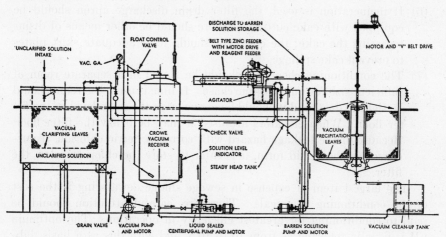

FIGURE 139. Simultaneous clarification-precipitation process using verticle leaf vacuum filter. (*Courtesy Merrill Co.*)

Where bronze, Monel, or stainless steel winding wire is used on drum filters it will serve for many cloth changes, and therefore should be spool-wound upon removal for ready replacement.

Sewage Sludge Filters. Sewage sludge in the larger plants generally is dewatered mechanically by drum vacuum filters. Filtration here is simply dewatering, without the necessity of cake washing, but there is the complication of a conditioning requirement before the sludge becomes filtrable. This conditioning affects not only the operation but also the installation. In addition to the special points previously enumerated, there are seven others which should be considered with a sewage sludge filter installation.

(1) The filter room should be well ventilated, particularly when stale raw sludge is being handled. This may be done by using filter hoods, or by a ventilating system.

(2) A concentration tank for sludge thickening is often desirable; it should be equipped with mechanical agitation.

(3) Large feed and drain lines (6 to 8 inches) should be provided, with drain connections both to the conditioning tank and to the sewer.

(4) The layout should be flexible enough to allow for variation in operation, *i.e.*, mixing time and speed, quantities of conditioning agents, points of conditioning application, and cake disposal, (*e.g.*, as a reversible conveyor).

(5) There should be convenient means of taking samples of the cake (as a cookie tester), filtrate, and conditioned and unconditioned sludge.

(6) If incineration is used, the filter drum discharge apron should be equipped with cake cutters, or there should be other means of disintegrating the cake; the conveyor should have adequate skirt plates to prevent cake spillage.

(7) The conditioning chemicals should be stored in a separate room of sufficient size for quantity purchase. If lime is used, the room should be tight to dust, and it should be above or on the same level as the filter floor. When elevators are used it may be below the filter floor. Because of the leakage hazard with corrosive ferric chloride, if purchased in the liquid form, it is safer to store the chloride below the filter.

The largest item of expense in sewage sludge dewatering is the cost of the conditioning chemicals. Therefore, careful attention should be paid to conditioning for greatest efficiency in operation. The optimum pH is usually reported as from 10 to 10.5, and with this as a basis, laboratory checks should be run on funnel filters. Normally, five minutes' time is considered the maximum allowable in laboratory filtering to get any practical filtering rate and still have the sludge sufficiently conditioned so that it will not clog the filter medium.

An increase in the solids content of the sludge tends to save conditioning chemicals; for this reason sludge thickeners are often used, although too thick a sludge is hard to condition and may slough off the filter drum. At some plants minimum conditioning is used giving a low yield, estimating that the greater filter area or filtering time required is more than overbalanced in cost by the saving in chemicals. The appearance of the sludge or filtrate often will indicate over-conditioning to the operator; a reddish brown cake or amber filtrate indicates an over-dose of ferric chloride.

Usually the second largest item of operating expense is the filter medium, and its renewal is more frequently due to clogging than to mechanical wear. Clogging itself may cause replacement. Cleaning with acids

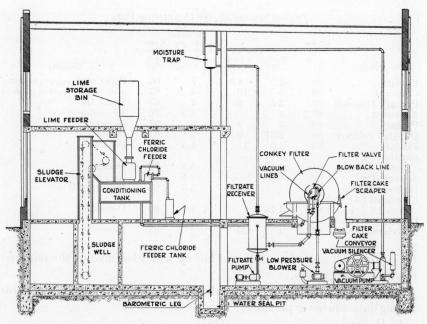

FIGURE 140. Sewage sludge filter layout. (*Courtesy Conkey Filter Co.*)

or harsh scrubbing may shorten the cloth life and cause repeated changings. Cloth clogging may be due to oils or greases; if these are present they should be removed before filtration, if possible by oil flotation, degreasing or other means.

Lime is one of the most common causes of gradual cloth clogging, as it tends to deposit, as a carbonate, in and on the filter cloth, as well as on the supporting screen beneath and in the connecting pipe lines. The quickest and surest method of removing the carbonate incrustations is by hydrochloric acid, which reacts with the calcium carbonate to form calcium chloride (soluble) and carbon dioxide. Oxalic acid also has been used successfully.

In any case the strength should not be over 2 per cent and the cloth should be thoroughly water-washed following cleaning, to avoid deterioration. The dilute acid may be applied to the top of each compartment, or the compartments may be dipped in an acid solution, brushing the cloth well for cleaning.

The filter cloth life of cotton ranges from 150 to 600 hours, averaging 350. The gradual clogging in some cases causes a drop of 2 to 3 per cent of capacity each day, so that at the end of 350 hours it pays to discard

Typical Sewage Sludge Dewatering Data

Type Sludge	Sludge Moisture (%)	Dry Solids FeCl₃ (%)	Dry Solids Lime (%)	Average No. sq ft/hr Filter Rate	Cake Moisture (%)	Remarks
Primary	90	2	8.0	7	66	Paper mill waste present
Chemical	89	3	10	4	67	Met. Plant wastes present
Primary Digested	90	2.5	0	7	65	Domestic
Activated	97.2	4	—	3.5	76	30% primary
Primary	10	3	9	6	57	Industrial
Digested Primary	88	2.31	9.25	8	61	Mixed
Primary	93	4.0	11	4.5	65	Domestic
Elutriated Digested	91	2.5	—	5.5	70	Domestic
Activated	2	4.7	—	2.5	80	25% primary
Digested Primary	88	—	4.4	3.5	68	Industrial Waste
Elutriated Digested	88	1.75	—	8	69	Domestic
Digested Activated	97	4	20	4	68	Domestic

the cloth. Not only does the yield fall off with clogging but the required conditioning increases.

According to Van Kleeck,[1] the daily plant log should include the following data whenever possible:

"(1) Gallons of sludge filtered (total).

(2) Per cent of solids in sludge.

(3) Per cent of volatile solids in sludge.

(4) Amount of ferric chloride, lime or other chemicals used, reported on a dry basis (total).

(5) pH of the filter feed. (The pH of the filtrate is determined, as this is also the pH of the conditioned wet solids and the sludge cake).

(6) Per cent moisture in filter cake.

(7) Per cent suspended solids and total solids in filtrate.

(8) Filter run in hours.

(9) Pounds of wet cake handled (total).

(10) Pounds of dry solids handled (total).

(11) Filter yield in pounds per sq ft per hour.

(12) If elutriation is employed, the total solids in the unelutriated and elutriated sludge, and the suspended solids in the elutriated sludge should be reported.

The cost of mechanical sewage sludge dewatering, by means of rotary drum vacuum filters varies from $2.34 per dry ton to over $8.00, depending on local conditions and the type of sludge handled."

Sand Beds. Most sand beds for dewatering sewage sludge are com-

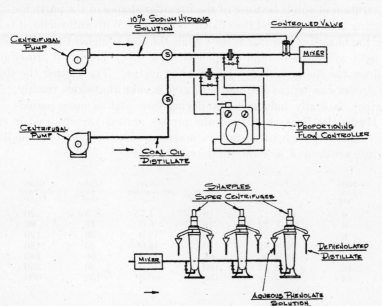

FIGURE 141. Typical centrifuge layout. (*Courtesy The Sharples Specialty Co.*)

Centrifuges

Application	Type	Capacity	Performance
Separation of cream from milk	Disc bowl	Up to 20,000 lbs per hour	Cream at 40% butter fat Skim at less than 0.1% butter fat
Conc. of rubber latex	Tubular and disc bowl	60 to 200 gal per hour	Cream at 62% rubber solids Skim at 1 to 8% rubber solids
Separation of fish oil from press liquor	Nozzle bowl	1800 gal per hour	Oil at 2% water Water at less than 0.25% oil
Dehydration of insulating oil	Tubular and disc bowl	Up to 1800 gal per hour	Dielectric value of oil to 32000 bolts
Dehydration of used lubricating oil	Tubular and disc bowl	Up to 400 gal per hour	Oil to less than 0.1% residual moisture
Dehydration of coke-oven tar	Valve bowl	1000 gal per hour	Tar to less than 2.0% residual moisture
Recovery of colloidal silver	Tubular bowl	100 to 250 gal per hour	99.8% recovery
Bacteria recovery	Tubular bowl	100 gal per hour	95 to 99% recovery
Sugar (refined) dehydration	Batch drier	7500 lbs per hour	3% residual moisture
By-product ammonium sulfate dehydration	Automatic drier	2⅓ tons per hour	1.5% residual moisture 0.10% residual H_2SO_4

posed of silica sand supported upon gravel, crushed stone and grating; or the sand may be directly supported upon porous plates. However, some beds are successfully operating wherein the medium is magnetite sand, anthracite, or other material. It is claimed for these that there is less penetration of solids because of the irregular shapes of the particles. The clogging is less rapid and the effluent is clearer. With anthracite, it is said that the hazard of freezing is less; while the cost is higher than silica sand, its light weight more than compensates for this. The usual procedure is to draw the sludge to a depth of **8** to **12** inches. The thinner the sludge the deeper can be the bed and still give a cake that dries readily. The weather naturally influences the drying time and cleaning periods.

Hydraulic Presses. Hydraulic presses are extensively used in cider pressing where high pressures are necessary whether large or small capacities are desired, as shown in the table below:

Ram Dia. (in)	Rack Size (in)	Pressure (tons)	Apples per pressing (bu)	Apples per hour (bu)	Cider per hour (gal)
4	17 × 17	10	1.75	5	20
4	22 × 22	15	6.0	15	60
6	28 × 28	35	12.0	30	120
8	32 × 32	50	18.0	45	180
8	36 × 36	63	24.0	60	240
10	42 × 42	100	36.0	90	360
12	48 × 48	150	60.0	150	600

References

1. "Vacuum Filtration of Sludge," Van Kleeck, L. W., Senior San. Eng., Conn. State B'd Health, 1938.

Appendix I

Surface and Interfacial Tension Separation of Immiscible Fluids

BY JOHN M. WALKER

Introduction. A new concept of the physical and chemical laws underlying long known facts has been brought forth for the industrial and scientific application of surface and interfacial tension separation to liquid-liquid and liquid-gas systems under various pressure conditions.

Present Methods. The various physical methods now used to separate such systems are based upon the differing characteristics of the fluids to be separated. Thus specific gravity is the effective factor in gravitational settling separation, inertial or baffle systems, and centrifugal separation, whereas distillation, in general, depends upon a difference in molecular weight, although modified in many cases by the great polar attraction of associated liquids.

Adsorption and Absorption. Adsorption is the attachment of particles to solid surfaces, for example, the taking up by activated carbon of hydrocarbons and other gases and liquids from water solutions, or their vapors from air. Similarly, the removal of water vapor from compressed gases by adsorption on activated alumina or silica gel is a surface adsorption, in contrast to the internal chemical absorption of water and water vapor by calcium chloride and other hygroscopic materials.

Internal Pressure. The various distinguishing characteristics of liquids are all factors of one fundamental force—the internal pressure, the molecular attraction between the molecules of the same or similar liquids, which holds the liquid together and in a separate phase, and acts to squeeze out molecules which are attracted with less force. Surface and interfacial tension, very closely related to internal pressure, similarly lend themselves to physical separation of fluids.

Familiar Examples of Natural Phenomena. The floating of a needle on water; the filtration of water from gasoline by means of chamois skin; fine metal screen; porous ceramics; the difficulty of drawing oil through a water-wetted filter paper and *vice versa;* the respiration of air through the porous, oil-tanned and water-repellant leather of shoes; water-repellant but porous and open fabrics, both natural and synthetic; steam and compressed air pipeline gaskets that sometimes leak the condensing liquid within, but not air or steam; the difficulty experienced in filtering mer-

323

cury through fine cloth or filter paper, these all are well known. "Wet the sails" was the cry during races of the clipper ships, because wet canvas is more nearly air-tight than dry.

Unifying Logic. The logic of such apparently unimportant and unrelated facts, when critically examined, leads directly to the following conclusion: the tiny holes or capillaries extending through a membrane, or thin wall of porous material, may be filled with liquid plugs, which do not permit the passage of another immiscible liquid or gas until a considerable pressure is reached. These liquid plugs do permit the flow of the same or similar liquids at any pressure difference. The length of the capillary or the thickness of the porous material has no effect upon the plugging action, which is a static equilibrium condition occurring at the entrance of the capillary, or at the point of maximum cross-section.

Fundamental Concepts. It is, therefore, possible to state that any porous membrane or material is pervious to any gas or liquid under exactly known conditions and is impervious under other exactly known conditions, depending upon the diameter or width of the largest unrestricted opening through the porous material and the surface or interfacial tension value between the two different fluid phases.

As in the case of the needle floating on the surface of the water, the elastic, diaphragm-like surface skin that a liquid assumes at its boundary with a gas or another immiscible liquid, suspended across a capillary opening by the adhesion of its rim to the walls, has strength to resist rupture. The smaller the span of this surface skin the greater the pressure it will withstand without giving way. For example, a membrane of water surface across a capillary $\frac{1}{25,400}$ of an inch in diameter will withstand 44 pounds per square inch differential pressure of air against it without allowing the air to disrupt it and enter the capillary. Water will flow through the capillary, however, at a fraction of an ounce of pressure, since there is no surface tension between parts of the same or miscible liquids, when in contact.

We may, therefore, consider a vertical membrane, which acts as a containing wall, in a pressure system higher than atmospheric. Initially the wall is wetted and the pores filled with the liquid to be discharged to the lower, atmospheric pressure region; the compressed gas in the system is to be retained. The liquid in the pressure system now coming into contact with the porous membrane flows through, driven by the pressure of the system, until no more is available to displace liquid filling the capillaries. Whereupon, at the entrance to the capillary, the liquid instantly assumes the characteristic skin against the gas and seals the entrance, until such time as more miscible liquid comes into contact with the interface, which as quickly disappears.

Multiply the one capillary by millions per square inch, all smaller than a certain limit, and no gas or immiscible liquid can flow through this containing wall, although the same or miscible liquid flows through freely under differential pressure.

Case A: As utilized for liquid-liquid separations, therefore, a porous membrane is chosen whose walls and surfaces are preferentially wetted by the liquid phase to be discharged and which will maintain a surface film of this phase even though in contact with the other, immiscible liquid.

Case B: As utilized for liquid-gas separation, where the liquid is to be discharged from the pressure system, a porous material is chosen which is strongly wetted by the liquid to be ejected.

Case C: As utilized for liquid-gas separations, where the gas is to be ejected from the system, a porous material is chosen which is not wetted by the liquid to be contained.

Wetting. The cohesion of the liquid to its own molecules, as contrasted to the adhesion between the liquid and solid molecules at the surface of the porous solid, thus is a determining factor in the selection of the proper material for a given separation. When a drop of liquid placed on a solid surface spreads to a thin film, the attraction of the molecules of the solid surface is greater for the liquid molecules than that of the liquid molecules for one another. The solid is said to be *wetted* by the liquid. An instance is the wetting of clean glass by water.

When a droplet of liquid placed upon a solid surface remains in a lens-like or ball-shaped droplet, the attraction of the liquid molecules for each other is greater than the attraction between the molecules of the liquid and those of the solid. The solid is therefore *not wetted* by the liquid. For example, mercury will not wet glass, nor will water wet a waxed surface.

When two dissimilar immiscible liquids, each of which is capable of wetting a given surface, are placed in contact with that surface, one will be more strongly attracted to the solid molecules than the other liquid and will actually displace the less strongly wetting liquid. The solid is then said to be *preferentially wetted* by the most strongly attracted liquid. For example, water preferentially wets glass, as compared to oil, oil preferentially wets lead oxides and sulfides, as compared to water.

Degrees of Wetting. A completely satisfactory evaluation of the degree of wetting remains to be developed. It is dependent upon the interfacial tension between liquids and solids, which has not yet been determined. The pressure, or adhesion attraction, between silica molecules and water may be taken to be in the neighborhood of thousands of pounds per square inch. Many other wetting adhesion tensions are probably of the same order of magnitude. In the case of mercury against glass and water against wax, the sum of the adhesion and cohesion forces is negative, resulting in an actual repulsion of the liquid molecules from the solid molecules at the boundary.

Classification of Surfaces. In the case of oil and water, solid surfaces are commonly classified as hydrophilic, *i.e.*, preferentially water-wetted, and hydrophobic, preferentially oil-wetted. In the case of non-wetting, the solid surfaces are said to be water-repellant, mercury-repellant, and so on.

These preferential wetting characteristics have long been used to effect the separation of pulverized mineral mixtures, according to their respective affinities for the liquid phases present, in mineralogical flotation equipment,[1-7] as well as being fundamental considerations in the formulation of paints and varnishes, leather-tanning compounds and processes, and protective coatings of all types.

Glass, portland and other hydraulic cements, paper, cotton, porcelain, most silicates and many other materials are preferentially water-wetted and are thus hydrophilic; lead, mercury and molybdenum, in fact most metallic sulfides, lead and mercuric oxides, unactivated carbon, sulfur, silver, lead, mercury, and other metallic iodides and halides are preferentially oil-wetted, or hydrophobic. Waxed and smoked surfaces and surfaces covered with precipitated heavy metal soaps are also hydrophobic.

Chemistry of the Interface. The strength of the interface membrane between two immiscible liquids, or a liquid and a gas, is affected to a marked degree by the presence of impurities; in some cases, a fraction of a per cent of a certain type of foreign material will reduce this skin strength several hundred per cent. This effect, which is the primary basis of the action of soap and the various wetting agents, depends upon the internal pressure. The molecules of a substance present in a liquid whose molecules have a greater attraction for each other than for the molecules of the foreign substance, tend to be squeezed out; this results in a higher concentration of these molecules in the surface layer of the liquid than in the interior. This is the positive adsorption predicted thermodynamically by Gibbs.

In the case of alcohols, stearates, palmitates, oleates, sulfonates and sulfamates, the surface tension or interfacial tension may be lowered to such a degree that separation by this means becomes impractical, as in the case of oil and water.

Physics of Capillaries. The rise of liquids in capillaries is a familiar phenomenon. If a glass tube of small internal diameter is held vertically and lowered into a vessel of water, the water will rise inside the tube to a level appreciably higher than the level of the water in the vessel. (See Fig. 142a). Furthermore, the smaller the internal diameter of the glass tube, the higher the water will rise. If the tube diameter were $\frac{1}{25,400}$ of an inch and the tube were 100 feet high, the water would rise 100 feet above the surface of the water in the vessel. Capillaries whose diameters are only a few multiples of molecular diameters, such as those occurring in silica gel, would cause a vertical rise of water five to ten miles in height, if arranged vertically. Thus, the force of attraction between the

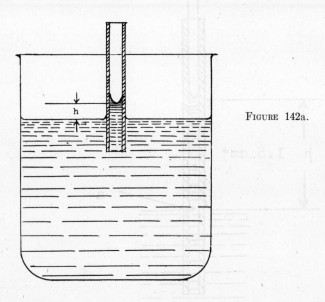

FIGURE 142a.

molecules of water and those of the tube wall is of great magnitude; when skin span of the water surface is small, as in the case of the smaller-diameter capillaries, this attractive force will lift the column to very great heights.

Simple considerations lead to a direct calculation of this capillary force, as shown in Fig. 142b. The weight of the liquid is expressed in terms of hydrostatic pressure, for any vertical liquid column of the same height would exert the same hydrostatic pressure at its base.

When water fills a glass capillary of any length, it is held within the tube and resists displacement by air or an immiscible liquid, with a pressure equal to the force of the capillary rise. It does not matter whether the capillary is horizontal or vertical, so long as it is filled with a wetting liquid. This liquid will act as a plug or barrier to the entrance of an immiscible phase, forming an interface against it across the diameter of the capillary. Thus a capillary tube one-eighth of an inch long, or more or less, if it has an inside diameter of $\frac{1}{25,400}$ of an inch and is filled with water, holds the water with the same force, 44 pounds per square inch, against displacement by compressed air, since 44 pounds per square inch is the hydrostatic pressure at the bottom of a 100 foot vertical column of water.

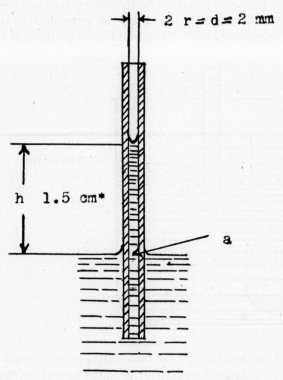

For the general case

Surface tension, σ, is a linear force exerted around circumferences

$$2\pi r\ \sigma = \pi r^2\ hgq_0$$

$$\sigma = \tfrac{1}{2}\ r\ hgq_0 \quad (1)$$

r = radius of capillary
h = height of rise of liquid
g = acceleration of gravity
$c_0 = q_1 - q_2$
q_1 = density of liquid
q_2 = density of atmosphere

For a particular case

r = 1 mm or .1 cm
σ = 73 dynes per cm
g = 980 cm/sec
q = 1 gram/cc
h = height of capillary rise
$\sigma = \tfrac{1}{2}$ x .1 x h x 980 x 1
h   1.5 cm hydrostatic column of liquid
* approximate
# water — glass — air

FIGURE 142b.

This relation has long been used to calibrate fine membranes and bacteriological filters. The membranes, in the form of closed cylinders, are carefully saturated with water, then immersed in a vessel of water and compressed air admitted to the inside. The compressed air will not rupture or displace the liquid plug until the critical pressure is reached; then by means of the capillary rise formula, the size of the capillary opening is obtained. (See Fig. 142c.)

The case of the displacement of one liquid by another immiscible liquid is directly parallel; however, instead of the surface tension value, the

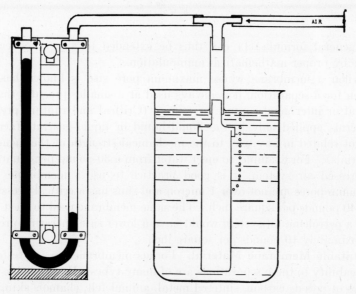

FIGURE 142c.

interfacial tension value of the two liquids is used. It must be remembered that although two immiscible liquids in effect repel each other, this repulsion is the algebraic sum of the forces of attraction and repulsion between molecules of unlike liquids, and the sum of the two forces is negative. We may thus quite properly speak of a water-filled capillary as having a negative capillarity for oil, and of glass capillaries as having a negative capillarity for mercury, molten metals, and so on.

It has been assumed that the capillaries in a separating membrane are circular in cross-section; this, however, is probably an extremely rare case. For capillaries of any geometrical cross-section, the formula developed

$$\sigma \cdot c = h \cdot A$$

where σ equals interfacial tension of the two immiscible liquids in dynes per cm, c equals length of the line of contact of the interface around the periphery of the capillary (in the case of a circular cross-section capillary, c equals circumference), h equals applied pressure against the interface or differential pressure, and A equals area of the cross-section of the capillary.

For a capillary of circular cross-section

$$2\pi r\sigma = \pi r^2 h \qquad (1)$$
$$h = \frac{2\sigma}{r}$$

The general formula (1) can thus be extended to any cross-sectional shape by proper mathematical manipulation.

When a membrane whose maximum pore size is known has been chosen for a separation, it is always used at a smaller pressure than the critical or interfacial rupture pressure. (Critical and rupture pressures are terms applied only to the liquid-liquid or liquid-gas interface, and are not related in any way to the mechanical strength of the membrane materials). For example, to eject water from a 30-pound per square inch compressed air system, it is good practice to use a membrane whose maximum pores are not over 1 micron and thus has a critical pressure of over 40 pounds per square inch. The same membrane used to eject water from a petroleum oil system would have a lower safe operating pressure, approximately 10 pounds per square inch.

Suitable Membrane Material. Porous membranes so far tested for applicability to these separations are of many types: Hydrophobic membranes of porous carbon, sintered metal, animal felt, chamois skin, vegetable-tanned leather, compressed metal shims, ceramics, whose surfaces are covered with precipitated or deposited hydrophobic films; water-repellant porous media, such as waxed ceramics, waxed fabrics, Vinyon and other plastics; hydrophilic membranes of ceramics, sintered glass, paper, cement, cloth, and so on. All of these have proved practical for some operations.

The following features should be kept in mind, however: the surface and interfacial tension values can be interpreted as being either positive or negative, according to whether or not preferential wetting or liquid-repellant surface conditions are involved. Also, a porous material whose surface is preferentially water-wetted may be very well adapted to the separation of liquid hydrocarbon from compressed gas systems, where no water is present in the system.

Shown on the chart size ranges of capillary openings from 1 millimeter (1,000 microns) to 1 millimicron ($\frac{1}{1000}$ micron), and pressures ranging from $\frac{1}{1000}$ of a pound per square inch to 10,000 pounds per square inch.

Immiscible Systems Studied. Since calibration procedure, by the methods described, involves driving through the wetting fluid present in excess, it serves also as a practical test separation, so long as the pressure is not allowed to exceed the interfacial rupture pressure.

The single-phase ejection separations investigated by this means include the separation of water from compressed air, compressed nitrogen, compressed methane, through porous membrances of paper, various ceramics, metal shims, annular glass rings, gypsum, portland cement, and silica gel. Similarly, naphtha, benzene, kerosene, chlorinated hydrocarbons, acetone, alcohols, and ether have been used for experimental and practical separations and calibration.

The inverse single-phase ejection of gases, which were non-wetting in respect to the liquid present, such as compressed air from water, and compressed air from mercury through calibrated ceramic materials followed the formulated relationship. Single and two-phase separations of water and kerosene, water and gasoline, water and benzene, water and carbon tetrachloride have been carried out both on laboratory and pilot-plant scale.

It should be noted that, even in the case of so-called immiscible liquids, there is a very slight mutual solubility. Thus, gasoline in contact with water may have a few parts per ten thousand of dissolved water, and the water phase in contact with the gasoline will contain a few parts per ten million of gasoline, the variance again being a matter of the very much higher internal pressure of the water, which thus resists intermixture of less polar gasoline. Fig. 142d presents the three cases diagrammatically.

Industrial Technicological Applications. Two classes of application are immediately apparent; the removal of condensing liquids from compressed gas systems, and the separation of oil and water phases, as well as various other undesirable immiscible liquid admixtures, in the case of liquid fuels and lubricants of all types.

The water in compressed air systems is almost always an undesirable and ever-present nuisance, interfering with flow through orifices, accelerating corrosion, and carrying dirt. Similarly, water in compressed chlorine and sulfur dioxide gas systems is a source of serious trouble, and its removal must be assured, usually by somewhat elaborate means. Surface tension separators would seem to offer an excellent means of reducing the load on adsorbent or absorbent driers.

Throughout the petroleum industry water problems are encountered. Those occurring in treatment are, of course, handled by baffle and gravitational separation. However, the continuous precipitation of dissolved water by hydrocarbons cooling from higher to lower temperature presents an entirely different type of situation, which contributes greatly to the trouble encountered in storage and transportation by ship and pipe-line.

Chlorinated hydrocarbons are sensitive to water, due to their tendency to hydrolize. Their use would be made more satisfactory by a safe automatic removal of condensed or otherwise accumulated water. The saving in mechanical energy or time as compared to other methods, the physical principle of action, which involves no mechanical movement, the re-

Single Liquid Phase Ejected   Both Liquid Phases Ejected   Gas Phase Ejected

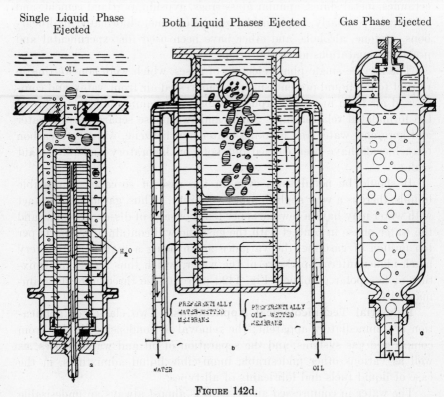

FIGURE 142d.

placeability of the separating membranes, all lead to a simplification of construction and operation and insure wide application.

Separatory Systems in Nature. The occurrence of surface and interfacial tension separation, according to the concept herein presented, ranges from geological formations to the action of human tissues. Impervious strata capping and containing gas and oil pools may well be, in some instances, micro-porous limestone or sandstone, saturated with ground water, holding both the gas and the liquid beneath the earth at the high pressures, as sometimes encountered in virgin pools.

Irrigation, both natural and man-made, depends upon the functioning of the tiny capillaries formed by the interstices between the ultimate physical particles of the soil. Water, from rainfall or other sources, wetting soils containing clay develops a natural separating system, permeable to water, impermeable to air. As the top water disappears by draining off or evaporating, that held in the porous soil against the pull of gravity and in communication with underground water-bearing sands or other strata establishes a continuous supply of moisture; capillary rise is capable of lifting this water vertically hundreds of feet and replenishing that lost to the atmosphere.

Similarly, in the vegetable and animal kingdom, micro-porous structures function alike through filtration, surface and interfacial tension separation, and osmosis. Any membrane or structure with pores or capillaries fine enough to exhibit osmotic effects is, of a certainty, capable of functioning as a fluid-phase separatory membrane as well, and it is undeniable that cell walls and living tissues, in many cases, act in accordance with this previously unconsidered concept.

Industrial Separators

Liquid-Liquid. Industrial separator units may well range in size from installations handling millions of cubic feet of natural gas per day through ordinary industrial filtration equipment down to individual oil-water or compressed air condensate filter separators no larger than a fountain pen. Due to the rapid evolution of micro-porous materials and surface treatments, no attempt will be made to give more than a few simplified diagrammatic sketches of equipment and certain phases of fundamental calculations of maximum pore size, surface or interfacial tension strength, and the critical pressures beyond which the immiscible phase would flow through the separating barrier.

As the first example, a gasoline storage tank, 20 feet high, will be considered. Assuming that, during normal operating conditions, gasoline in the refinery is given a final washing treatment, with water at a temperature of 70°, is then run into a storage tank, and subsequently cools to a temperature of 40°. Dissolved water in the gasoline, in true solution at the higher temperature, in amounts of a few parts of water to ten thousand parts of gasoline, is precipitated out of solution until the new temperature—solubility equilibrium is reached. This water settles continuously to the bottom of the tank; and, since large quantities of gasoline are involved, considerable amounts of water accumulate and must be drawn off to avoid loss of storage space, accelerated tank corrosion, and pipe-line freezing under cold weather conditions.

A 20-foot vertical column of gasoline of density 0.67 will exert approximately 6 pounds per square inch hydrostatic pressure. The maximum radius capillary in the porous separating membrane should, there-fore, be able to sustain 6 pounds pressure, when the gasoline-water inter-facial tension is 32 dynes. Selecting a membrane with a 7-pound critical pressure at 32 dynes, a porous medium with a maximum capillary radius of 1.2 microns fulfills the requirements; the closest listed mate-rial is paper or porcelain. Either material is preferentially water-wetted without further treatment; the paper, however, will withstand mechanical shock and repeated freezing and thawing cycles, and is con-venient and economical to replace as compared to the porcelain. Since either material will clog in the course of time from the water-borne dirt, a smaller, more frequently renewed paper membrane unit is the more feasible in this instance. A hollow cylindrical unit 2 feet diameter by 5 feet high, composed of compressed circular lamina, both the inner and outer surface acting as separating surfaces, would have about 60 square feet surface area and a final water flow rate of approximately 720 gallons a day, at which point it should be renewed. This type of unit could be lowered directly onto the tank bottom with discharge through a flexible hose syphon arrangement that would eliminate through-wall piping con-nections, to which petroleum refinery operators have well-founded ob-jections.

An alternative design for similar oil storage continuous automatic water-phase separators, where existing piping may be used and freezing temperatures are not encountered, is a small plate-and-frame filter press modified to permit use of separating filter media instead of cloth or paper.

In the case of smaller tanks, e.g., those of one tank carload capacity, a small quick-opening, replaceable, cartridge-type unit with either por-celain, paper, or other suitable separating membrane is employed. Since the total pressures are low, except in the case of vertical tanks, much coarser and faster materials can be used; consequently the size of the unit need not be more than 4 × 10 inches.

In those processes requiring the separation-ejection of both an aque-ous and organic phase, the standard plate-and-frame filter press, with the correct manifolding and alterations referred to above, may be conven-iently employed. Also very suitable, from a maintenance standpoint, are leaf-type filters. Both types would permit the use of filter aids or adsorbents if desirable.

Where only small amounts of one phase of liquid is present in large quantities of another, as is the case with lubricating oil containing finely dispersed water droplets, centrifugal coalescing devices may be resorted to, although future developments may simplify the problem. Moreover, the centrifugal effect may be produced by the liquid itself, if it is made to follow a short radius spiral path. This would be at the expense of line pressure, and may require extra pumping power, more convenient in most cases than high load centrifugal equipment.

Automotive gasoline-water separators have been designed which require no more space than the conventional glass bowl screen chamber and water trap. These units are automatic and need not be removed for cleaning, only an occasional replacement of the simple separator cartridges being necessary. The cylindrical copper screen or coarsely porous ceramics now used in these units serves as a gasoline-water separator to some extent; however, the size of the maximum openings is such that a very low differential pressure is sufficient to drive water through the barrier. The cup must be removed to empty it of accumulated water. As designed with precision-calibrated separatory media, in this case paper, to withstand freezing, the water is continuously ejected; the gasoline passing through the preferentially oil-wetted membrane is also filtered much more finely than is the case with metal screens or micro-porous materials. A maximum capillary radius of 5 to 6 microns is used.

Liquid-Gas. One of the largest fields of application of surface-tension separators is presented in compressed air equipment of all types. The removal of condensation from compressed air and simultaneous filtration of the air, to remove small droplets of water and particles of dirt, is accomplished in the standard surface tension-compressed air filter-separator by arranging an upper, water-repellant, air-permeable membrane and a lower water-permeable, air-impermeable membrane in a suitable pressure vessel, the proportions of the parts meeting the requirements of allowable pressure drop of air through the unit, general condition of the air, line pressures of operation, temperature ranges encountered, location of equipment, and so on. Where high rates of flow are to be handled, baffles that prevent velocity impingement of air-borne liquid slugs against the air-permeable membrane are incorporated.

In operation, air flowing into the apparatus is freed of slugs of water by the entrance bafflle. It next passes through the water-repellant membrane, leaving behind dirt and small droplets of liquid, which coalesce and fall by gravity to the lower portion of the chamber. The water coming into contact with the water-permeable membrane flows through it and out to the atmosphere. Emulsified oil formed by the condensation of oil vapor, along with water vapor, also flows through the water-permeable membrane, since in general the water is the external phase of the emulsion and the diameter of the droplets is smaller than that of the capillary. In the case of oil emulsion droplets larger than the capillary diameters, this simplified explanation does not hold; however, service records indicate that little trouble is to be feared from this source.

Taking an actual example in the filter separation of water and dirt from 250 cubic feet per minute of 80-pound pressure compressed air and the automatic ejection of the water to the atmosphere, a vertical 6-inch inside diameter steel pressure vessel 4 feet high is used; mounted in the upper half is a hollow, water-repellant micro-porous cylinder, 4-inches in outside diameter, ½-inch in wall thickness, of the correct maximum pore size and total porosity, which separates the water and dirt from the air passing through, and imposes 4 pounds pressure drop at nominal capacity. Seven vertical water-permeable cylindrical membranes, about 1¼ inches in diameter and 12 inches long, containing interior riser tubes discharging the separated water to the atmosphere, are mounted in hexagonal pattern on the bottom partition of the unit.

The maximum capillary radius of the air-permeable, water-repellant, large-diameter cylinder is approximately 30 microns; while not sufficiently small to separate water when totally immersed at the differential pressure of 4 pounds of air, this serves very effectively to remove the droplets and dirt particles. The maximum pore radius of the water discharge membrane units is 0.25 micron, and these have a critical pressure of 90 pounds; therefore, at 80 pounds air pressure, the water alone flows through and the air is perfectly retained.

The dimensions of units suitable for such capacities will in the future be very much reduced, since improvement in types of separating media, surface treatments, and engineering design will result in very compact and simplified separators. Similarly, in the case of compressed air-actuated control instruments, paint-spray guns, air-hose jets, and all small unit volume devices, very much simplified, improved, and compact units will shortly be available. Filter-separators of the same type, differing in materials of construction to meet the necessities of the conditions, are designed for the removal of condensed acids and gas-saturated water from chlorine and sulfur dioxide gas systems, as well as many others.

It is now practical to handle very large quantities of gas at low pressure drops through micro-porous materials, and to effect separation of very finely divided mist particles, with relatively coarse membranes, by further application of the surface tension concept combined with a dynamic flow concept. Such a development in the future may lead to the separation of gasoline mist from natural gas, where circumstances do not permit large central processing and collection plants.

Vapor Ejectors. The filter separation of liquids, to remove gas bubble or pocket entrainment, is a relatively untouched field of application for this type of equipment. In high-altitude flight, for example, dissolved air in the gasoline is evolved as the atmospheric pressure decreases; bubbles of air set free temporarily block small orifices, causing uneven flow and fluctuations in pressure. Small laminar metal disc partitions, strongly wetted by gasoline, allow the gasoline to flow through; the air bubbles are retained and collected by buoyant rise to an upper bell, from which the air is vented into the large fuel tanks.

Hydraulic systems encounter trouble from evolved air, which acts as a compressible material within the system itself, and of course reduces the effective control of the output pressure. Since the pressures encountered in such systems are very high, micro-porous separating media of special characteristics are called for, and investigation of materials for this purpose has been under way for some time.

The present synthesis of surface chemistry and accurate physical knowledge of the controlling dimensions of porous media used in this type of separation, and further intensive investigation of treatments and structures cannot fail to have a profound influence on conventional process filtration of the future. It is possible to visualize a similar unification of the present diverse and incomplete theories in this important field of engineering practice, founded, in part, on the same physical factors, which must be accurately known and correctly utilized in surface and interfacial tension separations.

References

1. Hoover, "Concentrating Ores by Flotation," London (1912).
2. Vageler, "Die Schwimmaufbereitung der Erze," Dresden (1913), also, *Metall und Erze*, **17**, 113 (1920).
3. Rickard, "Concentration by Flotation," New York (1921).
4. Gaudin, "Flotation," McGraw-Hill, New York (1932).
5. Sulman, *Trans. Inst. Mining Met.*, **29**, 44 (1920).
6. Edser, "Fourth Report on Colloid Chem.," H. M. Stationery Office, London (1922).
7. Lewis, Squires and Broughton, "Ind'l Chem. of Colloidal & Amorphous Materials," Macmillan, New York (1942).

Appendix II

TERMS

B.O.D. or Biochemical Oxygen Demand of a liquid is the oxygen required for the biochemical oxidation of the decomposable matter at a given temperature within a given time. The 5-day, 20°C test is the common basis of B.O.D. measurements. For further information see Standard Methods for the Examination of Water and Sewage by American Public Health Association.

CENTIPOISE is a unit of viscosity $\dfrac{\text{grams}}{\text{centimeter seconds}}$

Water at 68.6°F has a viscosity of 0.0100 poise one centipoise. It is customary to express viscosities in centipoises as viscosity relative to water at 68.6°F.

In English units viscosity may be expressed as $\dfrac{\text{lbs}}{\text{ft sec}}$

Since $1g = \dfrac{1}{453.6}$ lbs and $1 \text{ cm} = \dfrac{1}{30.48 \text{ ft}}$

$$1 \text{ poise} = 1 \text{ English unit} \times \frac{(30.48)}{453.6} - 0.0672 \frac{\text{lb}}{\text{ft sec}}$$

$$1 \text{ centipoise} = .00672 \frac{\text{lb}}{\text{ft sec}}$$

pH. The "pH" value of a solution or the hydrogenions concentration is a convenient measure of its acidity. A neutral solution is represented by a pH of 7. Any pH less than 7 represents a solution that is on the acid side—the smaller the pH the greater the acidity. Any pH larger than 7 represents a solution on the alkaline or basic side. Very slight changes in the pH number represent large changes in acidity. A pH of 5 represents ten times as much acidity as a pH of 6. A pH of 4 represents 100 times as much acidity as 6. Similarly a solution with a pH of 9 is ten times as alkaline as one with a pH of 8.

To find the amount (weight in grams) of hydrogen ions in one liter of water with a pH of 9 write a fraction with a numerator of 1 and a denominator of 1 and add nine zeros to the denominator. The liter will contain 1/1,000,000,000 gram (one billionth of a gram) of hydrogen ions.

Hydrogen ions give a solution an acid character. OH ions give a solution an alkaline character. At a pH of 7 the solution contains one H ion for every OH ion, therefore the solution is neutral at this point.

TABLES

Conversion Factors for Viscosity

To convert viscosity in centipoises to other units, multiply
0.01 to obtain viscosity in poises—gm/sec/cm
3.60 to obtain kg/hr/m
0.000672 to obtain lb/sec/ft
2.42 to obtain lb/hr/ft

The Brix hydrometer is graduated so that 1° Brix corresponds to a solution containing 1% of sugar at 17.5°C or 63.5°F. 2° Brix equals 2% and so on.

Baumé for liquids lighter than water.

$$\text{sp gr} = \frac{146.78}{136.78 + °Be}$$

Baumé for liquids heavier than water.

$$\text{sp gr} = \frac{146.78}{146.78 - {}^{\circ}\text{Be}}$$

Twaddell

$$\text{sp gr} = 1 + \frac{{}^{\circ}\text{T}_{\text{w}}}{200}$$

Weights and Measures

Board Measure. One foot board measure is a piece of wood 12 inches square by 1 inch thick or 144 cu inches. 1 cu ft, therefore, equals 12 feet board measure.

Shipping Measure. Register ton is used to measure internal capacity of ship. 100 cu ft = 1 register ton.
Shipping ton, for measurement of cargo:

40 cu ft
- U. S. shipping ton
- 32.143 U. S. bushels
- 31.16 Imperial bushels

42 cu ft
- 1 British shipping ton
- 33.75 U. S. bushels
- 32.719 Imperial bushels

Specific Gravity. The specific gravity of a substance is its weight as compared with the weight of an equal bulk of pure water.

For making specific gravity determinations the temperature of the water is usually taken at 62°F, when 1 cu ft of water weighs 62.355 lbs. Water is at its greatest density at 39.2°F or 4° centigrade.

Coefficient of Expansion and Contraction

For practical purposes of petroleum products.

Gravity	0 to 14.9—1% for every 29° temperature
"	15 to 34.9—1% " " 25° "
"	35 to 50.9—1% " " 20° "
"	51 to 63.9—1% " " 16⅔° "
"	64 to 78.9—1% " " 14° "
"	79 to 88.9—1% " " 12½° "

COMPRESSED AIR MOISTURE CHART

Gallons of water remaining in compressed air in form of vapor based on a capacity of 100 cu ft of air per min for an 8-hr day.

Temp. of Air	Pounds Pressure Compressed Air											
	30#	40#	50#	60#	70#	80#	90#	100#	110#	120#	130#	150#
32°	.575	.432	.36	.28	.25	.23	.21	.18	.17	.14	.13	.12
40°	.75	.60	.50	.43	.38	.33	.30	.29	.26	.24	.23	.21
50°	1.15	.89	.76	.65	.55	.48	.43	.40	.37	.34	.32	.29
60°	1.58	1.29	1.07	.93	.82	.71	.63	.55	.47	.45	.43	.40
70°	2.17	1.73	1.50	1.30	1.15	1.03	.94	.86	.77	.72	.69	.57
80°	2.90	2.39	2.00	1.78	1.58	1.43	1.27	1.15	1.03	.98	.92	.81
90°	4.03	3.28	2.76	2.42	2.16	1.96	1.73	1.58	1.44	1.35	1.26	1.10
100°	5.33	4.43	3.74	3.22	2.88	2.58	2.30	2.16	2.00	1.84	1.73	1.56
110°	7.00	5.75	4.90	4.25	3.75	3.34	3.02	2.76	2.60	2.36	2.18	1.95
120°	9.50	7.45	6.55	5.57	4.87	4.37	4.02	3.68	3.34	3.16	2.94	2.59

Example: Air at 100# and at 120°F, contains 3.68 gallons of water in the form of vapor for 100 cu ft capacity over an eight hour day. This same quantity of air when cooled to 60°F, contains only .55 gallons of water in the form of vapor. The difference between the two figures or 3.13 gallons condenses out as liquid water and must be removed with a filter to prevent the passage into air tools, spray guns and instruments. If the capacity of a compressor is 700 cu ft per minute, the above figure would be multiplied by 7 and represents the total quantity of water which must be handled by filters.

Index

341